MW00615150

# the deep sea quest for Amelia EARHART

To Robyn —

Best wishes!

*[signature]*

10-8-10

Courage is the price that life exacts for granting peace.
    —Amelia Earhart

Photo by Albert Bresnik with permission.

the deep sea quest for Amelia EARHART

david w. jourdan

Ocellus Productions
PO Box 7689
Cape Porpoise, ME 04014

© 2010 David W. Jourdan
All rights reserved. No part of this book may be reproduced or used in any form or by any means, electronic or mechanical, including photocopying and recording, or by any information storage and retrieval system, without permission in writing from the publisher.

Jourdan, David W.
    The Deep Sea Quest for Amelia Earhart / David W. Jourdan.

    ISBN 978-0-9843282-0-8

    Library of Congress control number  2010922725

Printed in the United States of America
First Printing

Book layout and composition: Bethany Jourdan, Anewgrafic

Also by David W. Jourdan:

Book I in the *Never Forgotten* Series
www.dakarneverforgotten.com

Portions of the proceeds of
*The Deep Sea Quest for Amelia Earhart*
will support future exploration.
www.earhartdiscovery.com
www.seaword.org

# Contents

# Foreword

**W**hy does a person dedicate a large part of his life and resources to finding and mapping previously unknown underwater geology, antiquities, and lost artifacts, while striving to educate the world about the major portion of our planet that lies beneath the sea? Maybe, when one is given the privilege of serving on U.S. Navy nuclear submarines and has spent more time underwater than over ninety-nine point nine percent of the earth's inhabitants, one might feel a special obligation.

Regardless of the reason, David W. Jourdan is one of those individuals who has heeded the call to explore and educate. His efforts over the last two decades have proven to be phenomenal. His first book, *Never Forgotten: The Search and Discovery of Israel's Lost Submarine DAKAR*, told a tale of disaster, mystery, discovery, and closure surrounding the loss of a ship and its crew, found by David and his team thirty years later. Book II of the *Never Forgotten* series continues the story of the adventures of Nauticos, a world leader in deep sea discovery. With the exploration of thousands of square miles of the ocean abyss, and a record of never failing to find what they were looking for, David resumes the narrative with *The Deep Sea Quest for Amelia Earhart*.

As leader of Meridian Sciences, David developed the techniques and software used to re-navigate the underwater voyages of nuclear submarines and improve the accuracy of their navigation. During his presidency of Nauticos, he added underwater search and marine education to his company's expertise. This unique combination has led to one successful adventure after another.

It is my pleasure to have worked with David Jourdan for more than a decade on the Amelia search, having dedicated so much of my own time and energies in the endeavor. If you have an interest in true-life adventure, oceanography, marine archaeology, aviation, or the solution of one of the great mysteries of the twentieth century, I highly recommend this book. Learn and enjoy, as Dave unfolds the story of *The Deep Sea Quest for Amelia Earhart*.

Elgen M. Long, author of *Amelia Earhart: The Mystery Solved*
(Simon and Schuster, 1999)
Reno, Nevada

# Preface and Acknowledgments

Discovery is news, but it is fleeting. It occurs in an instant. Usually, it is the result of exploration, a process that demands training, talent, time, resources, and the coordination of many parts to a common purpose. The news is exciting . . . but the process is richer, more enduring. And I believe that discovery of Amelia Earhart's Electra, when it comes, will be better appreciated and more thoroughly savored by knowing the story of the long, hard road that led to it.

The story that follows is a tale of exploration, a journey of discovery. Though the events are related chronologically, the narrative is part real-time journal, part recollection from notes, logs, and documents, and part from the writings of others, complete with flashbacks and changes in point of view. I have also shamelessly mixed units of measure, consistent with the practices of ocean engineering (contrary to formal scientific usage). I trust the reader's patience and ability to follow the story without confusion.

It is my privilege to thank many, many people and organizations for their part in this story. As with any team, contributors that play no obviously significant role can be just as important to the thread of the story and eventual success of the endeavor as those who lead. So, I offer my thanks in no particular order.

Shipmates deserve special recognition; at sea, we become family, and we share a common bond, hard to explain to those ashore. I have listed the crews of both the 2002 and 2006 expeditions at the end of this book, and I hope they all will enjoy my telling of their tale.

The members of the Collins Amateur Radio Club (CARC) of Cedar Rapids, Iowa, have contributed countless man-hours to this project, supporting our analysis and leading us in creative directions that we could never have imagined. These team members are also listed at the end of this book, along with Crawford MacKeand and other volunteers. Not a dollar has been rendered to the club for its time, expertise, and dedication; however, when we succeed I will ensure they will find some shiny new radios under their Christmas trees!

Investors, sponsors, and partners all helped us pay for the huge expense of mounting weeks-long voyages of discovery. Primary among these was Ted Waitt, whose Institute funded the 2006 expedition. Many others contributed funds needed to support the 2002 expedition and support efforts, and it all added up to millions of dollars. Special thanks go to the leaders of Earhart Discovery, LLC: Gary Bane, Bruce Crawford, Julie Nelson, Robyn Kravit, and Jon and Suzie Thompson. Sadly, John Shilling and Willard Derrick did not live to see their efforts bear fruit, but their contributions endure. Rockwell Collins supported us in the use of company facilities, equipment, a Cessna 206 for airborne radio propagation tests, and the means for CARC to participate in our quest. Cindy Dietz and Christine Rodriguez were enthusiastic proponents of this relationship. Irv Bjorkheim of Kongsberg-Simrad provided key sonar equipment to our venture, and film giant James Cameron (through Earthship Productions) loaned us lights to illuminate our way. Other companies helped us acquire the technical means to mount a first-class expedition, including Rochester Wire & Cable (Tyco Electronics), Klein Associates, Prizm Electronics, and Spectrum Offshore (Ron Raymond). We are grateful for key support and expert personnel from the U.S. Naval Meteorological Command and the Naval Oceanographic Office, and I highly value our Navy association.

If you go to sea, you need a ship. The folks at Ocean Services—Dan and Trevor Stabbart and their team—provided enthusiastic support during mobilization of the *Davidson* and during the 2002 mission. Cary Swasand, the owner of the *Mt. Mitchell* and a true believer in our purpose, along with the staff at Global Seas (Bob Desautel, Greg Shuey, and Dave Auckland) kept us afloat in 2006 and dealt with our maritime travails with professional grace.

There were many organizations that helped us along the way, many of them through the efforts of CARC. Thanks are deserved by: the Amelia Earhart Birthplace Museum, Atchison, Kansas; the Antique Wireless Museum, Bloomfield, New York; the Purdue University Library, Lafayette, Indiana; the Pima Air and Space Museum, Tucson, Arizona; the Hammond Radio Museum, Guelph, Ontario, Canada; the Radio Farm, Central City, Iowa; the Daytona Air Traffic Control Center, Daytona, Florida; and the Museum of Women Pilots, Oklahoma City, Oklahoma (particularly Margie Richison, who sadly passed away in 2008).

Many other people contributed to our venture in one way or another. Thanks to Ray (K7MLS) and Dorothy Adams, who handled logistics with sea wave experiments in Florida, including access to Cocoa Beach Pier—essential for the measurements; Peter Shilton (VE3AX), who conducted CGR-32 receiver measurements; Grant Maughan for Electra 3D drawings; Peter Palshook for Electra scale model used for radio antenna testing; Carl Panhorst, former First Class Seaman aboard the Coast Guard cutter *Itasca*, who related his memories of the Amelia disappearance; CDR Rocky Lee, USCG, Pacific Rescue

Coordination Center, for his help and encouragement during emergencies at sea; Astronaut Bill McArthur, NASA, for ship-to–International Space Station ham radio communications, and in particular for being willing to say "Hi" to everyone on board the *Mt. Mitchell.*

I am grateful to Steve Lyons and Paula Apsell of WGBH-TV in Boston for introducing us to Elgen Long and starting us down this long path of adventure, as well as Dr. Fred Culick, who conducted key fuel analysis studies and helped us not to feel so bad when we run out of gas on the highway. Thanks to Christine Olorenshaw in Vancouver, who introduced us to the wonderful world of Canadian media; Dav Kaufman and Mark Rosen, who helped elevate our thinking about the media business of Amelia; and Gordon Bowman-Jones, who helped create some of our promotional materials and gave me the most stirring introduction ever at the Hiller Air Museum in San Francisco.

Sallie Smith, leader of the education team, logged many hours and made many connections to help us be ready to share our adventures with students of all ages. The team enthusiastically continues to serve. Susan Loricchio has been an avid cheerleader and a great connection to the Ninety-Nines, Amelia's own group.

The book you are holding was created with the help of editor Michele Cooper, who continues to inspire and encourage, and copyeditor Patty Mitchell, who is a joy to work with (though I would like to know what she did with all of the commas and ellipses she removed from my drafts). Readers Pat Dugan, Tom Vinson, Rod Blocksome, Spence King, and Elgen Long helped me get my facts straight and offered many great suggestions. And, of course, my family, Lynn, Bethany, Eric, sister Susan (Sonar Girl) and brother-in-law Jeff, were constant sources of support and encouragement. Bethany in particular put her Media Arts degree to good use in the design, layout, and artwork in this book, including the cover painting (a present to Lynn and me in the summer of 2002, meant to offset the arrival of a new kitten to the household).

Finally, I would like to dedicate this book to the memory of Marie K. Long. She and Elgen inspired us to take up this quest, and gave us the means to set forth. My best thanks to them will be the discovery of the Electra.

Cape Porpoise, Maine
April 2010

# Prologue:
# The Start of a Mystery

A lush tropical forest drapes rugged limestone cliffs, surrounded by sand and coral. The varied textures and hues of the land are in stunning contrast to the intensely green vegetation on top and the deep blue sea below. Much of the coastline is limestone, worn by time, winds, and water into rocks so jagged they resemble giant coarse sponges, but much harder—hard to cut or dig—and lacerating to exposed flesh. From shore, the terrain rises steeply to thousand-foot peaks, more jagged limestone, and thick growth, before descending just as quickly to another shore, just a few miles distant. Breadfruit, taro, betel nut, acacia, and coconut thrive on the island with its unvarying warm climate and dependable rainfall. To the west, a coastal lagoon is fringed with mangroves and forests of coral reefs.

All of this is embedded in blue Pacific waters, plunging not far offshore to the deepest parts of all oceans on earth: the Marianas Trench. So deep is the Trench, that if one could magically lift Mount Everest and place it at the bottom of the sea, that famous peak would rest below over a mile of water.

Here, men drove themselves and conscripted laborers to work the island to serve the Imperial Japanese Empire. By the early 1940s, the island of Saipan—just twelve miles long by five miles wide—was heavily cultivated, with two-thirds of its arable land producing crops, mainly sugar cane. Thirty thousand Japanese troops garrisoned the island and its smaller companion just to the south, Tinian. A comparable number of civilians, including Korean laborers and other slaves of the empire, toiled on the sugar plantations, worked the fishing industry, and served the needs of the military.

The limestone was cut and gouged into tunnels, fighting positions, and command posts. Airfields were surrounded by concrete ordnance bunkers and air-raid shelters. Beaches were covered by machine-gun fire. Artillery was positioned in the mountains and pre-aimed to key locations. Saipan, just one

1

thousand miles from the Home Islands, was considered part of the Japanese homeland and would be defended at all costs.

In June of 1944, the Americans came. In one of the largest amphibious operations ever mounted, 8,000 Marines landed on the beaches of Saipan in the first few hours; by nightfall, 20,000 men of the 2nd and 4th Marine Divisions, supported by the U.S. Army's 27th Division, were ashore. The fighting was horrific, as Japanese soldiers and civilians alike were convinced that they must die rather than surrender, each taking at least seven Americans with them.

The landings alarmed the Japanese command as had no other operation. If the Americans were to take Saipan and its companion Tinian, the vast Pacific would no longer offer protection of the homeland from long-range B-29 bombers. Much of the remaining fleet of the Japanese Imperial Navy, including the super-battleships *Yamato* and *Musahi*, and nine aircraft carriers, were sent to challenge the U.S. Navy and the landings on Saipan. The Americans were ready for the Japanese. Admiral Ray Spruance, commander of the U.S. Fifth Fleet, had the ships, aircraft, and pilots to defeat the force he was certain would come. But as with all sea battles in the Pacific, the crucial first blows could not be dealt until the enemy was located.

The eyes of the Navy were in the air. The PBY Catalina Flying Boat, along with its cousin the PBM Mariner, was a slow, some say ungainly, twin-engine seaplane that could operate from a lagoon, land in the open sea, stay aloft for an entire day, and cover 2,500 miles at cruising speed. (According to the U.S. Navy aircraft designation system, "PB" stands for "Patrol Bomber" and "Y" is the code for the builder, Consolidated Aircraft Corporation; or, in the case of the PBM, "M" is the Glen L. Martin Company.) Its crew of nine included pilots, a navigator, a radioman, a flight mechanic, and gunners. It could carry depth bombs, torpedoes, and machine guns, patrol wide areas of ocean, rescue downed aviators and seamen, and was among the most widely used all-purpose aircraft of World War II.

In Saipan, the flying boats were assigned many roles, none more important than searching for the Japanese fleet. After submarines first sighted the Japanese battle group on June 15, the patrol aircraft helped keep contact. On the morning of June 19, the Battle of the Philippine Sea was joined. As the Marines were fighting for bloody ground on Saipan, their future depended on the Navy's ability to hold off the threat from sea and keep the invasion forces supplied.

Over the course of the day, the Japanese and Americans hurled hundreds of aircraft at each other, and submarines dueled with destroyers to penetrate defenses. But Japanese aviation had suffered great losses of experienced pilots since their glory days of Pearl Harbor, thanks to American victories beginning at Midway. American aviation skill and equipment had improved dramatically; it was no contest. In what has come to be known as the Marianas Turkey Shoot, the Japanese lost over 400 carrier aircraft, 200 land-based aircraft, and 3 aircraft carriers in that one day. From then on, remaining Japanese carriers could only be used as decoys, since they had neither the planes nor the pilots to man them.

Much fighting remained before the island was declared officially "secured" on July 9, 1944. Much fighting continued as Tinian was invaded in late July, and pockets of resistance remained for months. Before it was all over, there were more than 14,000 American casualties, including 3,426 killed or missing. Of the 30,000 Japanese troops that defended Saipan, fewer than 1,000 remained alive at battle's end, many dying in hopeless banzai charges. As many as 8,000 civilians perished in the end by leaping to their deaths at Suicide Cliff and other sites rather than be captured by the hated Americans.

The victory, despite its cost, was crucial to the defeat of Japan. Soon there-after, the government of General Hideki Tojo, who had led Japan into the war, toppled. American B-29 bombers were now able to operate against the Japanese islands. In fact, the most famous of those, the *Enola Gay*, flew from the airfields at Tinian with the first atomic bomb.

There were many heroes of the Battle of Saipan. Among them were certainly the aircrews of the PBYs, who spent countless hours aloft in the wide reaches of the Pacific, risking attack from the enemy they were seeking and being lost at sea if their machine failed or was unequal to the weather, or from poor judgment by young airmen. And young they were. One of the members of PBY Squadron VP-34 was Radioman Elgen Long, already a second-class petty officer, although he was barely sixteen years old. The Navy didn't know or care about his age; he had enlisted on his fifteenth birthday, with his parents at-testing that he was seventeen. Elgen doesn't resent that his parents sent him to war at such a tender age. He was sure he was going eventually, and as his older brother was enlisting they felt it best that young Elgen enlist with his sibling, who could watch out for him.

Over the next four years, Elgen saw his big brother for a total of two hours.

As it turned out, however, Elgen didn't need much watching over. He flew the skies over Saipan, and walked the jungle roads when ashore, worried that Japanese would appear at any moment. He saw the "invasion flies" that swarmed around the hundreds of dead soldiers who could not be removed or buried under battle conditions. He learned the art of aerial navigation and developed a life-long love of flying that would be the start of a remarkable and accomplished career. But it was at the age of sixteen, in 1944, on the barely secured island of Saipan, that Elgen began an association that would lead to a lifelong quest.

In the main town of Garapan, on the west coast of the island, sit several concrete buildings, damaged but not destroyed by the American bombardment. One of them is the old Japanese hospital, today still in use as an art museum. The other had been a Japanese jail, known as Garapan Prison, rumored to be the place where a famous American aviator and her navigator were incarcerated and eventually killed. It is one of the many rumored locations where Amelia Earhart and Fred Noonan were last seen.

Elgen Long and I had an opportunity to visit Saipan in February of 2007. I was working on a Department of Energy project, considering the feasibility of bringing cold deep-ocean water from 3,000 feet deep to the surface through a large pipe, and using it for energy-saving processes like sea-water air conditioning, fresh-water production through condensation, and even cold agriculture. My career has focused on the deep ocean, and it is exciting to work on these kinds of applications. I mentioned to Elgen that I was going, and he said, "You know, I was there once, sixty-three years ago! But I wasn't invited!" Then he wondered if he could come along.

Saipan is now the capital of the Commonwealth of the Northern Marianas Islands (CNMI), a U.S. protectorate. Its main town, Garapan, reflects both the influence of American money and government (including, on the one hand, good roads and signage but, on the other hand, McDonald's, Hard Rock Cafe, and KFC), as well as the trappings of a popular Japanese tourist destination (sashimi in abundance, oriental groceries, and advertisements in Japanese). All this on a distant Pacific island, a thousand miles from the equator, with tropical climate, flora, and island life. About 80,000 people are scattered about the islands of the CNMI, most on Saipan, which has a total area not much larger than Washington, D.C.

Besides work on the DOE project, there was plenty of time to tour. Of course, Elgen and I wanted to see the jail. We were shown the site by Sam McPhetres, a professor from the Northern Marianas College who taught history and current events of the CNMI, and for a while ran the Historic Preservation Society. As such, Sam is an expert on all of the folklore surrounding Amelia Earhart's supposed presence on the island. He graciously picked us up at our hotel for a fascinating tour of the Japanese prison, and told us many stories about the local people who were kept in the jail. He told us that the jailer, who was there during the time of Amelia's supposed incarceration, said there were no Caucasian women incarcerated (which did not surprise us). The tales of those who were unfortunate enough to visit were gruesome; he noted that the mess hall doubled as a torture room. Then Sam took us to the site of the old Japanese airport, complete with bomb shelters, old tanks, and the magazine for ordnance. He was a wonderful guide, and very enlightening.

There are many residents of and visitors to the island, including some prominent war veterans, who bristled at the numerous and elaborate Japanese memorials to the defenders of the island, especially compared to the lack of an American memorial. This situation was rectified in June 1994, on the fiftieth anniversary of the battle, with the dedication of the American Memorial Court of Honor. The names of the American soldiers who lost their lives are inscribed on the monument, and the entire site has been designated a National Park. Besides the Court of Honor, there is a visitor's center, amphitheater, and gardens, including a thirty-acre wetland and mangrove forest.

It was heartwarming to witness the reception of our World War II veterans, such as Elgen, on the island.

We ended our week's visit with an appearance on local Saipan radio, and a hop over to Tinian (a ten-minute plane ride in a six-seater). Our main purpose was to see the B-29 runways and the sites where the atomic bombs were loaded. Staring at the loading pits in the concrete runway, and looking at the full-size replicas of the bombs, we felt in the grip of history.

The more time I spent with Elgen, the more I discovered his connection with history. After the war, he flew Jewish refugees from East Africa to Tel Aviv during the 1948 Israeli War of Independence; he participated in the Berlin Air Lift; he even flew around the world, solo . . . but sideways (pole to pole!). He is the only man ever to fly solo over both poles. But the bit of history that Elgen and I share (although he owns a much bigger piece of it) is the quest to find Amelia Earhart's lost Lockheed Electra.

In a way, the quest began for Elgen on those days in Saipan in 1944.

Decide . . . whether or not the goal is worth
the risks involved. If it is, stop worrying.

—Amelia Earhart

Part I

# Expedition 2002

April 22, 2002; Monday, dawn. Near the Equator.

Deep-blue ocean meets an overcast sky as the morning light competes with the glow of high-intensity work lamps on the aft deck of the research vessel *Davidson*. The grey steel deck is covered with oily rags, hydraulic fluid, tool kits, and spare parts. Thick, black hydraulic hoses snake around winches, generators, and power units. Technicians and deck hands swarm around equipment, working in teams, each with a purpose. The ship's cook brings coffee and sandwiches. The group has been working all night, with no guarantee of success.

The ship lies still in a calm sea. From the aft deck trails a thin cable, dipping into the ocean, plunging into the abyss. Down it goes, one mile, two miles, three . . . and there, at a depth of 5,600 meters (over three miles) lies the bitter end of the cable, attached to a one-ton sled-like device called NOMAD. For weeks, NOMAD had been skimming the bottom, using a sonar to map hundreds of square miles of ocean floor. But now it lies still, helpless to move as the cable attaching NOMAD to the ship could no longer tow it.

Mission Operations Manager Tom Dettweiler is tired, and his bearded face shows it. He speaks quietly, working his jaw, teeth grinding with tension, as he haltingly explains. "Yeah, we've, uh, replaced one of the motors with a spare we had. . . . We've had to take apart one of the other motors, clean it out, rebuild it as best as we could . . . put it in place."

Tom gestures at the equipment with his talkie, and looks down at the deck. Then he returns his tired eyes to the camera, and continues, "Now we're getting ready to try taking tension on the winch and see if our rebuild jobs are going to work."

Ten hours earlier, all was well on board the *Davidson*. The crew was excited, heady with expectation, ready for discovery. It could happen any moment. Meanwhile, new underwater worlds were opening up, as the team was mapping territory never before seen. Volcanic calderas, extensive ridge systems, and massive seamounts were revealed as NOMAD imaged undiscovered terrain on earth's final frontier. Now the crew's measure of success would be recovery of a million dollars of equipment from the deep sea, returning home with everyone alive.

Tom looks around the littered deck, and gestures again with his ever-present talkie. "Uh, it's our only option. . . . We're down to our last option right now, this is it. If it doesn't work, then we have to consider . . ." he pauses, ". . . leaving the vehicle here."

Tom bites his lip, as if hearing his own words and considering their meaning. He looks down for a moment, then back at the camera. There is nothing more to say.

A ship in a harbor is safe, but that's
not what ships are built for.

— Rear Admiral Grace Hopper

# The Expedition Begins

March 12, 2002; Tuesday afternoon. At Sea.

Aloha Tower in Honolulu Harbor had slipped behind us, the beach and skyline of Waikiki had sunk below the horizon, and the jagged cliffs of Oahu were fading in the distance. After years of research, planning, equipment development, fundraising, and persistence, we are finally at sea on our deep-sea expedition to find Amelia's Lockheed Electra! We got under way at about 1530 (3:30 PM) this afternoon, right on schedule. We are steaming southwest at about ten knots, with a tired (but excited!) crew, and a long voyage ahead. We left some teary-eyed folks on the pier seeing family members leaving for the duration, planned to be as long as seven weeks, while other staff and supporters added their well wishes.

The expedition had officially begun many weeks before, when we made preparations for mobilization of our ship in Seattle, Washington. On February 22, a small fleet of trucks left Hanover, Maryland, for Seattle, loaded with tons of high-tech deep-sea equipment. Much had come together in the past couple of months to make that day (and many that followed) possible. We were embarking on a project that would cost over $1.6 million and last over seventy days. We would scan nearly 1,000 square miles of ocean floor at a resolution fine enough to detect a trash can at a depth of nearly 20,000 feet. We would operate far out of sight of any shore, several days' sail from the nearest inhabited island.

The trucks were loaded with an amazing array of equipment, ranging from state-of-the-art electronics and sensors, the latest computers and custom software, to powerful hydraulic engines, to simple hand tools. Supplies ranged from the technically sophisticated spare parts for sensitive electronics meant to work at massive sea pressures, to the more mundane pencils, paper clips, and whiteout. For seven weeks, our ship would be our home, office, factory, and recreation center, and we had to bring everything we need to be entirely self sufficient if at all possible. With at most five weeks of operating time on station, a week lost to retrieve a broken or forgotten item from the nearest inhabited island would be a devastating setback.

In some ways, it seems as though the hardest part was behind us. It had taken nearly half a decade for me and my company Nauticos to create this opportunity, and for Elgen Long, over thirty years. For Elgen, most of that was research, meetings, interviews and analysis. For me, it has been mostly business . . . making deals, finding sponsors and investors, and assembling a capable team that could do the job.

As we began mobilization, we were pleased to be on time and under budget. The funds for this expedition came half from investors (who hope to make some return from media and exhibition business upon success), and the rest cash and services from Nauticos. We also have some important sponsors who help offset some of the costs. Kongsberg-Simrad has provided a forward-looking sonar, Kodak has donated film, James Cameron (of movie fame) is lending lights, Rockwell Collins is supporting two engineers and communications, and the U.S. Navy is sending two people. Through the Naval Oceanographic Office (NAVO), and the Naval Meteorology and Oceanography Command (CNMOC), we were also getting weather forecasting and bathymetric data. Having the Navy along gave us some hope that if we would run into real trouble we could call up Admiral West or Admiral Donaldson and they'd quickly have a fast, gray ship on the way to help.

The common denominator for all contributors was the chance to support and participate in an adventure, a modern exploration into the unknown. All share in the excitement of seeing what is down there in the vast, unexplored reaches of the deep ocean. We would image territory on the sea floor that no human had ever seen, something that can't be said about any place on terrestrial earth, or even the far side of the moon.

All the equipment, supplies, personal belongings, two cases of Snyder's pretzels, and a small cadre of our team converged on Seattle, where our research vessel, the R/V *Davidson*, was waiting. Four days were set aside for our team to load, install, and test all equipment, and make ready for the ten-day transit to Honolulu.

The *Davidson* would be our little 175-foot universe for the next few weeks, where thirty-four of us would live, work, sleep, eat and play, surrounded by blue ocean and blue sky farther than one could see. To make up for this, I guess, the ship was painted blue.

The *Davidson* was built in 1967, and plied the world's oceans for many years as a National Oceanographic and Atmospheric Administration (NOAA) survey vessel, serving in the Pacific, Alaska, and West Coast. She was named for George Davidson (1825–1911), a pioneer coast surveyor, who came to California in 1850. Davidson was a geodesist, that is, one who deals with the measurement of the shape of the earth and its gravitational field. Anyone nowadays who uses a portable global positioning satellite (GPS) system to find the nearest restaurant can thank folks like Davidson, as the accuracy of these devices depends critically on knowing the exact shape of the earth.

Over his career, Davidson planned the 39th Parallel Survey from north of San Francisco through the Sierra Nevada Mountains, and measured the "Yolo Baseline," considered the most accurate geodetic measurements of the nineteenth century. He was president of the California Academy of Sciences for sixteen years, author of *Pacific Coast Pilot* (1889) and *Alaska Coast Pilot* (1869), and was instrumental in convincing James Lick to endow the Lick Observatory, among many other significant positions and accomplishments.

The ship bearing his name was acquired from NOAA in 1997 by Ocean Services, Inc., of Seattle, and began work doing submarine cable route surveys across the Pacific Ocean, and hydrographic surveys in Alaska's Cook Inlet and Peninsula regions. The *Davidson* was large and comfortable . . . for a research vessel. At 175 feet long and 38 feet wide, she contained an interior living space about the size of a four-bedroom house, providing accommodations for fourteen crew and up to twenty-eight charter passengers. With "only" thirty-four on board (crew and charter), we had just a little extra elbow room. Besides the living space, which included cabins, lounge, and mess, we had an operations space, spanning the width of the ship behind the bridge, large enough for a sonar analysis station. There was a large open deck space aft, which is where most of the ocean survey gear was installed and welded down.

The ship displaced 1,100 tons, and could carry 63,000 gallons of fuel. The rated fuel consumption for a cruising speed of ten knots was around 1,500 gallons per day; this included fuel for the generators that provided all power for the ship and its equipment. Of course, you can't burn every gallon, so with a planned reserve the ship was rated for an endurance of forty days and a range of 7,000 nautical miles.

We were planning a transit of "only" 1,700 nautical miles from Honolulu to the vicinity of Howland Island, a trip of about seven days. Over the course of five weeks of surveying, we would be moving at a snail's pace, only about two knots, covering another 1,700 miles total distance. Then the return trip. So, we would cover about 5,000 miles over the course of our seven-week expedition, and our calculations promised that we would have plenty of fuel. We were quickly to discover the limitations of pen, paper, spec sheets, and calculators when compared with the reality of operating at sea, far from land and a fuel supply.

In addition to fuel, our ship carried 2,000 gallons of lube oil, 6,000 gallons of fresh water, and enough food, drink, and snacks (including the Snyder's pretzels) to keep thirty-four of us well fed for the duration. We also had to bring supplies (everything from paper clips to mineral oil to super glue), spare parts (from hydraulic motors to electronics to o-rings), and personal effects (from soap to books to party supplies). There would be no opportunity to resupply or replace an item forgotten or lost. We had to be as self-sufficient as possible.

On the afternoon of February 28, with everything on board, tied down, and stowed for sea, the *Davidson* departed Seattle, sailed out of the Puget Sound, and headed southwest to Hawaii. On board with the ship's crew was a small group of technicians who would continue outfitting our spaces and readying equipment during the ten-day transit. Among them was Colleen Hughes, whose normal job was office manager at Nauticos.

A big part of the success of any endeavor, whether an office job or an ocean expedition, is teamwork. And a big part of that is everybody understanding and valuing the role of each of the teammates. At Nauticos, we didn't expect everybody to be able to do everybody else's job, but we liked to find opportunities to give people a healthy appreciation for what might be involved. Hence, the idea of "cross-training," and the reason that Colleen spent ten stormy days at sea. Battling seasickness, shivering in cold, wet weather, and working round the clock, she had little time for her favorite hobby, and had time to dash off only one quick email:

> This trip is a real eye opener. I knew there would be physical labor (I just didn't know how much). I have been too tired to quilt at night. Somehow out here it's not that important. There is so much to be done. I think we are going to try and put NOMAD in the water tomorrow. I guess we'll have a lot to catch up on when I get to Hawaii. Tell the ladies in the quilt group I said "hi!" Colleen.

During the transit, the team performed a rigorous schedule of integration and testing, including some test operations of NOMAD (Nauticos Ocean Mapping and Analysis Device, our deep-ocean sonar) in deep water. Some important progress was made, and some integration issues with the ship's power were worked out, so it was wonderful that we had a chance to face and address some of the technical challenges before starting the mission proper. Colleen and the others landed in Honolulu on March 11 all smiles, happy to be on dry land and proud of what had been accomplished. Colleen truly earned her new nickname (spoken in a "pirate" voice), "Colleen of the Sea!"

Meanwhile, our operations team was gathering in Honolulu. A couple of us came a few days early to make sure all was ready. Besides the Nauticos team, we had Rockwell Collins radio engineers, our Navy representatives from NAVO, and our media group. As is common in any major operation these days, folks were coming from all over, and the logistics for travel planning and shipping of gear from Maryland, Tennessee, Iowa, California, Rhode Island, and a few other states was daunting!

The trickle of people became a flood, which lasted until dinner on the evening of March 10, by which time everyone was present (some straight from the airport). We gathered at the Seafood Village Restaurant in Honolulu for a departure dinner and final briefing. Everyone dressed up and the atmosphere was festive. The gathering including Mike and Margaret McCormack, two of the many Amelia project investors, who were happy to see a little of what they were supporting. Also present to see us off were Arlinka, wife of Jonathan Blair (our photographer), who flew in from Molokai, and Susan, wife of Jon Thompson (one of our key investors and supporters) from Memphis. Though we had just met, Susan kept trying to get me in trouble wherever we went by introducing Lynn (whom I had married twenty-six years before) as my "first wife!" (Since Lynn and I are still married, I never really had time for a second wife. . . .)

Over dessert, assistant operations manager Tom Bethge (pronounced "BAY-gee") set the tone for the ensuing weeks with a no-nonsense briefing, making sure everyone knew their responsibilities for getting under way promptly in the morning. Though we needed no further motivation, I read an inspirational message from John Manuel, a member of the Nauticos advisory board (and former vice president of Lockheed):

> Fair winds, following seas, obedient electrons, tame running tackle, and here's to finding the Golden Fleece of modern times, not by luck, but by the vision, skill, dedication and professionalism of Dave and the Nauticos team. Godspeed, John Manuel.

Last, but certainly not least, we recognized the support of the others in our organizations who were not going on the expedition, and the families we would be leaving behind for as much as two months. Everyone played an important role in bringing us to that point, and our co-workers' and families' support and enthusiasm was critical and much appreciated. Although I had not fulfilled my ambition of calling all of the spouses, at least I managed to get out the following email, which I read to the group:

This message is to the families of all those about to embark on the Amelia expedition (and to the ones who already spent time at sea on the transit from Seattle)—

I just wanted to express my appreciation for the sacrifice you will all make for the extended adventure we are about to begin. I know it is a hardship for you to be separated for so long, and handle all of the day-to-day stuff that must continue over the next two months. You will have to be there for the crises, the sporting events, the good (and bad!) grades, and anything else that goes on that normally you both handle.

The best reward I can offer you is our best efforts at success, from which should stem a sense of achievement, worldwide recognition, and hopefully some financial benefit if we can conduct the business we hope to. We are "up to bat with the bases loaded," and you have helped us to get there. I hope you'll soon be cheering for that "home run!"

Regardless of the outcome, I feel very privileged to have this opportunity, to sail with a great crew, and to have the backing of the small army of helpers back home keeping us "afloat"! It is a worthy quest, and I'm confident in our team. Thanks again, and we'll look forward to the celebration when we return! Dave

Expedition Leader Elgen Long had a choice few words of encouragement, and then the exhausted travelers retired to our comfortable hotel rooms on Waikiki Beach for the night. We savored them, as our ship would arrive tomorrow and future nights would be spent in sparse quarters.

We learned that, owing to a mix-up having to do with how many days are in ninety-six hours, the Coast Guard would not let the ship in port until 1600 (4 PM) on Monday, March 11. This meant we would have to hustle to embark the team and be ready for our planned departure on Tuesday morning. The crew on board used the extra time to loiter off shore of Oahu and deploy the sonar in deep water for testing, taking advantage of calm seas and sunny skies. The weather had been notably harsh during most of the ten-day trip from Seattle. The media team arranged for a helicopter flyby of the ship, catching it in operation with NOMAD in the water.

When the ship arrived, we immediately began to move our gear on board, and to stow things anywhere we could to get it off the main deck. Meanwhile, the operations team was working to get NOMAD fully functional, having flooded a connector which led to a "smoked" capacitor on the sonar mother board. We arranged for a new board to be shipped from New Hampshire (ETA Tuesday at 1400). If the original could be fixed, the new one would serve as a spare. One of the banes of deep-sea equipment operation is flooding of connectors, allowing the highly conductive seawater to short delicate electronics.

Usually, once all connections have been made and properly sealed, there is no more trouble, so we purposely tested everything near shore so we could get new spares before heading far from any port.

After doing all we could, most of us (operations team excluded) headed out for a last dinner on the town. To save hotel costs, and to begin to adapt to our new homes, we spent the night on the ship. The dedicated operations team didn't quit working until 1 AM.

We were up early the next morning, and mustered on the pier at 0800. Tom gave us our Plan of the Day, which consisted of cleaning out and organizing the media lab, getting all gear in its place, and stowing for sea. Along the way, there were numerous errands, and cars going every which way. The time-limiting event was waiting for our part to arrive from New Hampshire via National Air Cargo. The item was picked up at 1430, and we made our way back to the ship in time for a 1530 departure. As we shoved off, there were plenty of teary eyes and waves and blown kisses. We would not be back for a long while.

So that brought us to March 12, 2002, finally at sea. The evening was warm and clear, heady with impending adventure. We all enjoyed seeing Aloha Tower, Waikiki Beach, and Diamond Head from the sea, and watched the skyline of Honolulu recede. Soon, only the peaks of Oahu were visible. A pod of whales came into view, as if to welcome us to their ocean world and the weeks ahead.

I had no trouble at all sleeping in the gently rolling rack. It was very soothing. . . .

I don't believe I thought one bit about Amelia Earhart that night. But she had been on our minds regularly since we met pilot and Amelia Earhart researcher Elgen Long, with Steve Lyons of WGBH TV, at our Nauticos offices in Maryland on August 6, 1997. Our company (then known as Meridian Sciences, Inc.) had yet to make many of our discoveries; the Israeli submarine *Dakar*, the 200 BC Ancient Wreck, and the Japanese aircraft carrier *Kaga* were still in our exciting future. But we had made a dramatic discovery of the Japanese submarine *I-52* at a remarkable depth of 17,000 feet, and already had established a reputation for deep-sea exploration. So, when WGBH (producer of the NOVA series) was looking to make a documentary of Elgen's quest for the Electra, and seeking validation of his theory, Nauticos was a logical choice.

The "Golden Submarine," the *I-52*, was a cargo-carrying submarine built by Japan to exchange critical war materials and technology with Germany when Allied blockades precluded any other form of commerce. On its maiden voyage in June 1944, the ship was carrying vital metals, raw rubber from Malaysia, three tons of opium (used to make morphine), and two tons of gold bullion. The latter was to pay for German bombsights, radars, and other high-tech products to be shipped on the return voyage. Through a combination of code-breaking, weapons technology, and brave, competent piloting, the *I-52* was sunk by an Avenger torpedo bomber launched from a converted Liberty Ship carrier in June of 1944 in the mid-Atlantic.

Nauticos was hired by historical researcher Paul Tidwell and a group of investors, led by Arkansas engineer Fred Neal, who were interested in recovering the valuable cargo. Tom Dettweiler, our operations manager for the Amelia expedition, led our operations team at sea. Back home, we analyzed data from the war patrol logs of the ships and aircraft involved in the attack. Using a system we developed for the Navy called Renav (short for "re-navigation"), we reconstructed the events of the engagement and redirected the search to a point nearly twenty miles from the position recorded by the U.S. Navy at the time of the sinking. We found the wreckage of the *I-52* barely one-half mile from the position we computed with Renav. Resting at over 17,000 feet, the *I-52* is still one of the deepest shipwrecks ever discovered.

The *I-52* discovery was a dramatic proof of principle of Nauticos' skill, business plan, and Renav technology. Our success was widely publicized, including spots on Dan Rather's *CBS News* and in the *New York Times*. A later trip to the site was featured on National Geographic. (As of this time, fifteen years later, Tidwell and his investors have not launched a mission to attempt salvage, or even determined if they have the legal rights to do so. This circumstance has little to do with technology, and a lot to do with business.)

So our team was more than qualified to assess Elgen's theory and analysis. At first we were skeptical; we had already been approached a year earlier to help another group (Tighar, The International Group for Historic Aircraft Recovery, led by Ric Gillespie) to search near a Pacific island, and had not been interested because we saw no reason to expect the aircraft to be there. The search for Amelia seemed based on folklore, like the legend of Atlantis, and we knew of little solid information to work with. A noble quest, for sure, but not good business. Still, the credibility of WGBH got our attention, and, after all, we were only being asked to evaluate Elgen's theory, not to conduct a search.

By the time the first meeting ended, we realized we could find the Electra. Elgen's ideas, research, and analysis were serious, professional, and quantifiable. It all made perfect sense, and our Renav process could probably refine his work to a reasonable search area.

We were hooked.

Elgen, of course, had been hooked for decades. He has claimed that he and his wife, Marie, were only researching the history and never expected to actually search, as the waters where Amelia ditched are nearly 20,000 feet deep and beyond the abilities of any technology he could use. But the goal of finding the Electra steadily took form as deep-ocean technology matured and became available outside the Cold War military. Available to companies like Nauticos.

Elgen M. Long was born August 12, 1927, in McMinnville, Oregon. At nine years old, his first memory of Earhart's disappearance came from selling newspapers headlining the event. He attended public schools in Taft and Marshfield, Oregon, until the tender age of fifteen. With his parents' permission and the exigencies of World War II, he joined the U.S. Navy and began a lifelong career in aviation: first as a radio operator, then as a navigator, and finally as a pilot. He accumulated over sixty years of experience and nearly 45,000 hours of flight time.

During World War II, he flew over one hundred combat patrols in Navy seaplanes throughout the Pacific theatre including many patrols over Howland Island. His service took him through the Marshall Islands, the Marianas, the Philippines, Okinawa, and the occupation of Japan. On the date of cease-fire in August 1945, his plane was directed to fly over all Japanese military installations on the island of Formosa (modern Taiwan) to see if the Japanese would shoot at them or honor the cease-fire. He remembers thinking to himself, "You have to be young and stupid to do this."

As a young sailor, Elgen was lucky enough to meet his future wife on a blind date in Los Angeles, California. On May 12, 1946, only a year after they met, twenty-year-old Marie Katherine Kurilich of Cleveland, Ohio, and Elgen were married. Throughout their fifty-seven years together they worked as a team, and Marie contributed to all of their life endeavors.

After World War II, Elgen was able to advance his formal education and graduate from the college of San Mateo with an associate degree in aeronautics. He also obtained his aircraft mechanics license and added that expertise to his radio and navigation skills. Although World War II had ended, there were still many regional conflicts around the globe. Elgen became involved in rescuing refugees from desperate circumstances and flying them to safety. The most dramatic of these was Operation Magic Carpet.

A humanitarian airlift program sponsored by legendary Alaska Air president James Wooten, Operation Magic Carpet saved more than 40,000 Yemenite Jews, bringing them to Israel between late 1948 and early 1950. Flying almost daily for over a year, overloaded C-46 and DC-4 aircraft flown by overtaxed pilots and crew dodged Arab airspace and found fuel wherever they could to save as many souls as possible. Despite flying conditions that would have been illegal under U.S. aviation rules, the operation never lost a life or even suffered an injury due to accident.

Later, Elgen flew in support of the Berlin Airlift as a radio operator and navigator. As if these adventures were not enough, in 1971, at age forty-four, Elgen set out to be the first man to fly solo around the world over both poles. The flight over the South Pole would make him the first man to have crossed Antarctica alone. It was the longest solo flight ever sanctioned by the French Fédération Aéronatique Internationale, and for this feat Elgen was selected as the outstanding sport pilot in the world and was presented the Gold Air Medal in Paris, France, in 1972. Elgen navigated the round-the-world flight using an inertial navigation system. This was the first flight around the world over both poles using this new navigation system, and the Institute of Navigation chose Elgen to receive their award as the outstanding practicing navigator for 1971. These are the world's top awards that can be presented in the two different disciplines.

In gratitude, Elgen and his wife Marie decided to travel throughout the world interviewing the people still living that actually participated in Amelia's last flight. This effort resulted in the historic collection of Amelia Earhart data and interviews that now resides at the SeaWord Foundation. Sadly, Marie passed away in June 2003, but the search for Earhart's plane continues using the data and information that she helped develop.

Our first full day at sea treated us to a sight we were to become all too familiar with: a vast, uninterrupted expanse of blue ocean, bordered by a horizon ringed with puffy white clouds and blue sky overhead. This part of the Pacific Ocean is sprinkled pretty evenly with cotton-ball clouds, widely scattered. These clouds are relatively low, so as one looks to the horizon they line up and give the appearance of solid overcast in the distance. So, wherever you are it seems that you occupy the only sunny spot in an infinity of solid cloud cover. This condition persists for days on end, the only variation being scattered (but very localized) squalls that seem to orbit the ship like satellites. Daily encounters with these weather blobs yield brief but intense sheets of rain, which end as abruptly as they begin. Only a few times did we suffer an all-day storm. Of course, it was often during these squalls or storms that the operations team had to be on deck to deploy or retrieve equipment.

Sailors over the centuries have recognized these weather patterns, and this area of the ocean came to be called "the Doldrums." To paraphrase Nathanial Bowditch's *The American Practical Navigator*, a belt of low pressure near the equator known as the Doldrums occupies a position midway between high-pressure belts at about latitude 30–35 degrees on each side. The atmospheric pressure along the equatorial low is almost uniform. Wind speeds are light, and direction variable. Hot, sultry days are common. The sky is often overcast, and showers are relatively frequent.

We can vouch for all of that! There is another low-pressure belt poleward of each side of the high-pressure region with similar weak winds known as the

Horse Latitudes, apparently so named because becalmed sailors threw horses overboard in this region when water supplies ran short! (This is one example of popular naval lore that doesn't make much sense and probably is not true, but it is the popular explanation.) There are two particularly helpful results of this meteorological phenomenon. Typhoons (the Pacific version of hurricanes) are absent from this region, and almost every day we were treated to magnificent sunrises and sunsets, owing to the arrangement of clouds.

In our circumstance, we tended to connect everything to Amelia. One of the curiosities of the final hour of her flight was her report that she was flying at 1,000 feet while searching for Howland Island. Why so low, when a higher altitude would have allowed her to see farther? Many researchers have sought the answer in the clouds, imagining that she was flying low to be below the cloud deck. They have scoured weather reports from the Coast Guard stationed on the island to imagine where those clouds were and therefore narrow down where Amelia must have been flying. I think the answer is simple. There are *always* scattered clouds *everywhere* just above 1,000 feet in this part of the Pacific. Unfortunately, this knowledge is of no help in finding Amelia.

Of course, by the morning of our first full day at sea we were barely 100 miles from Hawaii. The Doldrums were yet ahead of us and we had over 1,500 miles and almost a week of steady steaming to reach our operations area. But there was much to do, and we started work with enthusiasm (and only a little seasickness).

We had little time to adapt to our new surroundings, so as with everything else on this mission we approached the task with organized zeal. Operations manager Tom Dettweiler held a science team meeting to begin to organize our watchstanding, data collection, and analysis routine. This was followed by a safety briefing by First Mate Joe Litchfield. Joe looks and acts a bit like Popeye, and not surprisingly was the most experienced and competent sailor on the crew. His gravelly voice, squinting eye, and mock-gruff manner belied a sharp intelligence, keen professionalism, and a heart of gold. The briefing was followed by the first of our weekly Abandon Ship drills, where we practiced mustering at the proper station, bringing our lifejacket, long trousers, and long-sleeved shirts. We also got a demonstration of how to don the survival suits, Gumby-like one-piece outfits in stylish safety orange that promised to keep one alive for at least a little while in any conditions—if you could find one and put it on in time.

At 1030, Spence King, assistant operations manager, held the first "SEA School" session. A uniquely Spence invention, SEA School is a daily lecture or practical exercise on most any topic, partly to gain important working knowledge, partly to take advantage of the varied talents on board, partly for general interest, and mostly for team building. SEA School was generally optional, though well attended, but the first session on ship familiarization was manda-tory for the Nauticos team. We then toured the ship, from fo'c's'le (forecastle) to engine room; this helped to orient us, though it still took a couple of days for most of us to learn to navigate unerringly between any two places on the ship. After lunch, we had our first navigation analysis session, gathering Elgen, Renav expert Jeff Palshook, Tom Dettweiler, and the Rockwell Collins radio engineers Rod Blocksome and Tom Vinson to discuss our navigation estimates and put the finishing touches on our search plan. This was all documented by the National Geographic camera, hoisted by Bill Mills, with director Kristin Whiting and volunteer sound man Jonathan Blair. At one point, the director stepped in and stopped the proceedings because of a sound problem while I was in discussion with Elgen. I was really trying to listen to his answer, and didn't take well to being interrupted as though it was a "staged" meeting—especially since they insisted on candid shots. We worked out a new, more sat-isfactory protocol.

The latter part of the afternoon was spent outfitting the electronics room, meeting the ship's crew, and getting settled. After dinner, Elgen and I had an-other navigation meeting before we ran out of energy. There was big excitement on the fantail in the evening. . . . chef Scotty caught a four-foot mahi-mahi! Fish for lunch tomorrow!

Much of the activity of the first day, while having some immediate practical value, was geared to the team-building process. We had just assembled a group of thirty-four people from all walks of life, many of whom had never met, all with a role critical to our success. Some of us had never been to sea before, or away from home for so long. Others had experience at sea, but in far differ-ent circumstances. To the ship's crew, we were "invading" their home, and of course they wondered if we would be nose-in-the-air scientists whose work was "too complicated" for them to understand. Our junior members of the expedition, rookies at sea, were nervous in the presence of some of the grizzled old salts on board. Some were feeling the first twinges of nausea that would evolve into full-blown *mal de mer* in a matter of hours.

There are a number of tricks we use to help quickly mold this disparate group into a working team. Our philosophy is based on the premise that at some point in the course of a voyage everyone—no matter what skill, position, or pay grade—may become indispensable in a crisis or emergency. An em-barked VIP investor or egghead scientist who ignores a rugged-looking deck "grunt," assuming all he is good for is chipping paint and repainting, finds it is too late to be remorseful when that same grunt is deploying the lifeboats! In fact, the common able-bodied seaman on a research vessel is generally well educated, bright, and skilled in matters not readily apparent to the scientist, and his demeanor and appearance are not always a reflection of his talents.

We begin by assembling the charter team and set a few ground rules. Top among them is safety, but just a notch below is their relationship with the crew. We tell our people to make a point of sitting with the crew at the first meal, and asking them about their job on the ship and how they came to be on the *Davidson*. We encourage them to visit the bridge on the midwatch, in the wee hours of the morning, and keep the folks on duty company. We ask them to be on time for meals, and not to expect the cooks (who are the hardest working people on the ship) to make special meals or hold them for special times. (Of course, once the relationship is established they will do this without being asked.) The bonding among shipmates proceeds apace, and soon we are all working well together.

Getting there is half the fun!
    —Anonymous

When you're in the middle of nowhere, any
direction you head is somewhere!

    —The author, contemplating our location
    on the planet during the expedition

# Transit to Nowhere

March 14, 2002; Thursday, 0800 local time.

Another fine day at sea . . . and a busy one! We set up to deploy NOMAD first thing in the morning for deep-water testing. Our operations technicians Shawn Dann, Mike Davis, Jay Ellis, and Sue Morris had been tirelessly working to complete all repairs and make the system fully ready to withstand the crushing pressures at up to 20,000-foot depths. Their efforts could only be judged by a successful descent, as there was no way to simulate those conditions on the surface.

The NOMAD-6000 Deep Towed Search System was designed and built at the Nauticos Ship Point Research Facility in Lusby, Maryland. It was based on a tried-and-true design similar to the Argo system deployed by the Woods Hole Oceanographic Institution and the TOSS (Towed Optical Search System) built by the Naval Oceanographic Office. The development team was led by Bruce Brown, an ocean engineer with decades of experience in the design and operation of robotic vehicles. He had helped develop this technology for the U.S. Navy, and in 1998 helped Nauticos coordinate the Discovery Channel live broadcast from the wreck site of the *Titanic*. He was also a veteran of recovery operations to locate flight recorders and other wreckage from the 1996 ValueJet Flight 592 crash in the Florida Everglades, and the 1986 *Challenger* Space Shuttle accident, among others.

Of course, no project can begin in earnest without a name. Bruce wanted to call the system the Nauticos Acoustic Sensor and Telemetry Instrument (NASTI), but was vetoed by corporate counsel Julie Nelson, for some reason! With further thought, we settled on Nauticos Ocean Mapping and Analysis Device, hence NOMAD. The 6000 referred to its design operating depth, 6,000 meters (about 20,000 feet). Though there are ocean trenches that go deeper— including Challenger Deep in the Marianas Trench of the western Pacific, at just over 35,800 feet—95 percent of the ocean floor can be reached with the NOMAD system.

For those who enjoy reading spec sheets, here is what ours said about NOMAD:

> The Nauticos NOMAD 6000 Deep-Towed Search System is a 6,000-meter depth-rated tow body designed to be easily configured with numerous sonar and imaging sensors, as well as any customer-specified instrument. The heart of the system is a state-of-the-art fiber-optic data telemetry system providing up to 1.5 gigabits/sec data transfer. The basic system is a Klein System 2000 sidescan sonar modified for deep operation at both 50kHz and 500kHz and a Kongsberg Simrad MS1000 330kHz scanning sonar. This combination allows for wide area coverage (up to a 2000-meter swath with the Klein 50kHz and 200 meters at a 360-degree scan with the MS1000) as well as high-resolution sonar imagery for target identification and classification.

If it sounds complicated, it was. In layman's terms, NOMAD consisted of an aluminum frame with skids on the bottom—for that reason, it was usually referred to as a "sled." Fins on the back provided stability, as well as a flat space for logos and decorations. The frame surrounded two thick-walled stainless-steel cylinders that contained all of the electronics and anything else that could not live in salt water at high pressure . . . almost 9,000 PSI at 20,000 feet. That's four and a half *tons* of force on every square inch of the cylinder! Wiring connections could withstand the pressure, but not the seawater; hence, they were contained in plastic tubes filled with mineral oil. A simple spring-loaded pressure compensation device worked to keep the oil pressure just a couple of PSI above sea pressure, so any leaks in fittings would let oil out rather than salt water in. Because minor leaks were inevitable, an oil reservoir held an on-board supply, and often a dropping oil level meant an early end to a deployment. This feature was also a source of embarrassment to one of our female expedition members who once was sent to buy an entire case of baby oil at a local store to make sure we had enough for our mission.

The working elements of NOMAD are the sonars and cameras. A device called a sidescan sonar can image wide swaths of the ocean floor with acoustic echoes, detecting mountains, rocks, and man-made objects. Since the system must be towed near the bottom, within a few hundred feet or closer, a forward-looking sonar scanned the path ahead and warned of hills or cliffs, giving the operators time to winch in on the cable and pull up the sled. Otherwise, we might inadvertently conduct "bottom sampling." NOMAD was also configured with a number of cameras so that sonar targets could be visually imaged and identified. Special lights designed to operate at such depths were loaned to us by James Cameron (the film director of *Titanic* fame) since there is absolutely no ambient light in the deep ocean. Still, since light is strongly absorbed by seawater, even the best lights can only push back the darkness by a few dozen feet.

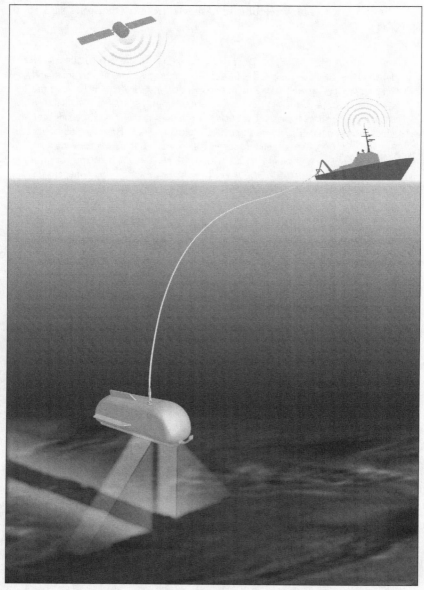

A sidescan sonar creates a burst of sound (ping) in a narrow "beam" to each side, and listens for echos from the seabed. Terrain features and man-made objects create echos that can be mapped, ping by ping, into an acoustic image. The sonar sled must be towed near enough to the ocean floor that the echos can be easily detected and accurately mapped. A long cable and slow speeds are needed to achieve this. Positioning is a challenge—GPS tells the location of the ship, but the sled position must be estimated.

That's why imaging operations are distinct and separate from sonar mapping; they cannot be done at the same time. The instrumentation package was completed by heading and attitude sensors to help correct the sonar data for positioning and pointing variations.

All of this would be useless without the cable and its fiber-optic telemetry system. In the year 2000, this was a state-of-the-art capability for underwater applications, allowing massive amounts of data to be sent over the six-mile cable, handling sonar and video signals with ease. The cable also provided electrical power to the NOMAD, and was its source of propulsion. Since the sonars like a very quiet environment, the sled had no propulsion of its own and was silently towed along by the cable. At thirteen tons, the cable was by far the most massive element of the deployed system, outweighing the 2,000-pound NOMAD by more than an order of magnitude.

And expensive! The system was designed and built beginning in 1999, and was first deployed for tests in the Chesapeake Bay in September of 2000. NOMAD cost just under $300,000 to build, but that did not include the 11,000-meter steel-armored fiber-optic cable that would be needed to deploy it. This was custom built at Rochester Cable in Culpeper, Virginia, for a price tag of $280,000. Jon Thompson put us over the top on that purchase with a key investment, so we were happy to have him out at sea with us to see it in action.

On the ship, telemetry from the fiber cable was fed into a collection of computers, monitors, and recorders, which also drew signals from GPS navigation systems on the vessel. An array of displays allowed our team to view the sonar images as they were collected, slowly, line by line, as the NOMAD was towed deliberately along the seafloor at a leisurely speed of just under two knots. A winch operator controlled the length of cable deployed, which in turn helped control the altitude of the sled. Changes in ship's speed also caused the cable (and sled) to rise or sink, which called for continuous monitoring of the altitude and frequent winch operations. This was further complicated by changes in terrain ahead, as indicated by the forward-looking sonar display. All information was recorded, and it was the job of Tom Dettweiler to go over every bit later, trying to tease out the slightest indication of a man-made target from the clutter of terrain features and noise.

Three quarters of a million dollars of sled, cable, and topside equipment would be useless without the most basic of machines, a handling system to spool the heavy cable and control its deployment. The 0.7-inch diameter cable was wound on a 10-foot diameter drum, and fed around a pair of large pulleys driven by motors powered by 3,000-PSI hydraulic fluid. The fluid was pressurized by a hydraulic power unit (HPU), powered by ship's electric service or a diesel generator. Having tapped all of our resources to build the

NOMAD and buy the cable, a new handling system was beyond our financial reach at the time. Fortunately, we were able to lease a used system through a Cooperative Research and Development Agreement (CRADA) with NAVO. Part of the Naval Meteorological Command, NAVO also sent two riders, Brag Shearer and Lieutenant Rob Witzleb, who provided analysis and weather forecasting support.

The cable left the ship via a huge pulley, called a sheave, that hung from an A-frame attached to the stern. The NOMAD was attached to the bitter end, with critical connections made into the NOMAD power supplies and fiber-optic telemetry system. These connections had to be absolutely watertight, even under the most extreme sea pressures.

Deploying the NOMAD was something of a ballet, with a ton of equipment suspended from the A-frame swinging like a pendulum as the ship rolled and pitched until it could be dipped safely in the water. A winch operator and an A-frame operator worked together to lift the vehicle off the deck, tilt the A-frame aft, and spool NOMAD out and over the side without smashing into the deck or the stern of the ship. To control its lateral swinging, "tag" lines were attached to rings on each side of the vehicle, manned by four crewmen each. These tag lines were released by a latch triggered by a smaller line when NOMAD was in the water. Hardhats, life jackets, and steel-toed boots were mandatory, as were long sleeves and no loose clothing.

Recovering the NOMAD was a bit more of a challenge. The trick is to get the tag lines attached while the vehicle is just awash at the surface. To do this, we used long telescoping poles that could reach down and latch the hooks at the ends of the tag lines onto the rings on the vehicle. It took quite a bit of practice to hook the lines, especially if the seas were high, or it was raining, or at night (or occasionally all three!) Tom Bethge set up a training session to practice on a test device Spence made. The device was a thin steel rod attached to a cable at the end of a line, such that it would trail upright in the water and give a target to hook. Jon Thompson was proud he snagged it three times. Others of us practiced, and Kristin wanted to try. She was proud to make the catch and officially become a "hooker."

The 2002 mission lasted seventy-one days, counting from the time the *Davidson* departed Seattle until it returned. Forty-five of those days were consumed simply by transiting (Seattle to Honolulu to the operating area, then to refuel, then back again). In the operating area, about a quarter of the time was spent in turning the system between search lanes, plus a little time for maintenance. So, out of the seventy-one days, we were able to spend only twenty-six days actually searching. If one considers the overall price tag of the mission, compared to the time spent searching, it cost about $3,600 per hour . . . every second, we were spending a dollar! Time was truly equated to money, and so we wasted very little. That's why we never delayed in a vehicle recovery or deployment, regardless of the conditions . . . day or night, in any weather. Thankfully, and owing to our location in the Doldrums, we never experienced weather severe enough to halt operations.

Fortunately, our test deployment of NOMAD could be scheduled, and the morning was sunny, bright, and calm. The *Davidson* slowed to two knots, and the ballet began. Everyone was carefully briefed and knew what to do, though our experience with this ship and equipment arrangement was close to nil. Regardless, the first deployment went well. Unfortunately, NOMAD was no sooner in the water when the port sidescan channel went blank. No choice but to retrieve it for repair. At least we gained extra practice in launch and recovery while the seas were calm. In the process, Carl Hoffman (our National Geographic–supplied journalist, and among our least experienced team members) suffered a rope burn on his hand from one of the tag lines. So Tom Bethge worked out a better system of deployment, including a couple of new cleats welded to the deck, and some new hand signals. After a few hours, the technicians tracked the problem down to a pinched wire, and we tried again after lunch. My journal reads:

> It is now 1645, and NOMAD is down with 4,000 feet of cable out. All systems seem to be working, and the deployment was smooth. Although this test will impose a delay in reaching the site, if we run into any problems which require spares we can get back to Honolulu before they arrive, or maybe even divert to Johnston Island for pickup. In the interim, we had fresh mahi-mahi for lunch, and then held another video-taped Renav session.
>
> 5,000 feet out! Our winch can run at a maximum speed of about 60 meters per minute, which sounds fast, but even at that rate it would take about three hours to deploy the entire 11,000 meter cable (which we of course would never do, needing to leave at least 1,000 meters or so on the reel). In practice, we count on close to four hours to deploy all the way to the bottom, and likewise to recover.
>
> Right now, we have ten folks in the Ops Center watching the proceedings. We've been concerned about high hydraulic oil temperature in the winch, caused mainly by the fact that our cooling water source is a tepid 80 degrees. The ship's engineer thinks this is OK, but we are being cautious and imagining better methods of cooling. We proceeded, checking the temperature every few minutes, and it did stabilize, and even drop, when the sun went down.
>
> We're at 9,000 feet. Although the water temperature is 80 degrees at the surface, our vehicle is in frigid 32-degree water. Up here, the hydraulic oil is holding at 132 degrees, well within limits, so it looks like we're OK.

22,000 feet of cable out, and we're seeing bottom with the sonar, over half a mile below it! We're still paying out cable, and trying to catch up with the bottom as it slopes away. The only other problem we've experienced is the oil compensation system level gauge, not a big deal.

The vehicle is now down to 5,880 meters (19,286 feet), and doing fine! The system is rated for 6,000 meters (almost 20,000 feet), so we're near its limit. Now we're testing lights and inching toward the bottom to check out cameras.

24,500 feet of cable out, vehicle depth 5,935 meters (19,467 feet). Altitude is 20 meters, now down to 16 meters . . . beginning to see the bottom on video! Now we're seeing manganese nodules by the hundreds, and very clear images of the bottom. The sonar works fine, lights OK, and sensors OK (except for the oil compensation level).

The big excitement came when we began to retrieve the vehicle. The electric HPU could not handle the load, probably because of reduced ship's power. A group of us donned work gloves and shifted all the hoses and cables to the back-up diesel HPU. Fortunately, that worked fine, is self-contained and reliable, and soon the vehicle was on its way back up. Sue, sitting snug in the Operations Center, was watching us on the security camera monitor scurry around the oil-coated deck manhandling the hoses and cables. She said we looked like mice wrestling with snakes. Bill, the cameraman, pitched in to help, which was good of him. Sometimes a camera is too much in the way, and he seemed to sense that.

Just before midnight, the NOMAD was back on deck, and everyone quit for the night. We went back up to full speed, heading toward our search area!

Meanwhile, we all worked to get our personal spaces "squared away" (a Navy term meaning "ship shape," also a Navy term) and our lab areas organized. Part of this process is "stowing for sea." Although we tried to do that before we left, there is no test like a rocking ship! We had to secure a number of items as the ship heaved through some modest swells, driven by a stormy wind. It is very hard to keep everything where it belongs, and to keep from slamming doors or avoid bumping into unyielding steel flanges.

It is *warm* here, and humid! We are struggling to keep the ship cool and somewhat dry, especially the Operations Center (with all the computers). After years of cruising the Alaskan coast and Bering Sea, the *Davidson* and her crew are unprepared for the tropics. The deck division spent a lot of time over the first few days repairing, adjusting, and in some cases jury-rigging the ventilation system. Fortunately, we did clue in the cook to bring double the normal load-out of syrup for the soda fountain!

## Nautical Term of the Day: **Jury Rig**

"Jury rig, while sounding similar to 'Jerry built,' has a slightly different meaning, emphasizing the temporary nature of the repair, and can imply an ingenious solution done with materials at hand. Jerry built, on the other hand, is often used for a permanent, but poorly built, construction and has no positive connotation.

The origin of jury rig is nautical and dates to 1788. It is from the nautical term 'jury mast.' This term dates to at least 1616 and refers to a temporary mast erected to hold sail when the normal mast has been lost due to storm or battle. It is commonly thought that this sense of the word is a clipped form of 'injury mast,' but no evidence of this longer term has been found. This form of jury is etymologically unrelated to the jury that sits in judgment at a trial." (from WordOrigins.org)

I thought this definition was pretty good, though some may disagree. The origin and use of nautical terminology is a fascinating subject, probably developed to help sailors while away the long hours at sea....

## March 15; Friday. Haircut Day.

Up early, with breakfast courtesy Scotty, one of our fine cooks. After breakfast, we had a safety briefing by the First Mate Joe Litchfield, followed by our first of weekly Abandon Ship drills, where we practiced mustering at the proper station, bringing our lifejacket, long trousers, and long-sleeved shirts. We also practiced donning the survival suits. Even in tropical waters, normal body temperature is well above sea temperature, and in time heat is drained from the body leading to hypothermia. An exposure suit can make all the difference.

Of course, one rarely remembers to grab an exposure suit while accidentally falling overboard. This is a real danger that we all recognized. While at sea, everyone spends most of the time in the indoor spaces; because of the intense tropical sun and heat, as well as the hammering noise of diesel engines running the survey equipment aft, people generally went out on deck for a reason. The reasons ranged from work activities to exercise to taking photos or just getting some fresh air, but most of the time the decks and rails were deserted, especially at night. So, if one went out at night to enjoy the stunning sky or have a smoke (not allowed inside), and slipped and fell overboard, no one would know right away—maybe not until morning. By then the ship would be many miles away, and once the "man overboard" was confirmed it would take hours to retrieve miles of sonar cable and begin to conduct a proper search. The Coast Guard would be no help . . . the nearest coast would be 1,600 miles away. The chances of being found alive or even at all would be slim.

Still, some of the crew had man-overboard stories, and were alive to tell them. Both Captain Dave Everhart and deck crewman Jesse Simms told similar tales of falling in the water in the winter in Alaska, and were both rescued within six minutes! That may seem like a coincidence, but I'll bet there are no seven-minute stories! Dave was carried overboard from a fishing boat while rigging down some equipment. It was night, and snowing. His shipmate saw him go, and immediately alerted the bridge. The captain executed a "Williamson Turn," a standard maneuver for a man-overboard emergency where the ship turns to one side sixty degrees of heading, then reverses the turn until heading in the opposite direction. This results in the ship heading back to the spot the man was lost. Somehow, they saw Dave in the water, who by then was too frozen to raise his arms to attract attention. They threw him a life ring, but at first he couldn't hold it enough to get pulled in. They tried again, and pulled more gently, while he put a death-grip (almost literally!) on the ring. After he was safely on board, they put him in the shower until the hot water ran out!

Jesse was also on a fishing boat, only seventy-five feet in length with a crew of four in the Bering Sea. He went aft to relieve himself, and a rouge wave came and swept him over. He was wearing just a t-shirt and shorts, and the water temperature was in the low 40s. He floated there watching the ship head off in the darkness. Meanwhile, his shipmate, only seventeen years old, noticed he wasn't on the mess deck where he expected him. He quickly checked his bunk, and then called the bridge. Jesse was astonished to see the ship reverse course! They pulled him out a few minutes later. I imagine he bought that kid a beer or two, underage or not!

We decided that if Spence, the consummate sailor, perchance went overboard in the middle of the night, he would fashion his trousers into a life vest, rig his shirt as a sail, and navigate his way over to the next survey line where he would be waiting for the ship when it came by the next day. He would haul himself aboard, carrying a fish he caught while waiting. And no one would know he was gone.

After a couple of days, we were becoming familiar with our little 175-foot universe, the R/V *Davidson*. Registered in Sitka, Alaska, the *Davidson* packed a lot of space and compartments into a small package. The main deck (also known as the D Deck) ran the length of the ship, the aft section being open deck space for survey equipment, the rest built into the superstructure. Moving forward from the aft deck, we enter the wet lab, an enclosed space to support maintenance of deck equipment. Most of our spares, tools, and small equipment are there. That's where we get our hardhats, gloves, and life vests before going out to do launches and recoveries. The area is crowded with gear, as organized as we can make it, and right next to the diesel HPU, so it's noisy and hot. But a lot of work is done there. Just forward of the wet lab is the laundry, which we can use any time except Saturdays (that's when they do the linens). It's kind of like a laundromat, except you have a dispenser for soap and you don't need quarters. We deposit our linens there on Saturday and pick up a set of clean ones from the linen locker. So there *is* a laundry fairy!

When we're not working, there are a few places to relax. Across the passageway from the laundry is a small space we call the "leather room," because it is outfitted with plush leather chairs, wooden bookshelves, and a desk. It's officially known as the ship's office. It is small, so it is not used often, but the media folks sometimes go in there to log their tapes in peace. The wardroom, on the main deck, has two sections, one like a conference room with a table and chairs, and a smaller area with a couch and chairs, TV, and stereo. We have Ethernet cable drops from the ceiling to the ship's local area network, so we do some of our computer work in the wardroom. A soda machine is in there, always pumping coke, orange, and root beer, along with an ice machine. The latter area is where movies are shown and SEA School talks are held. So, the folks on watch, but not on duty, spend a lot of time there.

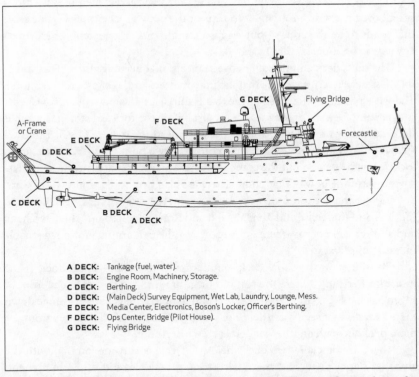

| A DECK: | Tankage (fuel, water). |
| B DECK: | Engine Room, Machinery, Storage. |
| C DECK: | Berthing. |
| D DECK: | (Main Deck) Survey Equipment, Wet Lab, Laundry, Lounge, Mess. |
| E DECK: | Media Center, Electronics, Boson's Locker, Officer's Berthing. |
| F DECK: | Ops Center, Bridge (Pilot House). |
| G DECK: | Flying Bridge |

A typical NOAA vessel, similar to the good ship R/V *Davidson*, our floating home for seven weeks in 2002. The R/V *Mt. Mitchell*, our ship in 2006, had a comparable layout.

Continuing forward we find the dining area, or "mess deck," the biggest space on the ship, with five tables, which can seat eight or ten each, plus a small lounge area (where video games are sometimes played). The seats are fixed to the deck and swivel, but they are sharp-edged and close together, so we are continually barking our shins on them. The tables are covered with a rubbery open-weave cloth, which tends to hold everything in place. There is a juice machine (orange, apple, cranberry, and lemonade, usually), and a fridge for ready access to milk, butter, condiments, and the meals being held for "mid-rats" (the midnight meal). There is a table for salads and fruits (while we still have them). You can always have coffee, make tea, toast bread, make a peanut butter sandwich, and there is often soup in the galley. There is usually a collection of snacks set out (I contributed a couple of boxes of Snyder's so far), and sometimes chocolate in the fridge. The galley faces half of one wall and has a cafeteria-style serving window. During meal times, Assistant Cook Jerzy Plata usually serves, and there is always quantity and variety. As the expedition stretched from days to weeks, we found that meal times offered a good opportunity to gather, and we always have a few words with crew members we didn't see all the time. Our group tries to respect the crew's space (there is one table that tends to be the crew's), but we also mingle to a large extent. There aren't any strong boundaries that I can tell.

The mess deck empties out between meals; no one hangs there. Forward of the mess deck is a storage area that includes freezers and "reefers" (refrigerators). There is a regular home-sized fridge that is full of ice cream, frequently visited.

Farther forward of the mess deck, just before the forward storage locker, is the ladder down to C Deck, and the forward berthing (where I live). There are six two-man staterooms, which each consist of two bunks, a sink, a shelf, and a locker. Maybe a desk, but the compartments are oddly shaped as the ship narrows toward the bow at that point. There are also two heads, and two showers. Sue and I each have rooms to ourselves, as does the assistant engineer. Carl and Jon, Bill and Jonathan, and Tom Vinson and Rod are paired up. There is a head and shower right across from Sue's room, so she can arrange for a reasonable measure of privacy.

Midships, on the same deck, but accessible by a different ladder, is the midships berthing, where the rest of our group lurks in two-man staterooms. Elgen has his own, but everyone else is paired up. There is a small lounge down there as well, so it seems a little more spacious. Further aft, accessible from the main deck through another ladder, is crew's berthing.

There are officially two decks below C Deck, as anyone familiar with the alphabet might deduce, that contain storage, tankage, and other equipment. Aft on B Deck is the engine room. Twin diesel main engines and all other major equipment for running the ship could be found in this hot, noisy, smelly compartment. A somewhat soundproof and air-conditioned booth held all controls and monitoring systems, with picture windows overlooking the engines. Anyone venturing into the engine compartment itself of course needed major ear protection. It is normally unattended, but the engine room watch will tour it from time to time.

Back up the ladder, and up twice again, we reach the E Deck. Aft is open passage with a railing overlooking the aft deck, a good place to observe launch and recovery operations. A door leads forward into the media center, where all the film gear and related equipment is kept. Bill, Kristin, and Jonathan spend a lot of time working there. Next is the electronics center, where Tom Dettweiler has set up his Isis sonar processing system, and Rod and Tom Vinson have set up their radio gear, as well as the bos'n's locker.

### Nautical Term of the Day: **Bos'n**

Many of you know that a bos'n, or bosun, is short for "boatswain," the "foreman" of a crew, who is in charge of a ship's lifeboats, rigging, sails, and deck fixtures. That is, all of the stuff that turns a floating office with engines into a functional ship. A very important person! I am told this derives from the Anglo-Saxon batswegen, or boatman.

Further forward on E Deck are quarters for the senior members of the crew, the chief engineer, mates, and captain, or master. We don't go there unless invited, respecting their privacy. A mate is qualified to man the bridge and stand the "deck watch," that is, take a turn running the ship. Of course, the master is always responsible, but he can't be on deck at all times. If one is qualified to be the master of a vessel, one is known as "Captain," even though not necessarily the master of that particular vessel. Thus, First Mate Joe Litchfield was "Cap'n Joe," even though he was not the master. The captain's cabin was quite comfortable, and was just below the bridge, so he could be handy at a moment's notice, even while sleeping.

There is one two-person stateroom on its own on that level, which was assigned to Julie and Kristin. It has its own head, so they don't have to venture into any other berthing areas. That deck also has outside "weather" decks on three sides, and it is where the two lifeboats are mounted (actually inflatable life rafts). We are each assigned a lifeboat (port or starboard), and have weekly Abandon Ship drills so we know what to do in that unfortunate circumstance. The life rafts are designed to deploy automatically if the ship sinks. There is a variety of lifesaving, communications, and survival equipment associated with each life raft, including a full complement of survival suits. There is also a motor launch (otherwise known as a "skiff") on that deck, which can be launched by crane.

That deck also leads (through watertight doors) to the fo'c's'le (forecastle), which becomes the Steel Beach on Sundays. It's also where we set up the rowing machine when we are moved to exercise. At night, it's the only dark place on the ship, and also the quietest (though not really quiet). So it's the best place to see stars or play guitar; some even try to sleep there (but are not normally successful).

### Nautical Term of the Day: **Fo'c's'le**

Short for "forecastle," this is the section of the upper deck of a ship located at the bow forward of the foremast. Since we have no foremast, it's just the forward deck. Some would include the spaces below, as "a superstructure at the bow of a merchant ship where the crew is housed." To us, it was the Steel Beach, a place to rest and recreate, avoiding, of course, the anchors, chains, windlasses, cranes, and other fittings scattered about the area. It was the quietest spot on the ship, as far as possible from the pounding engines aft, and also the darkest at night (especially if the mate would turn off the navigation lights for a while). Thus, it was used for sunbathing, guitar playing, exercise, and stargazing.

I am told that this term derives from the days of Viking galleys when wooden castles were built on the forward and after parts of the main deck from which archers and other fighting men could shoot arrows and throw spears, and rocks . . . but we rarely did this.

Up one more deck, to F Deck (I trust you are getting the pattern here), is the center of ship activity, the bridge or pilot house. The space spans the width of the deck, with "wings" cantilevering over both sides for best views, especially when docking the ship. The bridge is packed with electronics, including the latest in charting and navigation, fire detection, engine monitoring, communications, and ship control.

Aft of the bridge, easily accessible through a connecting door, is the Operations (Ops) Center. All control and monitoring functions for the survey equipment on the aft deck were managed from this location, so that the aft deck is normally unmanned except for a single watchstander handy for maintenance or emergencies. Ops is also where the e-mail server is installed, so we often get visitors (especially around the 0800 and 2000 satellite communication links).

Finally, we ascend once more to G Deck, sometimes known as the "Flying Bridge." There are open air, waterproof compass and ship controls up there, but they are rarely used. Other than the mast (for radars, radio antenna, and navigation lights) and exhaust funnel, there is just open deck space. The deck's main use was for observation, as it gave a clear view around the ship, and was our choice spot for sextant shots of the moon, sun, or stars.

We are settling into a bit of a routine. We have almost a week of transit to our operating area, and the equipment and spaces are all functional, so we are focusing on small jobs, training, and getting used to life at sea and each other.

The highlight of the afternoon was haircuts. Sue volunteered to play barber and clipped a bunch of us . . . she even overheated a set of clippers. There were "tumblehairs" all over the deck, and we're afraid the dolphins will be coughing up hairballs!

Some people on the charter team had a special problem to deal with. No one knows who will become seasick, or when it will strike, though most who get it suffer for only a day or so before they get their "sea legs." This process can usually be skipped or abbreviated by use of one or more remedies, none of which seem to work once *mal de mer* has struck. The favorite among the expedition crew was the scopolamine patch, applied just behind the ear.

Also known as hyoscine, scopolamine is an alkaloid drug obtained from plants of the nightshade family. But we didn't need to know that. What we cared about was that it acts by interfering with the transmission of nerve impulses and functions as a sedative; applied just behind the ear it inhibits the signal from the inner ear telling your brain that things are out of balance (in spite of what your eyes are telling you), and thus relieves (in most people) that feeling of nausea we call seasickness. This is all we *really* cared about. The patch also produces symptoms including dilated pupils, rapid heartbeat, and dry skin, mouth, and respiratory passages. So it's not for everybody, and should only be taken as long as it's needed. Many of us used only half a patch at the beginning of the voyage, just to get off to a good start, then never needed another dose.

Others, however, suffered longer, used many patches, and tried alternative therapies such as ginger pills, copper bracelets, and devices that put pressure on some body part. I did not see anyone stick their head in a pyramid! Kristen, in particular, had a pretty miserable couple of days that included some violent heaving over the rail, and took a little good-natured ribbing from those fortunate enough not to suffer.

Of course, First Mate Joe and all the other crew members think this is all much ado about nothing, but were generally kind enough to be quiet about it and occasionally even sympathetic. They are used to "flatlanders" coming on board, after all.

We switched time zones tonight one hour (and we'll do another hour tomorrow), so we'll be at +12 time. That should lead to some confusion for a while.

The novelty of endless transit has worn off, and we are all anxious to reach the search area and begin the job. Ninety hours to go!

Attempt the end, and never stand in doubt;
Nothing's so hard but search will find it out.
    —Richard Lovelace

# Opening Night

## March 16; Saturday. Meet the Crew.

S aturday at sea . . . another nice sunny day with some swells but a pretty smooth ride. We are steaming ahead of a following sea, and the wind is at our back, so we are making very good time. Speaking of time, Scotty decided he didn't want to switch the clocks, so he didn't. I had been cooling my heels waiting for breakfast to start, and dropped in to find it just about secured. So, half the ship was on +11 time zone, and half (the most important half, as it included the mess decks) was still on +10. The captain warned us this would happen. Theoretically, we will jump two time zones at midnight tonight, so we'll see.

We have been getting to know the crew; they seem to be a great bunch, and most have a good sense of humor. Especially, First Mate Joe. I noticed today the Abandon Ship procedure he posted:

IMMEDIATE ACTION FOR ABANDON SHIP
Sound alarm
Fix ship's position
Send Mayday
Secure engines
Collect available blankets, water & food
Collect radios, flares & logbook from the bridge
Collect emergency radio beacons
Muster at assigned life rafts
Bring cigarettes and coffee for Joe

I polled some of the folks on watch for "facts" about the crew. Now, mind you, I did no interviews or investigative journalism. I relied solely on rumor and innuendo.

There are fourteen crew members on this trip, starting with Captain Dave Everhart. We've had some nice talks up on the bridge during the midwatch.

Captain Dave has worked as a long-haul truck driver, played bass guitar for blues and rock bands, loves the Beatles and Bill Clinton, and is a sunglasses expert. His father was a Navy carrier pilot. Dave owned a Porsche for a while, but sold it because it attracted too much attention. He ran a crab-fishing boat in Alaska for twenty years, and survived an incident where he went overboard in near-freezing waters. The crew is used to working the Seattle–Alaska route, so this is quite a change for them; they usually don't spend any time out on deck, as it is normally too cold. Captain Dave is very excited about this project, and is doing everything he can to accommodate us.

Joe Litchfield is the first mate, and he talks, walks, and acts like the stereotypical sailor. Tall, thin, with a white beard, squinty eyes, a gravelly voice, ancient dungarees, and a faded t-shirt . . . he's perfect! He also is very competent, and always in good humor. Born in coastal Maine, Joe worked his first lobster boat at age thirteen, following in his father's footsteps, and jokes that he's been sailing since Moby Dick was a guppy. He claims he would never live more than one hundred yards from the sea. It is rumored that Joe went to Syracuse on a football scholarship, lasted three and a half years there, but never graduated. He says when his wife left him back home in Maine, he got in his car and drove until the highway ended. . . . There he settled, in Homer, Alaska. His brother was also a mariner, joining the Navy, and serving on the submarine USS *Halibut*. As a hobby, Joe likes to scan pictures on the computer and post them on the bulletin board, making a picture-journal of the cruise . . . but he doesn't own a camera! Joe is a real sea-going sailor, who puts in about 340 days per year on the water . . . so he says.

Although this is billed as a smoke-free ship, the captain, first mate, and a bunch of others smoke all the time. None of our group smokes, but it has not been an issue as the smokers always do so outside (except for the bridge). Joe says he smokes only right-handed cigarettes. Elgen told us he prefers not smoking, but he isn't a "heavy non-smoker"!

Rod Brumbaugh is the second mate, and he cruised the Caribbean on his own boat after a stint in the Coast Guard. He likes to call the women on board "babe," but then gets embarrassed when it slips out. He's quiet, mild-mannered, and very kind and thoughtful of other crew members. Rod, Captain Dave, and Joe share the conn (driving the ship), rotating on four-hour shifts.

R.J. Callahan is the chief bosun, and is responsible for the maintenance and operation of all the ship's gear. He runs a tight ship (although we later discovered that in port, after a visit to a local bar, he ran the ship "tight"). He doesn't want to hear "It's not my job!" R.J. is always smiling and cheerful, and has a great sense of humor. Tall and thin, he sports a big bushy mustache, accentuated by the buzz-cut Sue gave him when he got paint in his hair. He comes from the unlikely-named town of Frump, Nevada. He is not afraid of heights, and loves to drive people around on the skiff, any time. He and Paul Bingle share an affection for Mustang 5.oL convertibles.

There are three engineers who run the two diesels and related systems. Mel Kufeldt is the chief engineer, assisted by the second engineer Paul Bingel and engineer Leroy Rubinas. Mel went to college and got a degree as a graphic artist. He lives near Reno, Nevada, and loves to gamble, but wants to build a house in Montana. He owns a PDA (personal digital assistant), courtesy of his wife, a computer network administrator, but he doesn't know if it's charged, or where the charger is. He defends this circumstance by observing that a paper notebook can get wet and still be readable. Mel has finished writing and illustrating a book about his seagoing experiences, entitled *Tales of the Horseshoe Splice*. He says everything in it is true . . . or (when called on some of the amorous exploits depicted therein) could have happened. He has examples of some humorous prints he made of magazine covers for the fictitious *American Drought Fisherman*, and has also sold some serious prints.

Paul hails from Winchester, Massachusetts, and is a serious bodybuilder with long black hair. He looks like he could be a professional wrestler! He is building a house in the woods in Port Townsend, Washington, made of environmentally friendly concrete foam and equipped with wind turbines for power. He soon got busy making fancy knot bracelets for all the women on board. He reads *Bon Appetit* magazine, and loves to fish.

Leroy Rubinas is from Chicago, and worked for Great Lakes Shipping. He came out west for firefighting school, saw the *Davidson*, and signed up. Leroy has two published photos of a restored police car in the *American Encyclopedia of Police Cars* (bet you never heard of that one!) and is currently working on a re-creation of the Blues Brothers car. Leroy also likes to hang out in the wardroom, collecting all kinds of stuff to be stamped with "Earhart Expedition" as souvenirs.

The A/Bs (able-bodied seaman) are the backbone of any ship. Jessie Sims, Ron Curran, Harold Story, Bruce Nelson, and Bryan Lampi are in this group, and they do all the basic work of the ship, including maintenance, cleaning, painting, laundry, mess duty, you name it. We're not sure whether they like their job as much as they let on, but it's nice to have a group with such a positive attitude.

Bruce Nelson happens to come from the same town as Julie, who is also a Nelson (no relation). Bruce is a Marine Master Carpenter, and had been busy making beautiful trim, furniture, and bookshelves for the ship. He has also been a yacht captain, massage therapist, and dabbles with the sax, coming from a large family of musically inclined people.

Bryan Lampi is the most intense-looking member of the crew, with long, scraggly, dyed blond hair, wild eyes, earrings, and a half-row of front teeth. Sue cut his hair into a Mohawk, which enhanced the effect. Bryan drinks coke nonstop, morning to night, which could explain some of his unrelenting cheer-fulness! Ron Curran is also in the deck division, but his main job is to work with Jesse to help with the mess decks and keep the interior spaces ship-shape. This includes laundry, mopping, and any other menial task on the ship. Ron is always ready to help, and when things get busy on the aft deck, he is always bringing water, juice, towels, or offering any assistance.

Jesse Sims works with Ron. Jesse worked on a fishing boat in Alaska, and was also said to have fallen overboard while relieving himself over the side, and barely survived. After this incident, he quit the sea, went to Arizona, and worked as an electrical lineman for a couple of years, but was afraid of the scorpions, so he came back. He makes a point not to pee over the side anymore. Jesse has also been a tattoo artist, and he has restored a historic car which made the cover of *Hot Rod Magazine*. An image of the car is tattooed on his back.

Harold Story rounds out the deck division. He says he's working on his fourth divorce, and became a grandfather a few weeks ago. He is a prolific reader, but very quiet, so is chided often for being "too noisy." He will some-times not move out of your way when you encounter him in the passageway because he wants to have a conversation, but doesn't quite know how to start one. Harold always shies away from a group, but when least expected, he can become quite the chatterbox.

Of course, the most important man on the ship is the head cook, Scotty (Stephen) Swistchew. Scotty is short, white haired, and very Scottish. He ran a restaurant in Canada last year, but everyone brought their own food, so he went broke. He works logging camps when not aboard ship, and has also worked as an auctioneer. He loves jokes (especially Irish ones), and has been married for over thirty years . . . to the same woman! He says she's so good with money, she can turn $1 into $10, and brags of a sure-fire way to beat the lottery.

Scotty is assisted by Jerzy Plata, who is Polish (not Latino, as his surname would suggest). He knows little English, but speaks Polish, Russian, Italian, and some Africani. He attends a Polish church in Tacoma, Washington, and has a happily married daughter to talk with on the HF (high-frequency) radio in rapid-fire Polish. He can do any job on the ship from deck hand to A/B to mate. Having little English at his disposal, Jerzy doesn't say much, but he always serves us with a "bon appetit." I believe he thinks this means, "More potatoes?"

Scotty and Jerzy keep the food coming, and prepare it well. Saturday is supposed to be the best day of the week for chow, and tonight we had grilled steaks (on an outdoor barbecue) and king crab legs. One item that's always on the menu is "stuff," either "lotsa stuff" or "more stuff" or "other stuff" . . . you get it. Scotty said that, by the end of the cruise, the menu will consist of "Stuff, stuff, stuff, stuff, and Spam."

So, we are in good hands. Hopefully, our group will be appreciated as much as we appreciate the crew.

Meanwhile, we are making progress. At noon I spent some time on the bridge, looking at the chart. The seamounts in this area are astonishing. The most dramatic is a small-tipped mount that rises abruptly from a depth of over 3,200 fathoms (almost 19,000 feet) to a shoal just 3 fathoms (18 feet) under the waves! We have traveled almost 900 nautical miles so far, with about 750 nautical miles to go (about three days steaming time) to the nearest corner of our search area. So we should be there by mid-day Tuesday, ahead of schedule.

As usual, the ops team was not idle today. Jay spent the day rebuilding a gasket on the junction box, which was leaking enough to limit vehicle deployment. Mike was working on some camera control software, Tom D. was setting up the search area and waypoints; Bragg got the NAVO bathymetry (depth data) dumped into the computer; Sue, Shawn, and Tom B. continued to organize stuff, Spence seemed to be supervising everything; and Julie helped Jay by bolting on zincs, removing the vehicle fins, and other similar jobs. Of course, there were media interviews going on, and Rod and Tom were setting up their HF radios to do some background noise checks. If someone didn't have a particular job, he or she was helping out wherever possible.

It is a tradition in deep ocean expeditions to create special, unique souvenirs by placing ordinary Styrofoam coffee cups into a mesh bag attached to the sonar sled, allowing them to descend to the depths and be exposed to the extreme sea pressure. The result is a perfectly formed shrunken cup, not much bigger than a thimble! Lettering and decorations applied beforehand with a Sharpie will be quite legible, though reduced to fine print. Anticipating this while preparing for the mission, our team designed a special holder, consisting of a length of PVC pipe with holes drilled in it and screw-on caps at each end. Built by our teenage son Eric, it was dubbed the "Cup Crusher 6000," and allowed us to compress loads of cups without distortion or fear of a mesh bag becoming entangled in important equipment. Jon collected the sets of Styrofoam cups that went down on the test dive, and assumed the duty of reloading the device for each deployment. Under Jon's supervision, people gathered in the wardroom in their spare time and decorated cup after cup for friends, family, sponsors, and associates. Some of the loads went down to almost 20,000 feet, maybe the deepest a Styrofoam cup has been and come back!

## March 17; Sunday. St. Patrick's Day.

What we wouldn't do for a Guiness! Did I mention that we were on a "dry" ship? Not a lot of activity today, as we inch closer to our search . . . watchstanding begins tonight at midnight; I have the noon-to-midnight watch. I conducted SEA School lectures today on the project for the benefit of the crew and anyone who hadn't heard the story yet. The crew really appreciated it, as normally the customer doesn't clue them in at all on what they're doing.

So, what was so compelling about the Amelia Earhart story that had us expend all the time, effort, and money to mount this expedition, so far from home and comfort?

There are many books written about Amelia, her life, her achievements, and her disappearance. Elgen himself published a book entitled *Amelia Earhart: The Mystery Solved* (Simon & Schuster, 1999). (He admits that he did not choose or approve of the title.) The book lays out the details of his investigations and was the starting point for our analysis and search. The more we studied the events of Amelia's life and the circumstances of her demise, the more we were inspired by her and convinced we could locate her Electra. Considering such a project from a business perspective, we realized that if we found her plane we could raise it, conserve it, and make it the centerpiece of a traveling exhibition that would pay for the expeditions and help us fund other ocean exploration projects. Also, we could help inspire others, especially young people, to dream and achieve.

But all of those ideas and ambitions were nurtured in time as we learned more about Amelia and thought more about the quest we had embarked upon. What first attracted us was the technical challenge of solving yet another mystery of the deep ocean. The story Elgen presented to us on our first meeting in the summer of 1997 captured our professional attention from the start.

The story of Amelia's final flight really begins with her first attempt, in the spring of 1937. Elgen in his book describes to the smallest detail all of the preparations, motivations, and circumstances of this flight, which started from Oakland, California, on the afternoon of March 13. Accompanying Amelia were Paul Mantz, experienced pilot and owner of a charter airplane company; Harry Manning, Merchant Marine captain, navigator, and Congressional Medal of Honor winner; and Fred Noonan, chief navigator for Pan American Airways. The latter was asked to accompany the team to assist with navigation as far as tiny Howland Island, an uninhabited speck of sand roughly midway along the route from Hawaii to Lae, New Guinea. Rightly considered the most challenging leg of the journey, the flight would benefit from Noonan's experience in Pacific air navigation.

Amelia and her team flew to Honolulu without major incident, though a number of small problems arose that needed attention in Hawaii. A week later, on March 20, she began her long journey across the vast and empty reaches of the mid-Pacific Ocean. As she sped down the runway, barely ten seconds before her Electra could lift off the ground, disaster struck. A failure of one of the landing gear (either a blown tire or a failed shock absorber) sent the plane into a "ground loop," twisting it onto its wing tip as it skidded along the runway at high speed. Both landing gears collapsed, dropping the plane onto its belly, continuing to skid and spin in a shower of sparks for hundreds of feet.

Amelia calmly shut off the aircraft master switches, opened the overhead hatch, and stood to watch the fire trucks approach (although, miraculously, there was no fire). Her World Flight had come to an ignominious end.

Undaunted, Amelia and her husband, the publicist George Putnam, immediately began planning another attempt. Some fateful decisions were made on the way home from Honolulu, including the outright replacement of Manning by Fred Noonan. Though Noonan was more than capable of handling the navigation duties alone, Amelia would later face her inadequacies in radio communication, a job that Manning had performed very well. And although Paul Mantz was never deemed responsible for the accident in Hawaii, he was removed from the team as technical advisor. Thus, only Amelia and Fred set out together for the second attempt at the World Flight, leaving again from Oakland on May 20, 1937.

There were two major differences with the second flight. First, the departure from Oakland was a quiet affair, and Amelia did not admit she was embarking on a World Flight attempt. Second, and much more important, she decided to reverse her route, flying east across the United States and tackling the Atlantic and Africa crossings first. Her considerations had to do partly with weather along the route, and also to be sure the Electra would be fit for the flight after extensive repairs. Only after she had crossed the country, and was sure of her machine, would she admit to the public that the World Flight had resumed.

Fred and Amelia crossed the United States, stopping in Burbank, Tucson, and New Orleans before arriving in Florida. With renewed fanfare they departed Miami for the Caribbean and South America. After several stops they left Natal, Brazil, and crossed the Atlantic to Dakar, French West Africa (now the Republic of Senegal). This was to be a "dress rehearsal" of their anticipated Pacific crossing later in the journey. It did not go well.

Amelia's primary means of locating a landing field was a new technology known as a "radio direction finder." This device could receive radio transmissions of a certain frequency and indicate the direction to the source. If a radio beacon was placed near the destination, she could follow the indicated direction and fly there regardless of weather conditions and visibility that might render celestial navigation useless. Even if the weather was clear, a direction finder was more accurate than navigating by the stars and sun, which was considered

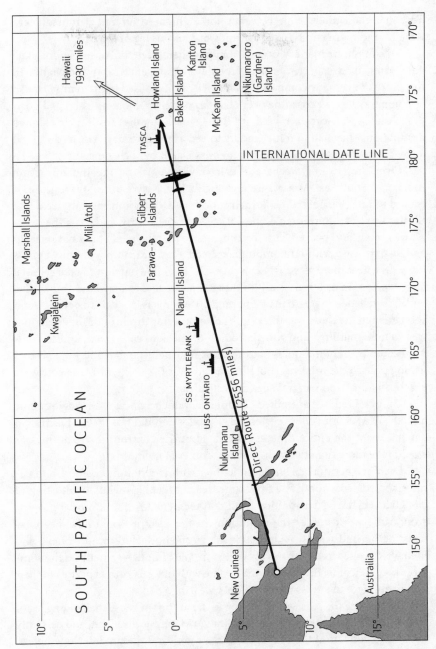

The Lae to Howland leg of Amelia's world flight. Note the location of Tarawa and Kanton islands, the nearest ports to our operating area. A transit of two or more days to one of these islands would be required for any resupply or emergency.

no better than fifteen-mile accuracy for high-speed aircraft. Unfortunately, Amelia's radio direction finder did not work on this leg of the trip.

To complicate matters, poor visibility rendered celestial observations marginal. And, in retrospect, there was probably a significant unknown deviation in the aircraft's magnetic compass heading. All of this caused them to miss Dakar, crossing the African coastline over 60 miles north of Noonan's estimated position. Amelia was forced to land at Saint-Louis, 120 miles from their planned destination. They had to refuel and fly to Dakar the next day. Amelia and Fred never figured out what caused them to miss Dakar by such a distance.

Over the ensuing weeks, the pair traversed Africa, the Indian Ocean, India, and Southeast Asia before arriving in Lae, New Guinea, on June 29. It is hard to imagine how difficult their month and a half journey had been. The Electra was not a comfortable ride—it was cramped, noisy, and cold. The cockpit was small, and packed with instruments so that the pilot could not raise up and lean forward without bumping her head. Fred probably spent most of his time aft, where there was a window on each side, allowing him to take celestial observations. In order to return to the cockpit he had to crawl over bulky fuel tanks, installed to increase the flight range. The air was frigid at 10,000 feet, and soon enough the cabin was freezing. The hammering drone of the huge engines was so loud that Fred and Amelia could not speak to each other, and so communicated by handing notes back and forth, usually attached to the end of a fishing pole so the missives could be passed over the fuel tanks. The pair were practically deaf upon arrival at each destination.

Though Fred had a "limited commercial pilot certificate" for single engine aircraft, he was not very experienced as a pilot and did not fly the Electra. So Amelia spent the entire time of each flight at the controls. Some of the legs would take more than twelve hours, sometimes at night.

Even in a comfortable modern jetliner with entertainment, food, and climate control, crossing a few time zones leads to jet lag owing to adjusting of circadian rhythms, dehydration, and confinement for hours on end. Flying around the world under the conditions in the Electra would have been exhausting beyond words. As a final insult to the body and mind, Amelia and Fred were treated as celebrities at every stop, and although sometimes the comforts were welcome, the obligations to dine with officials, attend parties in their honor, and face the press were no doubt wearing.

By the time the pair was preparing to depart on the most challenging leg of their World Flight, they were mentally fatigued, physically spent, and certainly not able to perform at their best or exercise the clearest judgment. Nonetheless, late morning of July 2, 1937, the fuel-laden Electra and its famous passengers struggled off the runway at Lae for the eighteen-hour, 2,556-mile flight to little Howland Island.

Why was this leg to Howland the most difficult? There are two main reasons, which were exacerbated by a number of complications. First, there is simply the distance, which was at the extreme range of the aircraft, even with extra fuel tanks and stripped of all unnecessary weight. Second, the island is so small—about the size of the Washington D.C. Mall, and rises only a few feet above sea level. It is also remote. Other than its equally nondescript companion, Baker Island, there is not another scrap of land within 350 miles, and no major land masses along their path within thousands of miles. An error in position, such as experienced on the flight to Dakar, would leave nothing but a virtual infinity of open ocean ahead.

The original flight plan, aborted by the Honolulu accident, would have had them flying the much shorter leg from Hawaii to Howland, and the ensuing leg from Howland to Lae would have an entire continent as their destination, hard to miss.

Of course, all of that was known to Amelia, and she took the circumstances into account in her planning, in keeping with her own words of wisdom, "Preparation, I have often said, is rightly two-thirds of any venture." But ordinary and foreseen circumstances rarely lead to tragedy; in a disaster, it is the improbable that is most likely. In Amelia's final flight, several unrelated factors conspired with fatigue and stress to overcome all preparation, skill, and experience, and lead to the demise of the famous flyer.

An astounding array of resources was committed to support the Howland leg of her flight. In some ways, this was the Apollo moon mission of the day, an unprecedented journey at the limits of technology, worthy of international attention and national backing. Howland Island was inhabited at the time by a small handful of colonists from Honolulu, who had arrived just two years before, and existing facilities were meager and primitive. A temporary airstrip was constructed for the project and the island was outfitted with facilities for refueling and overnight accommodation for Amelia and Fred. The U.S. Navy provided communications equipment, and even vessels stationed at key locations to record weather conditions and provide waypoints for navigation. Although this was a privately funded enterprise, the national interest had a stake in Amelia's success.

As the Electra flew east into the morning sky and the vast Pacific, problems arose right away. Her flight plan called for a route just north of the island of Bougainville, but weather reports indicated a severe storm along that path. Amelia must have decided to fly farther south to skirt the storm, based on a position report radioed back to Lae early in the flight. This caused two problems. First, it made for a slightly longer flight in a plan that was already near the limit of range. But more important, it required Amelia to fly over the mountains of Bougainville, climbing to an altitude of 10,000 feet according to the radio message. Her plan called for a slow rise to higher altitude, not to burn so much fuel early in the flight when the plane was so heavily laden, but taking advantage of better efficiency in the thinner air later in the voyage. To climb right away, in Elgen's words, "would require them to burn an unconscionable amount of extra fuel," and cut further into her limited reserves.

Still, Amelia ended her terse message with her customary "EVERYTHING OKAY." This was the last message she would ever again end with that reassuring sign-off.

Another, more severe problem was the wind. A steady wind in excess of twenty knots faced her almost the entire flight. She and Fred recognized this from his navigation calculations, and it was confirmed by several weather stations along the route. For an aircraft that cruised at under 150 knots, this was a significant headwind and called for a significant excess of fuel to cover a given distance. There is also a question of how much fuel the Electra could carry; in the tropical heat of New Guinea, a gallon of warm fuel weighs less than in cooler conditions, yet it is burned by weight, not by volume. All of these circumstances conspired to consume almost all of Amelia's fuel reserves. Nevertheless, she and Fred pressed on to Howland.

One key element of preparation was to ensure that Amelia would have a working direction finder to use. Three of these devices were employed—the one on her plane, one installed on Howland Island, and a third on board the *Itasca*. The latter two units could provide a bearing to the Electra, and the information could, in theory, be radioed to Amelia. Unfortunately, and for various reasons, Amelia and the *Itasca* crew were unable to obtain useful information from any of the direction finders. Amelia was never able to get a bearing to Howland, and the *Itasca* could never get a bearing to the Electra. So, even after she was lost, there was no way to know which direction to search!

Even if the *Itasca* had a bearing to the Electra, there was no way to communicate it to the aircraft, as radio communications failed dismally. Now, the technology has advanced quite a lot from the early days of wireless, but a modern observer would find a 1930s vintage radio to be cumbersome, complicated, and of limited performance. Radio sets were large, consumed much power, and had to be manually tuned. Transmitting and receiving were different functions that had to be timed so as not to overlap. Transmissions were scheduled according to agreed-upon protocols. It was not possible to pick up a handset and just blare out a message for anyone to hear, even an "SOS." It took experience and skill to communicate effectively.

Amelia was not an expert in radio communications, and was limited to voice transmissions on certain frequencies. She could not communicate by the more reliable continuous-wave Morse Code. Owing to mistakes in protocols, operators did not use the same frequencies or even send or receive at the right times, not accounting for the fact that Howland Island was in an area of ocean that (unusually) observed a half-hour time zone. It is also possible (though impossible to verify) that her receiver simply did not work properly. The result of all of this was that Amelia could not receive anything that was sent to her, and those on board the *Itasca* could only hear her increasingly desperate voice reports and calls for bearings.

But a breakdown in communications and direction finding in itself was not the cause of disaster. Fred Noonan was perfectly capable of navigating the Electra near enough to Howland Island to see it. If he could get the plane to within the fifteen-mile uncertainty in celestial navigation, they should have been able to arrive safely.

The men in the *Itasca* radio room, led by Chief Radioman Leo Bellarts, listened to Amelia's call, almost eighteen hours into her grueling flight, "ABOUT 200 MILES OUT." The sun was about to rise before them, giving Fred a chance to take an observation and calculate a navigation "line of position" that would lead them to Howland. A half-hour later she asked the *Itasca* to take a bearing on her, and reported that she was about 100 miles out. We assume around this time that Fred computed his line of position, a line running from slightly west of north to slightly east of south (157-337 degrees true bearing) and advanced it on his chart to pass though the position of the island. Knowing her speed, and based on Fred's calculations, Amelia would know how long to fly to reach that imaginary line, then turn on its heading to lead them to Howland.

At this point, Fred and Amelia were probably quite confident of their position and had no serious concern about reaching the island safely. They flew on for another hour without further contact. It was then, at 1912 GMT (Greenwich Mean Time—7:42 AM local time), that Amelia sent the fateful message, "WE MUST BE ON YOU BUT CANNOT SEE YOU. GAS IS RUNNING LOW. BEEN UNABLE TO REACH YOU BY RADIO. WE ARE FLYING AT ALTITUDE 1,000 FEET."

This message, according to the reports of the listeners in the *Itasca* radio room, had an air of anxiety in the pilot's tone of voice and pace of speech. Some listeners recall that she said "half-hour of gas remaining," which would have given her very little time to to search for her destination and avert disaster. The few remaining messages from Amelia, rising in pitch and tempo, belied her growing concern and even fear as she was coming to realize she and Fred were in deep trouble.

The few words of her 1912 GMT message capture the essence of the problems she was facing. "Gas is running low" succinctly summarizes all that went before to consume her fuel reserves; in fact, she would fly only about an hour longer before almost certainly running her tanks dry. That left very little time to search for the island. "Been unable to reach you by radio" reflects her communications dilemma. She could get no help, no radio bearings, and didn't even know if she was being heard. "We are flying at altitude 1,000 feet" suggests that she had descended below the ever-present cloud deck to look for the island, but at 1,000 feet, looking into a rising sun, could not see far. The island is very small, and the scrubby vegetation that covers it blends into the ocean background. The most visible feature would be brilliant white surf on the shore; but here, the winds aloft that opposed her were calm near the surface. The seas were flat and the surf was minimal. Even an attempt by the *Itasca* to make thick, black smoke with their boilers was to no avail; the sooty cloud hung low over the ship, and failed to rise to offer any signal.

But most importantly, "We must be on you but cannot see you" tells us that she arrived at the point in the ocean that they expected Howland Island to be, but were met with a view of only endless sea. Despite Noonan's best efforts, they were not close enough. Without any further information, they didn't even know which way to begin to search. We presume they continued on their line of position for a while longer, to be sure they were not short of the mark, but after sixteen more minutes Amelia called, more tensely, "WE ARE CIRCLING BUT CANNOT HEAR YOU." She probably realized then that obtaining a radio bearing was her only hope of survival.

Silence for another long forty-five minutes. We can imagine that Fred and Amelia were intensely scanning the horizon for any sign of the island. What else could they do? With nothing heard on the radio they could expect no help from their army of supporters, and no new round of sun observations were going to tell them which way to fly. Finally, at 2013 GMT, Amelia was heard for the last time, frantically: "WE ARE ON THE LINE OF POSITION 157-337, WILL REPEAT THIS MESSAGE ON 6210 KCS. WAIT. LISTENING ON 6210 KCS. WE ARE RUNNING NORTH AND SOUTH."

According to calculations by Dr. Fred Culick of the California Institute of Technology (Cal Tech), who was commissioned by NOVA (WGBH-TV in Boston) and has worked with Elgen to perform fuel consumption estimates, it was at about this time that the Electra's tanks were exhausted. Elgen imagines that Amelia's full attention was diverted to flying the now powerless aircraft down to the ocean surface and ditching so as to give Fred and herself a chance of survival, at least for a while. Since no one knew where they were, the chances were essentially nil.

Why did they miss the island? It is certainly possible that Fred miscalculated or took a poor sun observation. Or the compass problem could have cropped up again at the most inopportune time. But there is another possibility, one more problem they had to overcome. Charts in the 1930s were not up to today's standards, especially in remote locations such as Howland Island. The chart they had been using was updated after they began their World Flight, and it showed the position of Howland Island to be in error by about six miles. New charts became available before they left Lae, and there is some evidence that they were sent to Fred and Amelia, but there is no evidence that they received them and used them. Six miles would have been a critical error to overcome, and possibly more than enough to put them outside of visual range.

We may never know. Though if we can find the Electra we may be able to recover, preserve, and read the notes between Amelia and Fred, see his charts and calculations, and solve the mystery of why they missed Howland Island.

Sue carefully applied stickers for all of our sponsors for this trip on the fins of NOMAD. Rockwell Collins, Simrad, Rochester Cable, and Klein all got stickers. After she was done, I taped on a Snyder's of Hanover logo I cut out from a pretzel box. Everyone thought I was serious! Actually, I probably should contact Snyder's for a sponsorship, as everyone is eating the pretzels I brought. The two cases will be gone in no time.

We passed a sign that said "Nowhere" about ten miles back.

## March 18; Monday. They Call This the Doldrums??

Nasty weather today, with some overnight squalls. Most everyone seems adjusted to their surroundings and routine, although Julie is getting over a cold and Kristin is not yet weaned off the seasickness patch. I just gave her the bad news this morning that we are *not* getting re-supplied after twenty days as she was promised. She's doing much better, though, and will be an old salt in a few more days. The question is, will she run out of outfits? We see a new one every day!

This morning I saw a rainbow in the direction of Howland Island, still nearly 300 miles ahead of us. I checked with First Mate Joe, expert in nautical lore, to see if this was a good omen or a bad one. He assured me a rainbow is a good sign. However, this led to a discussion about whistling on the bridge. Apparently, one of us has been guilty of that transgression, and Joe is not happy about it! You see, sailboat sailors will try to "whistle up a wind," but a wind is no good to us. Joe is convinced that the strong breezes and whitecaps we've been having are a result of the bridge whistling. Now that the culprit (who shall remain nameless, but it wasn't me) is clued in, things may improve.

Preparations for survey operations are almost finished, and everyone is excited to begin. We are attending to minor issues now; the "Equipment Action List" includes low-priority items such as "set up 12VDC for music." At noon today, our Collins radio guys hooked up with "Comm Central" in Cedar Rapids,

Iowa. Using HF radio, they patched us into the regular telephone system, and a few of us were able to place a quick call home.

We began standing regular watches at noon, starting with a watchstanding briefing by our section leader, Tom Bethge, followed by an operations briefing by Tom Dettweiler. My watch section, noon to midnight, includes Section Leader Tom B., Mike Davis, Julie Nelson, Bragg Sherer, Jon Thompson, Jay Ellis, and Tom Vinson. The other section, led by Shawn Dann, includes Spence King, Sue Morris, Jeff Palshook, Robert Witzleb, Rod Blocksome, and Carl Hoffman. Tom D., as the operations manager, is on call at all times. The media team (Jonathan, Bill, and Kristin) are on their own schedule, and Elgen (expedition leader) is free to spend time with either watch section. Of course, we'll call Tom, the media folks, and Elgen for any events.

After dinner, and after a driving rain had subsided, we went out to the fantail and checked out NOMAD. Although we had all seen it in action, it was helpful to review its current configuration. During this watch, we are taking turns familiarizing ourselves with the operation of the equipment. We have two main centers of activity supporting survey operations. The Operations (Ops) Center, just behind the bridge on the third (F) deck, is the location of all the real-time processing equipment. There is a lot of ship equipment in there already (like the INMARSAT satellite communications gear). We have added two GPS systems for ship navigation, which feed into a central computer system, integrating all data. Several flat-screen monitors (including one on the bridge) display ship and sled position relative to the search grid and available bathymetry at all times. The water depth around this area will be about 5,400 meters (about 17,500 feet), with a few seamounts sloping at a rate of as much as 100-meter-per-kilometer distance.

The fiber-optic feed from the sled makes its way through the 11,000 meters of cable and finally up to the Ops Center, where it is de-multiplexed into its separate sonar, video, and control/telemetry signals. The sonar signal from the Klein 2000 sidescan sonar goes into the Klein control unit, as well as an Isis sonar processing system for better display and further analysis. There are two Isis monitors in Ops, allowing real-time analysts to mark and quickly assess targets, as well as record all of the raw data for further study and archiving. Isis, by the way, is named after the deity in Egyptian mythology. She is the goddess of fertility and motherhood, which has nothing to do with sonars and computers, as best I can tell. Still, that's what they call it. . . .

The sled also has a Simrad MS-1000 forward-looking sonar, which will serve as an obstacle-avoidance sonar and a "gap-filler" to help cover the area directly beneath the sled, a weak spot for the sidescan. There are also two video monitors for display of video cameras mounted on the sled, and controls for the 1,200-watt HMI lights we'll be using for optical imaging. (HMI stands for "Hydrargyrum Medium-Arc Iodide," a name that is hardly illuminating. However, the lights, which work by creating an electrical arc between two electrodes within the bulb that excites pressurized mercury vapor laced with metal halides, produce very high light output with great efficiency.) Video recorders save all camera feed, and two other video monitors mate with them so we can see what we're recording. Other displays cover vehicle telemetry, such as heading, speed, attitude, leak detection, and electrical bus voltages.

Another handful of small surveillance monitors allow the watchstanders in Ops to keep tabs on the after deck, the cable drum, the traction winch, and the level-wind, with little security cameras mounted on the aft railings. There is also the winch control, a joystick that is normally operated from Ops to control sled altitude. There are high voltage power supplies (Julie made some sharp-looking warning signs), UPS (uninterruptible power supplies for the electronics), and the computer LAN (network) file server, with drops to the wardroom two decks below and to the electronics lab one deck down. Finally, there is the ship's computer mail server. All in all, it is quite an impressive operation, and we are all working to become competent at as many jobs as we can. The seven of us in the watch section will keep three bodies on critical positions at all times: a winch operator, Isis sonar monitor, and supervisor (who will keep tabs on the forward-looking sonar and our general track). Those not on-station will be conducting tours of the aft deck, keeping logs, swapping and logging video tapes, gofer-ing for coffee, fixing whatever breaks, and training.

One deck down, and just aft, is the electronics room, where Tom D. has set up four flat panels displaying track and Isis windows for post-processing and analysis. He intends to scrutinize every bit of sonar to be sure we haven't missed anything. Tom V. and Rod also set up a radio room in electronics, which is how we communicate with Comm Central in Cedar Rapids. They have also contacted other ham radio friends around the world, and are preparing to collect background noise measurements to validate some of their radio analysis.

We finished our watch at midnight, turned over a few minor problems to the next watch, and hit the rack to get rested up for the big day tomorrow. . . .

### March 19; Tuesday. Launch Day.
We have logged one full week at sea, but are just beginning our mission. After watch last night, I took in a bit of a movie, read for a while, and had no trouble falling asleep and staying there until 0800. Today dawned sunny and hot, with patchy clouds all around but none overhead . . . a typical Pacific day! I had time for a workout on the rowing machine, then figured out the laundry system before getting called to a 1000 pre-launch briefing on the aft deck. We went carefully over all the preparations and precautions one more time.

Spence treated us with his "Explorer's Thought of the Day," posted on the wardroom white board:

"Today is the Day [of discovery]"—words spoken by Mel Fischer every day for 15 years to his (mostly unpaid) helpers until discovery of the Spanish galleon Atocha in 1983.

With that kind of motivation, who can fail?

At 1130, I was back up to the fo'c's'le for interviews by Kristin, to record the sense of anticipation for the launch. It's exciting, but it's hard to be concerned when so many capable people are working so diligently. She asked me what worried me, and I said it was safety, and the thing we haven't thought of. Anytime there is an accident or disaster, it is either because of carelessness or because too many things happened that were not anticipated. I know our team is not careless, and our preparation is meticulous and deliberate. So, I really don't need to worry.

I grabbed a couple of eggrolls from Jerzy on the way aft to prepare for launch. It was nice to be able to depend on competent supervisors like Tom D., Tom B., and Shawn, so that I could serve as a tag line handler and be part of the launch. The launch went perfectly, and was certainly well documented with dozens of video and still cameras from all angles.

Julie has relieved Jay on the winch control, and has winched out to 4,300 meters (14,000 feet), with vehicle depth about 3,500 meters (over 11,000 feet). Comp (pressure compensating) oil level is down to 50 percent, which is worrisome, and we stopped reeling out for a while when winch oil temperature got too high. We were concerned until we discovered that the bos'n was using the hose that normally provides cooling water to the hydraulics to hose off the deck! It has cooled down now, so we're on our way back down.

The survey lines we planned and set up in the computer were meant to be parallel to the current, as reported, but in fact the current, winds, and seas are from nearly abeam. This makes it hard to run lines (at such slow speed), and also makes for a very rough ride as the ship rolls considerably. Tom is considering adjusting lines.

Comp level is down to 41 percent. Not good; it seems that we have a leak. We have reeled out 5,000 meters (over 16,000 feet) of cable, with vehicle depth 3,600 meters (nearly 12,000 feet). Sea pressure at this depth is nearly 5,300 PSI, enough to crush a scuba bottle from the outside! We are going to haul back in to see if the comp level comes back up (which could indicate a sensor problem).

1640. We have hauled the vehicle up to nearly 2,000 meters, and the level has risen to 44 percent. This is hopeful. If we hold for a while and get a real positive indication, we may continue back down.

*1700.* We are hauling in to 1,500 meters to see if comp level continues to rise. Now it's up to 50 percent, so we've decided to go back down. The theory is: the oil is not going to sea, but rather is being forced up the cable, filling the little gaps in the strands. Once filled, it should stop. So, we go back down.

*1820.* The vehicle is down to 4,300 meters (14,000 feet), and we are hoping to see bottom soon on the 1,000-meter range scale of the sonar. Comp level is 32 percent.

A lot happened in the next hour and a half! The bottom was quite a bit deeper than advertised . . . as much as 5,500 meters (18,000 feet). This is not surprising, as historical depth survey information is very sparse in this part of the world, and bathymetry contours are freely extrapolated from just a few depth points. We did begin to pick up the bottom, and got within 200 meters of it, but only by letting out lots of cable. We reached the last wrap on the drum at 9,600 meters out (of a 11,000 meters cable!) The ship's mate is having trouble controlling our path at speeds below two knots, and we can't keep close to the bottom unless we run around 1.7 knots. It will take some time for the mates to learn how to hold a line, deal with winds and currents, and do it slowly. This is a practice line. But anyway, we are searching, and things will improve with practice. It will take a while, since each watchstander will have to learn.

The deep-sea search for Amelia Earhart had finally begun.

Greatness is not where we stand, but in what direction we are moving. We must sail sometimes with the wind, and sometimes against it—but sail we must, and not drift, nor lie at anchor.

—Oliver Wendell Holmes

# The Art of Search

March 20; Wednesday. More Recoveries and Launches.

It is 1630, almost halfway through the next watch, and we have been busy. Last evening, things really settled down, and we collected lots of good sonar data. Over time, the cable sank so that we could haul in a couple thousand meters and still image the sea bottom. But the process of reeling cable in and out affected control of the ship, as the forces on the stern changed dramatically. Considering that the ship displaces about 1,000 tons, and the cable with vehicle weighs nearly 15 percent of that, plus higher dynamic loads as the winch pulls the system in or lets it out, it is not surprising that this makes it difficult to steer the ship. We are working out better communications between Ops and the bridge to alleviate this. It is amazing how some aspects of this system (such as reeling the cable in or out) cause an instant reaction, and others (like the sinking of the cable) take hours to respond.

The bottom during our watch was boringly smooth, and there were no significant features to see, so that we were not sure how well the sonar was working. However, as the line progressed, we "flew" over some very interesting terrain during the midwatch that showed that the sonar was performing very well indeed! The highlight of the watch was a one-mile-diameter crater that the NOMAD passed directly over, forming a beautiful image. We called it "Dann's Depression," in honor of Shawn Dann's watch-section. The midwatch finished the line, but at the end Tom D. decided it would be best to retrieve the system to check the comp oil system, as it was uncomfortably low. So, up it came. Since it was during a time we would have been turning anyway, it did not delay the start of the next line too much.

We held our first daily ops (operations) and navigation briefing at 1100. Spence started a "discovery pool," where everyone will put a buck on a search grid square; whoever's square is where the discovery is made wins the pool. He also put up a "thermometer" showing by degree how far along in the search we are (not very!). After much research, analysis, and consideration of all practical constraints, we have set out an ambitious search area of 600 square nautical miles, encompassing the most likely resting place of the Electra. We consider this a minimum goal; if we can cover (on average) a square mile in an hour with high efficiency, we should be able to examine over 800 square miles in the time we have available in the area. The latter would require us to stay out for the entire seven weeks, including transit time from Hawaii. Within this area, our NOMAD sonar will create swaths of sound "images" with a resolution of one meter—that means in a square mile we will have over three million pixels in our image, about the same as the average "point and shoot" camera. Over the 600-square-mile planned search area, that amounts to over two billion pixels and six gigabytes of raw data. In today's high-density digital world, that may not sound like much, but each pixel is gained at great expense . . . almost $1,000 per megapixel. (Rod pointed out that we are really only interested in the few dozen particular pixels that will represent the Electra . . . about a nickel's worth!)

At that resolution, we should easily be able to detect an object the size of the Electra, even if it is broken in several pieces. This I consider unlikely, as the plane was ditched in calm seas at slow speed, and even if there were structural damage the pieces would be expected to hang together connected by pipes, wires, and the aluminum skin. Even if pieces separated, they would tend to fall near one another (judging by our experience), and in fact create a larger "target" of debris. Our search plan was designed to detect these eventualities.

Our team settled on a plan to cover a nearly square rectangle, divided into 39 search lines (or lanes). We decided to start in the middle of the box on Line 18, the area of highest probability, and work our way down to Line 39. Then we would return north and cover Line 19 next, then continue by decreasing numbers to Line 1. The large search area allowed us to run very long search lanes, in swaths about a mile wide and over thirty miles long. There is a major advantage to this: we waste proportionally less time in turning around at the end of each lane as compared to shorter lane lengths.

By the time my watch section returned to go back on watch at noon, the vehicle was nearly up, and we readied for recovery. Tom Bethge organized teams and a process akin to a race track "pit crew," in which everyone had a job to do, and was to descend on the vehicle as soon as it was secured to the deck to make it ready for launch as soon as possible. Earlier in the watch, Tom had to explain to landlubber (but quick study) Tom Vinson what he meant when he told him to "secure" a piece of equipment:

## Nautical Term of the Day: **To Secure**

The verb "to secure" means different things to different people. The nautical version is not mentioned in most dictionary definitions; it is probably most instructive to explain by example. If you tell a sailor to "secure" a building, he will turn off all the lights and lock it up. If you tell a Marine or Army GI the same thing, he will assault it with troops and occupy each space. If, on the other hand, you tell a member of the Air Force to secure the building he will issue a contract and buy it for you.

So, when Tom B. told Tom V. to "secure the fan," he just wanted him to turn it off! It takes a while to educate "flatlanders" in the arcane and mystifying language of the sea, and nuances exist even between naval sailors, merchant marines, sailboat crewmen, and offshore fisherman. Traditionally, this special vocabulary helps make communication clear and concise, once you understand the lingo. . . . Of course, in olden times much confusion arose from the use of the terms "starboard" and "larboard" for right and left, respectively. Eventually, the more distinguishing term "port" was substituted for the latter.

Recovery of NOMAD was successful, although exciting as usual. We had to make several tries to hook the tag lines, but otherwise we were pleased with our effort. Once on board, we strapped the vehicle down, secured the sheave, replaced the safety net, and got to work. We swarmed over the vehicle, replacing comp oil, moving a camera, adding ballast weights, checking tie-wraps, checking connectors, and recharging the Styrofoam cup holder. Jay found a leak in the oil comp filler connection (which qualifies as ironic, as without the leak we would have no need to refill!), and repositioned one of the cameras to aim at the comp reservoir so we could monitor it visually.

We secured the diesel so things would be quieter on deck, and refueled it (supervised by the Diesel Queen, Julie), but it wouldn't restart. Fortunately, Mel, the ship's engineer, took over and repairs were quickly completed. It is nice to have the crew's cooperation when we need it, and they are very eager to help.

We also repeated a compass calibration while the system was on deck, done by circling the ship to allow the compass to cycle through its full range. By the time we had done about ten circles we were quite a way from our next lane start point, owing to current and wind drift. We spent forty-five minutes steaming over to the launch point, and we were ready to launch NOMAD long before the ship was. The launch was very smooth, and the vehicle is now most of the way back to the bottom. Jon likened the last few hours to "two-a-days" he remembers from his football practice experience. Between the heat and wicked sun, the physical effort, the ship motion, and the anxious waiting, we are all tired. But it is a long way to midnight, when our watch is relieved.

The midwatch (midnight to noon) section that we were waiting for so eagerly is led by Shawn Dann, operations assistant and ocean engineering technician. Shawn came to us from the Navy, and sailed with our *Dakar* expedition in 1999 as a Navy representative. He is a storehouse of practical knowledge on all of our systems, and is a natural leader. He is also unassuming, and loves a practical joke. He and Sue duct-taped thirty-six–pound lead weights to Tom Bethge's steel-toed shoes last night (Tom carelessly left them in Ops when he switched to sneakers). Shawn feels that NOMAD is his baby, and you feel confident he can fix anything (especially if Jay is around).

Spence King, our most experienced sailor, is Tom's assistant operations manager, and assists Shawn with the watch-section. The Swan Island Shipyard in Portland, Oregon, was Spence's playground when he was a youngster, and his love of ships persisted through adulthood. A retired Navy commander, Spence was captain of the USS *Brunswick*, a salvage ship, and last served at the Naval War College. For over twenty years he worked with surface ship operations, towing, salvage, demolitions, underwater survey, mixed gas diving and recompression chamber operations. He now represents Nauticos up in Newport, Rhode Island, and in his spare time captains small fifty-passenger high-end cruises. He holds a license as master of motor vessels of unlimited tonnage, sailing on any route. On trips from Maine to Florida, he would often give talks on exciting Nauticos projects. Now working for Nauticos, he tells quirky and amusing stories about his cruises.

Spence is helping to make the most of our expedition by leading the SEA School program, organizing numerous activities that help relieve stress and boredom, which helps build us into a well-functioning team. Spence can actually take a celestial fix with a sextant, and is a fount of nautical lore. He is comfortable and competent at sea, which is a great asset.

Jeff Palshook is our lead Renav engineer, former submariner, and an important member of our Navy support team back east. Fortunately, thanks to others pitching in and an understanding customer, Jeff was able to be spared for the duration of this trip. Jeff has worked on this project for several years, and has recently completed a Monte-Carlo statistical analysis of the problem, which has helped define our search area. Being the only one to request a supply of diskettes for our load-out earned him the nickname "Floppy."

Sue Morris is the operations tech on the watch, and also happens to be my sister. It is fun having her along, and she is doing a great job working vehicle maintenance. She is also Spence's cohort in organizing activities, and Shawn's cohort in practical jokes. Although she has only been working in the operations division for a year or so, "Sonar Girl" has caught on very well and seems to enjoy the work.

From Rockwell Collins, Rod Blocksome is a radio engineer who helped us immeasurably with the navigation analysis. He is serving as a general watchstander, and like everyone else, gets to "fly" the sled, watch the Isis, check the aft deck periodically, and participate in launch and recoveries. When not on watch, he and Tom Vinson are working radio communications, both with other ham-radio enthusiasts and with Cedar Rapids, where we get HF communications links to regular telephone lines. We are grateful for the occasional opportunity to briefly call home!

Robert Witzleb, a lieutenant commander from the Naval Oceanographic Office, is tasked to provide weather forecasting. Unfortunately, there is little known about this part of the world and few observations are regularly made. As Rob says, one can *make* forecasts with no data, but they aren't very good. Robert is a former Tomcat fighter pilot, and he is now attempting to put an oceanography degree to use.

Carl Hoffman is a freelance journalist who was sent by our media partner, National Geographic, and has been assigned to the watchbill as a general watchstander. He has written a book called *Hunting Warbirds: The Obsessive Quest for the Lost Aircraft of World War II* (Ballantine, 2001), and has done some writing for *National Geographic* and other magazines. He has now recovered from the rope burns he sustained during the first practice NOMAD launch, and is busy trying to stay awake all the time so he won't miss anything. Carl is always asking if NOMAD is currently in a "sweet spot," or area of high probability.

Tom Dettweiler, as noted, is the operations manager, as well as vice president of Nauticos. Tom does not stand a regular watch, but sets up the search plan, analyses results, coordinates with the ship's operation, and leads daily briefs. He is on call for anything interesting. He is the best in the business, having spent his career learning how to manage operations at sea. Tom was science officer on the *Calypso* with Jacques Cousteau, spent years developing technologies to mine the deep oceans (leading to today's search technology), and worked with Dr. Robert Ballard at the Woods Hole Oceanographic Institute's Deep Submergence Laboratory. In fact, Tom was the operations manager for the RMS *Titanic* discovery mission. Tom has also worked extensively with U.S. Navy underwater programs. Being with Nauticos for over twelve years, Tom has led the company to many of its discoveries, and has had no small hand in building the team running this operation today. Tom is one of those unique individuals who can perform well at a wide range of tasks on many levels. He is best at running operations at sea, but is also a great analyst and adept at using a heavy machine tool or the latest computer software program. He is equally comfortable splicing a line, identifying a nematode, interpreting a sonar image, directing a vehicle recovery, or briefing an admiral.

These crew members and others from the Nauticos team are my shipmates, employees, and friends. When I consider the array of talent and experience that we have assembled over the years, I marvel at the result. My background as a nuclear submarine officer has been an asset to the business, as well as my experience in underwater navigation, mapping techniques, and analysis. But I derive a perverse pride in admitting that I don't know how to do 95 percent of what my company does! I do know how to assemble a team, inspire my staff, engage investors and supporters, and lead us all to remarkable and unique achievements. It is an honor and privilege to lead this group, and I know in the end we will succeed, as we always have.

## March 21; Thursday. The Bat Turn.

We have been so busy and so much is happening, it is a challenge to keep up a journal. We had a very productive day since our launch on March 20, and expect to finish our third line during the night. As each line is around thirty-five miles, at our slow speed and with the turn at the end, it takes the better part of a day to finish one, and each opens the window on the world four miles below us a little wider.

Somebody posted a picture of "Dann's Depression" on the white board . . . it is quite a spectacular underwater volcanic caldera, almost a mile in diameter. We went directly over the top of it in a 750-meter range scale (about a mile-wide swath), so it filled the sonar screen. It was arresting to think that we were the first explorers to see this dramatic feature of the earth.

The sonar image included a strongly reflecting ridge-top feature with a half-dozen radiating "arms," looking as if some tentacled creature was sprawled akimbo on the edge of the crater. Though it was clearly geological, it was interesting enough to catch attention, and we began to refer to it as "the Hectapus." In time, the fanciful deep-sea monster was blamed for all kinds of unfortunate occurrences aboard the *Davidson*. The creature's most heinous and persistent crime was drinking the comp oil from NOMAD.

Today at 0845 and 1245 I was the SEA School lecturer. I told the story of the discovery and salvage of the Israeli submarine INS *Dakar*. I have since published the account in the book *Never Forgotten: The Search and Discovery of INS* Dakar, *Israel's Lost Submarine* (Naval Institute Press, 2009). The crew is very interested in these talks, especially the captain, so even though the lectures are strictly voluntary we have excellent attendance. Tomorrow, Shawn is doing a mandatory (for Nauticos personnel) talk on shipboard electrical safety. As billed:

Nauticos's very own electrical whiz kid Shawn describes why electricity on board ship is different than the stuff you find at home. This is a topic where what you don't know can *kill* you!

Spence and Sue officially launched the Electra search pool today, and collected $200. With the help of Mike Davis' random number generating program, they assigned squares at $1 each in a grid. We are all hoping that the winner will invest his earnings into a big party when we return.

We took over watch at noon today near the end of the second sonar line, and immediately rushed out to capture a fairly unique event: the equinox at the equator at noon. Since today is the first day of spring (the equinox), and we are pretty close to the equator, the sun should be directly overhead at noon. We proved it by taking pictures of ourselves with tiny shadows.

Shortly after we took over the watch, we executed our first "Bat Turn," an attempt to turn the whole ship-cable-vehicle system around as quickly as possible. In this case, "quick" is a relative term . . . if all goes well it normally takes at least four hours to completely reverse course and stabilize on the next line when towing near 20,000-foot depth. Huge dynamic loads can develop on the cable and handling system if this process is not managed well, so the desire to execute the turn quickly and get back on line to resume surveying must be tempered by avoiding damage to the equipment or (even worse) parting of the cable and leaving a million dollars of sophisticated technology at the bottom of the ocean.

We started around 1430, after hauling in 1,500 meters of cable (so the vehicle wouldn't hit bottom during the turn, an event Tom Bethge refers to as "unintended bottom sampling"). We started with a 90-degree turn, and headed off track well past the next line. We had to carefully watch the angle of the sheave and the vehicle depth, as it immediately began to descend. It took about fifteen minutes for the vehicle's heading to begin responding to these ship maneuvers. After almost an hour, we turned again, this time greater than 90 degrees, in order to return to our new track. In another hour, we hit our new track and began heading along it. It was after 1800 before we were back in action again, with the sonar near operating altitude. So, it still took almost four hours. But I think we'll get better.

The term "bat turn" came into vogue during previous Nauticos operations, as the path the ship follows in this technique loosely resembles the silhouette of a bat. This is distinguished from a more conventional and less aggressive "Williamson Turn," as used for locating and recovering an overboard sailor. (The name is attributed to naval officer John Williamson, who popularized this maneuver during World War II, though there were certainly earlier uses of the technique.) Just to be irreverent, we in time started to refer to this as

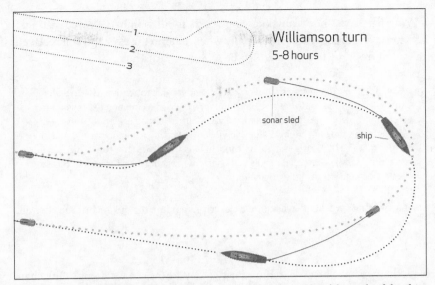

A standard Williamson Turn causes the sonar to drift to the side of the path of the ship, and requires a long approach to stabilize the sled on the reverse course. This method is simple to execute and does not require large angles on the tow point, but it takes many hours to complete.

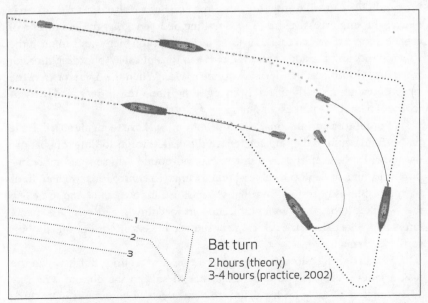

The experimental Bat Turn causes the sled to twirl on its axis in a relatively short time, but it requires a precise set of maneuvers, careful timing of winch operations, and extreme vigilance of operating parameters.

61

a "Wombat Turn," not really knowing much about wombats. My educational horizons were broadened considerably when, later in the expedition, I received an e-mail from my friend Peter Brodie in Sydney, Australia:

> Wombats! My thoughts about wombats when you first mentioned a "wombat turn" in your Amelia story was that it must have been a common expression to describe a very tight turn. Wombats live in burrows that are about the same diameter as they are themselves, and while they have a chamber at the end, it too is quite tight. So my immediate thought was that a wombat turn indicated a real tight turn as a wombat makes in its burrow. I can find no reference to this so it's a piece of Peter Brodie originality!

So, it arose that "wombat" was quite a descriptive name for our technique after all.

Now that we have been searching for two days, how are we doing? Our challenge is trying to maintain a particular "course over ground" (that is, the ocean floor) at a speed between 1.5 to 2 knots, with a current on the order of 1 knot coming abeam. This means we have to "crab" the ship's heading 40 degrees or more off our desired course! We would like to stay close to the planned survey line, and GPS can tell us that to within meters. But we also don't want to maneuver the ship excessively, as we are trailing between 8,000–10,000 meters of cable behind us! Add to this a 20-knot variable wind which wants to push the ship around, and the added effect of over ten tons of cable (plus drag through the water) tugging on the stern at varying angles. When the operators reel the cable in or out, it nearly instantly changes the 1,000-ton ship's speed by two-tenths of a knot (15 percent of our speed)!

In order to drop our sonar near the bottom, we have to juggle speed, cable payout, and depth. If the ship goes faster, the vehicle wants to "kite" out behind us, and rises. Conversely, if we slow, the 1,500-pound vehicle—and more importantly, tons of deployed cable—want to sink. To control this, we haul in or pay out cable, as necessary. In order to reach as far down as 18,000 to 20,000 feet, we have to pay out a lot of cable, and go very slowly, generally less than 2 knots. We'd like to hold the vehicle a constant 80 meters off the bottom, for best sonar performance.

We can't go too slowly, or we never cover any ground. But if we go too fast, it takes more cable to allow the sonar to sink to the bottom. We have 11,000 meters of cable on the drum, so Shawn gets very nervous if anything over 10,000 is out (we had it up to 10,200 at one point). So, the sonar is about three and a half miles below us, and two and a half to three miles behind us. And we are holding it to 80 meters over the bottom, to a tolerance of 5 meters.

Also, speeds over 2 knots begin to compromise the quality of the sonar data, as we may actually start missing spots in between sonar "pings." To complicate matters yet further, if the ship drivers make drastic corrections to speed, the altitude and pitch of NOMAD can begin to bob around, blurring our images and potentially creating gaps in coverage. Just as with a regular camera, we get a much sharper image if the instrument is stable.

Yet another complication is the bottom itself. The water depth here is around 5,400–5,500 meters (nearly 18,000 feet), and (according to the bathymetry charts we have) varies by only a couple hundred meters over most of the area, with fairly gradual inclines. Over 90 percent of it is flat as Kansas, but it is dotted with volcanic ridges, cinder cones, calderas, and pillow lava flows that occasionally stick up from the bottom as much as a hundred meters or more. There are even larger seamounts just outside of our search area, the most dramatic rising over 3,000 meters from the seafloor (but the peak is still over 2,000 meters deep). We have a fathometer on the ship that measures depth at a spot about three miles ahead of the vehicle. That gives us warning of ridges a couple hours in advance, and our team has become adept at noting and marking these obstacles, bringing the altitude up (by reeling in the cable) so we don't get too close to the bottom. The extreme case of this, as mentioned earlier, is known as "sampling," or even "violent sampling." To be avoided.

None of this terrain we are mapping has ever been seen by humans before, so we give prominent features our own names: Mt. Vinson, Thompson's Ridge, Ellis Escarpment, and, of course, Dann's Depression. Technically, we can submit name suggestions to the cognizant government agency, which can choose to officially sanction them in future maps. According to the Web site of the U.S. Geological Survey (part of the U.S. Department of the Interior):

> The U.S. Board on Geographic Names (BGN) is a Federal body created in 1890 and established in its present form by Public Law in 1947. Comprised of representatives of Federal agencies, appointed for 2-year terms, the Board is authorized to establish and maintain uniform geographic name usage throughout the Federal Government.

However, they don't like to name things after living people, so no one is volunteering to have an undersea mountain named for them any time soon.

Our improvement in performance in all of this is partly practice, and partly adjusting our parameters. "Close" is a relative concept . . . just because we *can* keep the ship within five meters of track, with great difficulty and strain on people and equipment, what is the point? The vehicle, five miles away, is unaffected by even larger wobbles in our track. So we set constraints on track following that are looser than we *can* do, in favor of restricting maneuvering so we don't over-stress the rudders and towing equipment, or create such fatigue that someone misses something important. Now, working on our third line, we seem to have the process down much better. This may sound like everybody is frantically busy, but it all happens over hours-long time scales. In some ways, once everything is going well, this is very much like watching paint dry! However, when things unravel, events can happen *fast*.

The objective of this entire exercise is to lower the sonar to the right altitude over the seafloor and tow it along deliberately and smoothly. The sidescan sonar is a common tool for ocean mapping and search. It takes advantage of the distance that sound can propagate in water, but suffers from lower resolution and sensitivity to motion as compared to an optical image. It also represents acoustic reflections (like an ultrasound image of a baby) rather than light reflections, so there is some difference in interpretation. We can never be certain what we have "seen" with sonar, and must identify it optically.

Sidescan sonar works by using an array of transducers, which are made with crystals that vibrate when electrically charged and make sound in the water. (See illustration on page 24.) The proper arrangement of the array and timing of its discharge will form a butterfly-wing shaped "beam," or area of sound intensity. This beam is oriented so the thin edge strikes the bottom, in a line on each side of the sonar. The system "pings" a burst of sound, at a specific frequency (in our case, both 50 kHz and 500 kHz), and then "listens" for a period of time (the transducers can also convert sound back into electrical signals). Any echoes are timed and correlated with distance from the sonar. These echoes are plotted on a line on our computer screens (and saved to disk for later analysis). This all repeats up to several times per second, and line by line, an image of the bottom is collected. This can all be corrected for geometry and vehicle motion, and ultimately mapped into a mosaic. But we are mostly interested in detection of targets.

The sound will reflect stronger as a result of several factors. If the bottom is rocky or composed of hard sand, it will reflect stronger than if it is mud or silt. If there is a slope or cliff, the face will reflect stronger. And if there is something very hard, like metal, or with sharp edges, like man-made objects, the echo can be very strong. There can also be acoustic "shadows" as the sound is blocked from some area . . . the length of the shadow can be used to calculate the height of the object casting the shadow.

Our sonar can "see" up to 1,000 meters to a side, but the farther the range setting, the worse the resolution. So, as always in our universe, there is a trade-off. (I consider this evidence that Mother Nature has a wicked sense of humor!) Also, the image degrades in the far reaches of the swath, and we have to account for some error in navigation, so we work with some overlap between swaths. In the current circumstance, we are covering something just over one square nautical mile per hour while searching, but there is "overhead" for maintenance, weather, and turns. You have heard about turns.

There is much more to tell, including gapfilling, mosaicking, image processing, target detection, grazing angles, resolution cells, and other complications. These make the effective analysis of sidescan images both a technical challenge and a skill that comes only with experience and a knack for recognizing a likely target from a shadowy blob. The "Art of Search" is practiced well only by the few who are talented, intelligent, experienced, and patient.

### March 22; Friday. Another Day, Another Line.

The midwatch finished the third line last night, and by noon the vehicle was on its way up for another comp oil refill and other maintenance "of opportunity," that is, repairs that can wait until the opportunity arises and don't require suspending operations. We have about 8 percent of the area completed, right on schedule. Shawn insisted that his crew retrieve NOMAD this time, as they hadn't had a chance yet. It went smoothly (though exciting as usual), and the team descended on the vehicle and winch with a purpose. In only two hours we refilled the comp, retethered the drogue (a parachute-like device that stabilizes the vehicle), moved the camera (which was pointed at the comp reservoir) back to normal position, chased down a few leaks, replaced a cable run that had an air bubble in it, checked for sources of noise, tie-wrapped everything in sight, and jacked up the level-wind so the cable wouldn't rub on it. Oh, and reloaded the pressure-compensated Styrofoam compression device (the Styrofoam Cup Holder 6000).

Our watch section is definitely coordination-challenged. In the interest of good housekeeping, I'm always cleaning off the Isis monitors, as a number of people treat the screen as a "touch panel." So I took a good swipe with an alcohol-soaked rag and stroked the "Power" key. The entire Isis system went black. Jay had to dive into the panel under the winch control station and reset everything. The only saving grace was that we were not yet on the bottom, so Isis was unnecessary at that moment, and we developed another "training opportunity."

For a good salty conversation, there's no one better than Joe. I saw Joe by the fo'c's'le deck rail last night, and asked him how he was. "Arrgh," he says, in his authentic gravelly voice, "You know, the sea looks different every day, and she's full of surprises." He proceeded to tell me about how he was relaxing, looking at the sea by that very rail, very peaceful, when all of a sudden he was doused with a deluge of water. It turns out, someone we shall not mention (Mike Davis) chose that moment to empty the dehumidifier tank over the bridge wing, and misjudged the wind. Just another one of the sea's surprises.

Now, the vehicle is on the bottom, five and a half hours after we began winch-in this morning at the end of the last line. That's hardly any longer than a normal turn takes, so we accomplished all of our repairs without any significant loss of time! Of course, with practice we hope to make the turns shorter.

## March 23; Saturday. Bat Turn Number Two.

As we finished the line we neared our second attempt to do a Bat Turn. We are trying to blend Joe's experience with towing trawl fishing gear in Alaska at 4,000 feet, with Tom's experience towing sonars at 20,000 feet, Spence's ship-handling skills, and Jeff's analytical mind. Jeff and Spence did a marvelous analysis of the first turn, using data we collected on the computer and photos Julie took of the monitors along with hand-written logs she kept of the event. They have dissected the detailed events and interpreted the parameters, leading to a step-by-step procedure for this next try. If it works, we could cut the turn down to two hours, a big time savings. It would also be an advance in the art of deep-ocean survey.

It is now 1230, and we finished Line 15 (our fourth line), and began to haul the vehicle up while increasing ship's speed.

Fifteen minutes later, and we are turning 90 degrees. This tends to slacken the cable and allow the vehicle to sink, but we are continuing to haul in to slow that effect and hopefully shorten the process.

We had covered much of Line 15 before midnight, and the midwatch finished it. There was nothing exciting to report on the bottom, but we did have a surface contact which caused some excitement. We picked up on radar a ship about fifteen miles away, with a twelve-mile CPA (closest point of approach). This seemed unusual in itself, way out here, but it was even odder due to its slow speed, about fifteen knots. A merchant would normally be moving much faster (time is money). Then he changed course—toward us! We were really wondering what was up. Soon, we could see navigation lights on the horizon, about ten miles out. Of course, we were displaying towing lights, and had very limited maneuverability.

After a while, he reverted to his previous course, and passed ahead at about eight miles. He was definitely a large (150-meter-long) merchant ship. It was unexpected to see another ship out here, but I guess if you are going from somewhere to somewhere else, you just might pass through the middle of nowhere.

At just after 1300, we are thirty minutes into the turn. The cable is trailing nearly directly behind, and the vehicle depth has stabilized and even begun to come up. So far, so good. Now we're executing another right turn to head back in the direction of our next line. We are also beginning to haul in fast, as altitude is dropping as the ship is heading back toward the vehicle. Vehicle heading is starting to respond.

*1345.* The ship is just passing over the vehicle, miles below, with the cable snaking around in a corkscrew. We have regained contact with the bottom with the sonar, and are actually collecting data after only one hour. Of course, the vehicle is pointed the wrong way and will take a while to recover. But things are looking great.

*1400.* About ninety minutes into the turn, and we've had to secure paying out due to a level-wind problem with the winch, but Jay and Bragg are working on it. The "level-wind" is a device that guides the cable onto the drum so that it wraps evenly and the cable doesn't lay over an adjacent wrap. Very important, given the forces involved and the cost of the cable!

*1415.* Back in action, paying out to the bottom. The vehicle heading is on track, altitude about 300 meters, and the ship is on Line 14 (our next survey line).

Our watch-section leader is Tom Bethge, who is also the operations department manager back home. As his entire department is here at sea, it's appropriate that he is here, too. Tom is a logistics genius, and was in charge of the entire operation preparation and mobilization. It is to his credit and the Ops team that we are so well prepared. Tom is very patient and meticulous, especially with procedures. We plan, rehearse, prepare, and are ready with a purpose when things start happening. And if anything goes wrong, he is ready to help us learn from the experience.

The captain told me yesterday that he and Joe, the first mate, were talking about how with each passing day they are beginning to appreciate what a world-class operation Nauticos is, and they are proud to be a small part of this operation. I assured him that it couldn't happen without the ship and crew, of course. I am very proud of this team.

Jay Ellis is our ops technician extraordinaire. He is indefatigable, and can be called upon to fix any mechanical problem (and usually is). It is fascinating to see him reconfigure the vehicle sensor arrangement or cable runs, making modifications as necessary in the field. His albatross of the moment is the winch level-wind; he has found that, when it hangs up, a tap with a hammer will usually get it going again. Now that we have traced it to be an electronics problem, he still wants to tap it with a hammer!

Mike Davis is our very talented software and electronics engineer who keeps all the electrons flowing and the bytes in their places. Mike has been a major architect of most of the software we are using. He puts us to shame by working out every day and eating well. (Somebody has to bring the average up!) Mike has been indispensable out here, making sure the software is working, troubleshooting electronics, and helping Spence generate random numbers for the Electra search pool. Mike also plays bass guitar for Naked Blue, a great local Maryland band, and brought his bass along to keep in practice.

It is now nearly 2200, and we have had a long afternoon and evening. Shortly after we completed our great Bat Turn, we had some real trouble with the level-wind. Cleaning the connector was no help, so Jay, Bragg, and Mike began serious troubleshooting. Before long, Shawn and Sue were up working on it, and a major repair effort was under way. It began to rain steadily, and we rigged a tarp so they could open up the electronics box. Shawn and Sue worked under the level-wind itself, coated with grease, working on the sensor and connections, while Mike worked on the control board. Bragg and Jay searched for parts and ran tools, and the media team documented it all. This went on for hours, the rain continuing to fall, soaking everybody. They finally managed a temporary fix. Still, the system could not be adjusted properly for automatic operation, so we have resorted for now to local control of the winch (that is, operating it from the control station by the winch). There someone can control the level-wind manually and make sure it tracks. The problem is that we cannot see the altitude reading from there, so we have to communicate winch-in, winch-out commands via walkie-talkie. It is also noisy out there, and tomorrow it will be hot. And for now it is raining.

However, we are back searching, a bit late on the lane, and with some inconvenience but just as effectively. We are still ahead of schedule, and should be able to pick up more time with our Bat Turns.

## March 24; Sunday. Back on Line.

Mike and Rod were seen late last night poring through the level-wind circuit diagrams and puzzling out the difficulties we've been having. Mysteriously, sometime during the night it decided to start working properly and now is running smoothly.

Back to the watch team. Julie Nelson is our corporate counsel, Diesel Queen, sonar watchstander, tie-wrap debris scavenger, star log-keeper, and is at this moment portraying the "victim" in the crew's SAR (search and rescue) training drill. She was tasked to hide somewhere in the berthing spaces while teams of the crew tried to find her wearing blindfolds (simulating search in a dark and smoke-filled room). Then they strapped her to a board and carried her out of the wardroom, to the aft deck, up one level, and to the fo'c's'le. Julie is making an effort to experience everything she can on this trip, doing mechanical work on NOMAD, standing all of the watch stations, operating the diesel, and in general making herself very useful. She is always cheerful, but at the same time serious about our work. She was a big contributor to the development of the project, and supported ship-checks in Seattle, as well as writing the ship charter document. Julie eventually became general manager of Nauticos, and no doubt her experience at sea was invaluable in that role.

Bragg Sherrer is on loan to us from the U.S. Navy, specifically the Naval Oceanographic Office, and we are very happy to have him aboard, as we had worked with him on other projects and knew he was good. Bragg has been a willing worker, great shipmate, and talented technician. He has spent a lot of time on the Isis, and helped do some of the initial contact analysis that gets passed on to Tom.

Dave Jourdan, that's me. If we don't find it, it'll be my fault, as I got us into this. I (along with partners Joe Crabtree and Dan Schoenberger) founded Nauticos in 1986. I was a Navy submariner, and have worked with ocean projects my entire career. My specialty is underwater navigation, and I have been successful on a number of search operations both with the Navy and with Nauticos. Though I am president of the company, I believe a good leader is also a good follower, and I am pleased to focus on my area of expertise while leaving the operational management to those like Tom Dettweiler and the others with more appropriate experience. However (as I will find later in the mission), there are times when the president must step forward and make a critical decision. Meanwhile, I am a happy sonar watchstander, NOMAD line handler, and chronicler of our endeavor.

Jon Thompson is our exhibits manager (sometimes known as the "Exhibitionist"), as well as an investor. He is pitching in any way he can to stand sonar and winch watches, as well as perform collateral duties as "Drogue Mon" (handling the drogue during recoveries and launches), Cup Meister (preparing, loading, and unloading the Syrofoam cups), and Newscaster of the Stars (thanks to email feeds from wife Susan). Jon has been at sea before with one of the *Titanic* expeditions, and managed the Wonder Series of exhibits for the City of Memphis. He also organized two successful *Titanic* traveling exhibitions. A graduate of the U.S. Military Academy and Vietnam veteran (where he flew O-1 Bird Dog observation aircraft in combat), he is our sole Army representative.

Tom Vinson is our lead Rockwell Collins radio engineer, and co-operator (with Rod) of our HF radio station, which allows occasional phone calls home through Comm Central in Cedar Rapids, Iowa. We all really appreciate their support, as well as that of Rockwell Collins, which is sponsoring their time and the equipment. "Comm" Tom and "Rod-io" have worked for three years and (with their cohorts in the Collins Amateur Radio Club, CARC) have spent about 3,000 hours conducting radio transmission analysis for our project. Tom is a pleasure to have aboard, and even though it's their first time at sea, he and Rod have proven to be great sailors.

A successful search for anything . . . whether it be Amelia's Electra or a set of missing car keys at home . . . requires the satisfaction of two basic conditions: one must be able to "see" the object one is seeking, and one must look where it is! All of the discussion about sonars and cables and computers addresses the first condition. So, how do we satisfy the second condition: where to search?

Nauticos relies on a process we developed called "Renav," short for "re-navigation." This refers to a comprehensive re-computation of navigation parameters using raw data collected during a voyage and an in-depth under-standing of navigation system operating principles and error behavior. Since all of this information is uncertain, the inputs and results are necessarily statistical in nature. In most cases we use a statistical estimation process called a Kalman filter, which is programmed into a software program, also called Renav.

The Renav system was originally developed to analyze modern submarine inertial navigation systems, using a Kalman filter to estimate parameters for sophisticated error models of these complicated devices. This was very success-ful, but relied on massive amounts of data and detailed models of error behav-ior. In 1995, we showed how this technique and software programs could be applied to historical information from World War II, with much sparser data, in the discovery of the Japanese submarine *I-52*. Other Nauticos discoveries relied on this technique, and we have become quite confident in its use.

In order for this to work, one must be able to correctly judge the statistical uncertainty in historical information, and to understand how this uncertainty affects navigation. This part of the problem relies on experience and judgment, and sometimes involves clever ways to objectively rate the quality of data. It is sometimes more art than science, and the overall process is far from a cook-book recipe.

One of the hardest parts of the analytical process is to maintain objectivity, as most people already have an idea of the answer and spend a lot of time seek-ing data to support their premature conclusions, while rejecting information that contradicts them. Over many years and successes in this field, I have sum-marized a few key principles that help guide me in my quest for objectivity and have contributed in no small way to our successes in underwater discovery.

*Consensus about the wrong answer is still wrong.*

In any study of historical events, one finds a collection of "conventional wis-dom" that is commonly accepted. Sometimes these "facts" are the product of a mistake or misinterpretation that is propagated over time and becomes "true." It is never a good idea to accept a piece of information solely on the basis of consensus, though this is a very powerful temptation.

*In a disaster, it is the improbable that is most likely.*

Systems are designed to be reliable, and people are trained to deal with problems and emergencies. Especially in the case of experienced professionals, rarely will a single equipment failure or isolated mistake cause a disaster. So, even though the likelihood of a combination of unrelated events is normally small, in the special case of a disaster one has to turn this thinking on its head. In the case of a disaster, it is that unlikely combination, in fact, that led to the tragedy.

*Answers assimilated in the heat of battle are least reliable.*

I have seen many cases where an erroneous datum has been calculated based on source information from perfectly good navigation and excellent record keeping. This is because the time of a disaster is never the best circumstance to analyze and report. When ships are sinking, planes are crashing, and people are dying, the parties involved are much more concerned with recovering from the disaster and moving on to the next mission or event. Conversely, with the perspective of time and the comfort of a lab or office, as well as the benefit of a wide range of information before, during, and after the event, an objective analyst can do a much better job of assimilating information and computing a better result.

*False associations are easier to swallow than logical reasoning.*

Michael Shermer, publisher of the magazine *Skeptic*, explains why anecdotal reports from eyewitnesses are so unreliable, yet so readily accepted. Writing in *Scientific American* (May 2005), he says, "Humans evolved brains that are pattern recognition machines, adept at detecting signals that enhance or threaten survival amid a very noisy world." He calls this capability "associative learning," and it explains how our ancestors could associate the seasons with the migration of game animals, or connect the position of the sun, change of season, and time to plant crops. Animals know some of these things by instinct, but human brains can reason out connections and make subtle inferences.

Humans can also communicate and pass on these learned associations to other humans. This awesome capability to reason out casual connections and pass on accumulated knowledge can be a great asset, but it also leads to false associations. Superstition, rumors, and conspiracy theories are all fueled by this associative learning ability. We do this naturally, whereas logical reasoning and scientific inquiry require more training and discipline to apply successfully.

All of the above came into play in our analysis of the Amelia Earhart disappearance. First of all, since she vanished without a trace, there was plenty of room for speculation, and the vacuum was quickly filled with folklore. Since she was last heard from over deep water, beyond the reach of any technology of the day, one had to assume she fetched up on an island somewhere to have any hope of finding any evidence. Thus, every major island in the South Pacific seems to have an Amelia Earhart legend, and all are mutually exclusive. Over time, the lack of real evidence led to suspicions of coverup, and the fact that the U.S. government had no information to produce only heightened the suspicion that they were hiding something.

We at Nauticos had declined some earlier invitations to conduct searches for Amelia just offshore some Pacific islands, as it was easy to see there was no hard evidence to support any specific location. This changed when Steve Lyons from WGBH/NOVA and Elgen Long visited us in 1997. In an initial effort to confirm Elgen's conclusion that Amelia ran out of gas near Howland Island (the "crashed and sunk" theory, as it is known among Amelia Earhart enthusiasts), NOVA commissioned a study of the fuel consumption of the Electra, conducted by Dr. Fred Culick of Cal Tech. Dr. Culick, who also was present at our 1997 meeting, is a leading aeronautics expert, and is published widely in technical journals, as well as more popular magazines such as *Scientific American*. He helped create a full-scale replica of the Wright Flyer and is the co-author of *On Great White Wings*, the story of the Wright brothers and the race for flight (2001, Madison Press). Dr. Culick was assisted by Professor Grant Swenson, also of Cal Tech.

This analysis was armed with some new information, recently uncovered. In late July of 1937, Eric Chater, the general manager of Guinea Airways, Ltd., on Lae Airport in New Guinea, wrote a full report on Earhart's activities at the airport and her departure from it. This report was misfiled and lost for many years; however, in 1991, the document was located in a filing cabinet that was being cleaned out of old company records. Owing to publicity surrounding the search for Amelia, it was brought to light, and eventually made its way to Elgen Long. This report had much to say about Earhart's fuel load and maintenance concerns when she left Lae.

Based on all of the evidence and considering all that was known about the plane, the pilot, the environment, and the flight plan, Culick and Swenson estimated that the most likely flight endurance for Amelia's last flight was twenty hours and thirty-eight minutes. Amelia's last radio message was sent twenty hours and thirteen minutes after takeoff from Lae. This analysis was detailed in an exhaustive twenty-two page report that left little in doubt.

Furthermore, the analysis finds that Amelia could not have remained aloft for longer than twenty-two hours and fifteen minutes, even under the most generous range of assumptions. Culick and Swenson conclude in their report:

With less than two hours of fuel remaining, there are only two islands that might have been within her range: Howland and Baker, both manned by Coast Guard personnel. [*Author's note*: The Coast Guard was not on Baker, but colonists were present on the island at the time.] Since she landed at neither, the inescapable conclusion is that Amelia Earhart crashed at sea. Her airplane lies at the bottom of the Pacific Ocean, waiting to be found.

So we can be confident that Amelia and Fred never reached an island . . . unless they escaped the sinking Electra, and swam across hundreds of miles of open ocean to encounter one of the tiny specks of land scattered thinly about the region. Regardless of that improbable scenario, the Electra itself sunk. But knowing when Amelia ran out of fuel in itself does not tell us where to search.

Elgen's research and analysis took two paths. One was to consider the wide range of possibilities for all elements of navigation and determine an "area of probability" that encompassed all conceivable outcomes. If done correctly, this should yield an area of the ocean that almost certainly must contain the sunken Electra. Unfortunately, his result projected a region of deep ocean about five times the area of the State of Rhode Island, around 6,000 square miles. Since we can cover about one square mile per hour at a resolution sufficient to detect the plane, it would take 250 search days to cover this area. Considering fuel, food, and human endurance of a typical research vessel and embarked survey team, a seven-week mission, including five weeks on station and about twenty-eight to thirty effective search days (considering weather delays and maintenance time), is a realistic limit for a single mission. Thus, eight or nine "typical" missions would be required to cover this area of probability. At $1.5 to $2 million each, we are talking about $12 to $18 million and two years or more of steady work to complete such an agenda.

The other path Elgen followed in his analysis was to consider a "most likely" approach and choose the best assumptions based on his research, analysis, navigation knowledge, and aviation judgment to arrive at a best estimate for the Electra's splash point. Elgen was well equipped to do this, based not only on his impressive experience in general aviation, communications, navigation, and historical research, but also in his specific and detailed experience with the particulars of Amelia's situation. Elgen actually flew near Howland Island under conditions similar to those that Amelia experienced, and did his best to judge the parameters she would have faced, such as cloud cover, visibility, and wind conditions. He crafted a very plausible scenario for Amelia's final flight, which he outlines in detail in his book.

This result, unfortunately, has the opposite problem from the area-of-probability approach: it predicts a single point in the ocean and does not tell us how large an area we must search to achieve a reasonable chance of success.

This is where the Renav process could be used to good effect. Even if one can contemplate searching the entire 6,000-square-mile region in time, it's best to start with the most likely area.

In 1997, Nauticos set about to renavigate Amelia's final flight based on Elgen's research and any other information we could glean. The first thing we did was to strike an agreement with Elgen and his wife, Marie, to have access to their vast archive and to get their help. This was mutually beneficial and was the beginning of a partnership that has lasted over a decade. Along the way, Nauticos saw value in acquiring the entire research collection from Elgen and Marie so that we could digitize and preserve the historical information and eventually set up an archive that would complement a museum exhibition and be available to the public and other historical researchers.

Elgen and Marie had, over thirty years, acquired newspaper clippings, video and audio recordings, books, maps, letters, and photographs, contained in nearly two dozen neatly packed boxes and inventoried to the item. After we got to know the pair better, we used to joke that, if you had a question about a circuit in Amelia's radio, Elgen could tell you the particular alloy of copper used in the wires, and Marie could find the document in the archive to prove it! This was only a slight exaggeration. But we were concerned that the paper and magnetic tape materials would deteriorate in time, especially as they were being stored in a hot garage in San Diego.

I visited Elgen and Marie at their San Diego home in November of 1997. They were very gracious hosts, and were proud to show me the mountain of data they had collected and how well it was organized. I was interested to see, prominently displayed, a LeRoy Neiman painting of Amelia entitled *The Adventuress* . . . also notable and prominent was a similar painting of Elgen himself, entitled *The Adventurer*. As Elgen explained to me, he met the famous painter through a friend of Marie's, Evelyn Tate, who was sponsoring an art show in San Francisco. Though successful as an artist, Neiman was at heart an explorer, and over dinner he became enthralled with Elgen's stories and adventures. One thing led to another, and with some conspiring among Marie, Evelyn, and LeRoy, the artist presented Elgen with *The Adventurer* in 1977 in honor of his fiftieth birthday. A few years later, Elgen and Marie commissioned Neiman to paint *The Adventuress*, which he completed in 1981.

Eventually, Nauticos arranged to acquire the Longs' archive for about $200,000, along with the services of Elgen as our expedition leader and technical advisor. We offered to work through the non-profit SeaWord Foundation to digitize and archive the collection over time, in honor of Marie, who suffered from Parkinson's disease and passed away in June of 2003 at the age of seventy-seven. Elgen and Marie were married for fifty-seven years, and those of us who knew her could tell that she was a remarkable woman who played no small part in Elgen's success and recognition.

Over the years, with the help of the SeaWord Foundation, Nauticos, and a collection of interns and researchers, we have digitized thousands of photographs and slides, scanned reams of papers, and converted hundreds of hours of audio cassette recordings to digital audio CDs. Notable among the recordings are interviews conducted by Elgen with the eight men who were posted in the radio room of the Coast Guard ship *Itasca*, listening to Amelia's last radio transmissions. Among them was Leo Bellarts, chief radioman, whose observations figured significantly in our analysis.

Armed with all of this information, we set about to formalize a Renav analysis to try narrowing the Earhart Project search area to something under 800 square miles, an area we thought could be searched in one long mission. The approach we normally take is to make a first estimate of the path taken by the ship or aircraft in question, then "model" the uncertainty in this path. This model is a collection of error behaviors and quantifiable factors that describe the growing uncertainty in position starting with the known point of takeoff at Lae. One of these parameters, for example, is the compass heading. We can estimate the heading flown at any given time, but there are a number of uncertainties including the quality of our guess, the performance of the instrument, the accuracy that could be read from the instrument, and the precision of the path flown. All of these parameters can behave differently and have different numerical values associated with them. Also, different types of errors have different effects on navigation position; for example, heading and other angular errors tend to be seen as an error across the track, while speed errors tend to be along the track. Wind direction and speed are also factored in.

Once a plausible track with modeled uncertainty is created, this can be compared with "measurements," that is, known locations, speeds, distances, or headings as reported along the way. These measurements have their own uncertainties that must be modeled. Once this work is all completed, the set of data can be run though a Kalman filter algorithm which compares all of the parameters according to a complicated set of statistical rules, and yields the best estimate of position and uncertainty along the track. This answer is known as the "maximum likelihood" result. Our goal was to compute the maximum likelihood position at the end of Amelia's flight, which would define the search area location and size to any desired probability.

This technique had stood up well over the years and many successful deep ocean searches. Unfortunately, it would not be that simple for the case of the

Amelia Earhart disappearance. We had two major problems. First, we had very sketchy information about her flight path and few solid measurements to go on. Still, these things could be modeled and did not in themselves present an intractable problem. In fact, at the time when Fred and Amelia reached the point over the ocean where they expected to find Howland Island, and reported "WE MUST BE ON YOU BUT CANNOT SEE YOU," I believe we have a good idea of where they were. However, this leads to the second, more serious problem. After that 1912 GMT message, they flew around searching for the island with increasing desperation until their last message at 2013 GMT, a full hour later. What path did they fly? How fast? We have a few bits of information, such as "WE ARE ON THE LINE OF POSITION 157-337 . . . WE ARE RUNNING NORTH AND SOUTH," but that leaves much to question. Where was that line? Were they running north or south at that moment? They reported they were circling, but was that to reverse course and to run back north (or south) along the line, or to be able to scan the horizon, or for some other reason? Elgen's scenario included his best guess at the path flown, based on impressive logic and reasoning. But we had to admit there were many other scenarios that fit the radio reports just as well.

When faced with this kind of uncertainty, not just in the quality of the data, but in the scenario itself, one approach that had been successful in the past was to create a "decision tree" of plausible possibilities based on well documented assumptions, and to try to encompass all likely outcomes. Each of these could be rated by some statistical method, and analyzed separately. The collection of Renav results, weighted according to their likelihoods, would define a search area . . . admittedly a much larger one than would result from one scenario, but probably more realistic.

This is where the radio signal analysis became important. In a couple of her messages, Amelia estimated her distance to Howland. Though we know this was off, it was nonetheless a measurement with an uncertainty. Elgen made his own estimate of the relative distance at the time of each transmission, noting that the signal strength was judged to have been increasing each time up until the last message, where it declined somewhat. What we needed for Renav was a quantitative estimate of the distance from the *Itasca* to the Electra at each transmission, and the uncertainty in the estimate.

One of the key members of the Nauticos team was Gary Bane, the leader of our West Coast operations. I met Gary in 1997 just after he had officially retired from many years of service with Rockwell International, which had culminated with a position as Director of Ocean Systems. His retirement was short-lived, as he soon joined Nauticos, and became a major contributor to the Amelia project planning and development. He saw immediately that a special resource might be available to us, and he had the right connections.

In 1973, Rockwell acquired a company by the name of Collins Radio. Founded in 1933 by Arthur Collins in Cedar Rapids, Iowa, the company captured the world's attention when it supplied the equipment to establish a communications link with the 1933 South Pole expedition of Rear Admiral Richard Byrd. The Collins Radio Company built equipment for America's space program, including the Apollo, Gemini, and Mercury capsules, providing voice communication for every American astronaut traveling through space.

Gary knew the folks at Collins Radio, and, in the fall of 1998, asked if they were interested in helping our efforts. The answer—a resounding *Yes!*—came from the Collins Amateur Radio Club (CARC), a group of professional radio engineers who spent much of their spare time as amateur (ham) radio enthusiasts. With support from the company, and led by Tom Vinson and Rod Blocksome, CARC put its full effort, the club's resources, and the brainpower of a dozen talented and experienced radio experts to our problem.

At about the same time in Philadelphia, in early 1999, commercial pilot and Earhart researcher David Dunlap contacted Crawford MacKeand, a retired electrical-electronics engineer in Delaware, to see if his published radio propagation program could be of any aid in locating Amelia's aircraft. Crawford made some initial calculations with the help of documentation unearthed by Dunlap. In the summer of 1999, Dunlap sent these results to Elgen Long, who passed the connection on to Nauticos. Crawford was working on a book *The Friendly Ionosphere* (2001, Tyndar Press). Though the title and subject did not argue for a future on the *New York Times* Best Seller list, the book caught our attention, especially as Crawford included a chapter with an analysis of the Amelia Earhart signal propagation. We, in turn, connected Crawford and Rod Blocksome of CARC, who established a good working relationship and began to pursue the analysis in parallel.

Crawford became a welcome and helpful partner in this endeavor, helping to maintain objectivity, provide insight, and sometimes offer an alternative view of an issue. Crawford also contributed a lot to the design of the experiments. Nauticos's own Jeff Palshook followed this work very carefully, and made some of his own contributions, particularly to the listening tests (described later). David Dunlap, meanwhile, continued to provide helpful research and offer a skeptical voice to keep us from being too closely wedded to particular assumptions.

Over the course of many years and uncounted thousands of volunteer hours, using the latest software and test equipment that Rockwell Collins could provide, as well as the resources of the University of Delaware library,

Crawford, Tom, Rod and the CARC team have tried their best to answer the question, "How far away was Amelia at each of her transmissions?" They have also taken their own independent approach to navigation, a great complement to Renav. In pursuit of these goals, the team has attempted to model exactly how the radio signals propagated from Amelia's airplane to the receivers on the *Itasca* by considering the signal loss at each step of the way, and then to compare the transmitted and received signal strengths to compute a distance. Over the course of this work, the team has conducted hundreds of tests, computer runs, and field experiments.

For starters, the group used well-established computer models and the known specifications of the radios in question to compute the transmitted signal strength, the Electra's antenna pattern, the propagation through the atmosphere, the *Itasca's* antenna pattern, and the *Itasca's* radio reception. One day, they heard of the existence of a vintage radio of the same type as the one on the *Itasca*, located at the Antique Wireless Association Museum in Bloomfield, New York. Taking a long weekend road trip, a party traveled by car, converging from Cedar Rapids and Delaware, visited the museum, conducted tests, and added that knowledge to their estimates.

Rod, Tom, and their team have studied scale model planes on antenna ranges, have flown aircraft similar to Amelia's offshore to measure ocean propagation effects, and have conducted "listening tests" to compare the judgment of a collection of modern radio engineers with the reports of signal strengths recorded in 1937. One of the more remarkable studies they conducted was to have a young woman, Lisa Carrara, read the script of the Amelia's radio transmissions, attempting to mimic her voice as heard on recorded broadcasts. It was reported that Amelia's voice became higher pitched and the words came faster as she became more desperate; Lisa attempted to reproduce this effect to match the descriptions of Leo Bellarts and the other radiomen. Then, the radio engineers added the appropriate amount of noise to replicate the quality of the signal strength as heard on *Itasca*.

It is an eerie feeling to listen to the recordings of Lisa's voice. One can easily imagine that it is Amelia herself that we are hearing, a voice from the past.

All of these efforts were documented in great detail in a series of over a dozen reports, and our team gathered in Cedar Rapids on several occasions to hold a conference on their findings and discuss how we would use them in the development of a search area.

This work has been of immense value and is a story unto itself. The thousands of hours of work done by CARC were all voluntary. Rockwell Collins has backed these efforts as part of their Community Outreach program, and has even supported the expeditions by sponsoring Rod and Tom to go to sea and bring special radio communications gear. The CARC folks have given many lectures to school kids in an effort to promote science and engineering among young people.

The results tell us pretty well how far Amelia was from the *Itasca* at each transmission, and the range of uncertainty in that estimate. Unfortunately, there is one source of error that has defeated all efforts to mitigate: that is, the level of electronic noise present on the ship *Itasca*. We have very little historical data on this parameter, and estimates are fraught with debate. Was it more since equipment of the day was of poorer quality than today's devices, or was it less as the vessel in 1937 was equipped with few electronic devices as compared to today? There are no surviving examples of this ship. This is the biggest source of uncertainty in our estimates. Still, the results are perfect fodder for Renav.

Another major conclusion of these studies is that there is no possibility that Amelia's radio transmissions were heard much beyond the *Itasca*. All reports of her voice being heard in California or elsewhere in the Pacific are almost certainly not true. Also, all of the reports of "post-loss transmissions," that is, messages reportedly from Amelia after 2013 GMT, are most probably red herrings. This conclusion is supported by the fuel analysis, which says that Amelia's plane could not have reached dry land anywhere to transmit from. There are many explanations for the plethora of confounding reports and transmission, some of which are straightforward, such as a listener mistaking a commercial news report that included a re-enactment of the last transmissions received by *Itasca*. Sadly, it is not uncommon for spurious transmissions to be sent by "hoax-sters" as soon as the news is out of a disappearance. Others remain unexplained, like a small portion of UFO sightings. It is not my purpose here to try to explain each of these anomalies; suffice it to say that our team was convinced that the 2013 GMT transmission was the last message ever heard from Amelia Earhart. (See "Interlude: Where is Amelia Earhart?," for further discussion of the "post-loss" radio transmissions and alternative theories of Amelia's disappearance.)

It would be impossible for me to do any serious justice to the contributions made by CARC and Crawford MacKeand by trying to explain in detail all of their analyses and conclusions. It would take another entire book, and it would be a tome that only a radio engineer (or a Renav expert looking for Amelia Earhart) would enjoy reading!

One other bit of information proved to be useful, but also difficult to assess. That is, the distance from which Amelia could just barely see Howland Island under the conditions of her approach. Obviously, if she or Fred saw the island, they would have flown to it. This placed a lower limit on the distance to the shores of Howland that we would expect her path to have crossed.

There were many factors against her easily spotting Howland (or Baker, which would have been almost as good). She was fairly low (1,000 feet), presumably to be below the cloud deck as mentioned earlier; this limits the distance one can theoretically see. In spite of the stiff winds aloft that hindered her progress and consumed fuel throughout the flight, ironically the surface winds were very slight. This made for calm seas and little surf, which, as mentioned, would otherwise have made a bright white, highly visible line along Howland's shore. The *Itasca*, in an effort to create some kind of visible signal, made smoke with its boilers, but without wind the greasy cloud hugged the surface and did not rise to any height.

The sun was rising in front of the Electra's path, making a harsh glare in the direction of Howland. And the visibility was limited in any case from the small windows, with oversized engine nacelles and the bulbous nose of the aircraft in the way. Amelia could not even rise up in her seat to change her angle of view, as there just was not enough room in the cramped cockpit.

Elgen made his own observation of the visibility, flying in similar conditions to Earhart, and estimated this distance all around the island. To confirm this, we consulted with Professor John Andrews of MIT Lincoln Laboratories, who conducted visual range analyses based on similar work he performs for the modern U.S. Air Force. With his help, we were able to refine Elgen's estimates and increase our confidence in this parameter. Still, it is hard to imagine just what the conditions were inside the Electra's cabin during those final moments. Were Amelia's senses dulled owing to fatigue and stress, or were they heightened with fear and adrenalin? This adds to the uncertainty of the estimate.

All of this information—the fuel analysis, the scenarios, the radio signal results, the visual range estimates, Amelia's occasional position reports, and possible sightings of ships or islands along the way—were combined in our Renav filter to yield our best statistical estimate of a search area. Meanwhile, the CARC team created their own estimates, relying heavily on the assumption that Amelia was flying somewhere along their reported line of position bearing 157-337 degrees, regardless of any flight path or scenario. Led by Tom Heifner at CARC, the detailed statistical analysis also included visibility statistics, radio signal distances, inbound-course probabilities, ocean current drift, and even weather factors. All were integrated with formal statistical techniques, but presented so clearly that anyone could understand the process. Though there was some notable difference in these results as compared to Renav, the bulk of the regions overlapped, which was a satisfying outcome.

However, as I have said, *"Consensus about the wrong answer is still wrong!"* Was there another approach we could use? Renav analyst Jeff Palshook came up with another idea that overcame the weakness of the "traditional" renavigation, which relied on a specific set of assumptions and scenarios about the final hour of her flight. His approach, based on a well-understood statistical method called a "Monte Carlo" analysis, did not use any assumptions about the path of the plane, but (unlike the Collins approach, which used no path) tested many different paths. He programmed an algorithm to try a path at random, compare it with the measurements we had and other constraints (like visual distance to the island) and compute its likelihood. Then, just like rolling the dice at a Monte Carlo casino, the program would generate a new random path and test it.

With several days' running time on his laptop computer, Jeff generated a probability space based on about four million paths. To our satisfaction, the core of this region coincided with our other estimates. However, the nature of the approach generates a lot of unlikely, but not impossible, answers, so the estimate wasn't able to narrow down the search as much as we wanted. After all of this, we still had a large area to consider, but it was collapsing to 1,000 square miles or so of highest probability.

When we set out on the 2002 search mission, we realized that we would be hard-pressed to search anywhere near 1,000 square miles. But 600 was quite doable, and 800 was not out of the question. If we could achieve this, we would have, statistically, a quite good chance of success. We set our minimum goal for the mission of 600 square miles, encompassing the best combination of all approaches, and set our sights on mapping as much as 800.

By the morning of March 25, we were closing in on a week of solid surveying, and had completed our first 100 square miles of coverage. The teams were working smoothly, the sonar was performing well, and bit by bit we were revealing mile after mile of new territory, never before seen. Our sonar was probing the heart of the Renav area, and though we were prepared for more weeks of work ahead, we knew that discovery could come at any moment.

Anyone can hold the helm when the sea is calm.
    —Publilius Syrus (~100 BC)

Anyone can hold their lunch when the sea is calm.
    —Sue Morris (AD 2002)

## No Joy

**March 25; Monday. Flybys and Teasers.**

We finished the line last night, and by 0500 it was time to recover the vehicle. We had a long list of maintenance tasks to perform, but the main reason was to refill the comp oil reservoir. The NOMAD came on board at about 0730, and here's what the team had to do: replace the aft traction winch hydraulic motor (the rotary seal was leaking, so we did it as a precaution), fix hydraulic leaks on the forward motor hoses, relocate one of the cameras and lights to eliminate chatter on the sonar projector, refill the comp, check for vehicle oil leaks, service the diesel (do a "Jiffy Lube" on it), reposition the tow-point, and of course, reload the Styrofoam Cup Holder 6000. Guess how long before the vehicle was back in the water and on its way down? One hour and forty-five minutes! By late morning we were back on the bottom, searching Line 12. Jon, Julie (the Diesel Queen) and Jay got up extra early and worked with Shawn and the midwatch to do everything as quickly as possible. Great job!

Julie got a news download from our business manager Carla Bowling back home, so she issued the first edition of *The Daily Doldrums*. We should achieve a near 100 percent subscription rate.

This afternoon, we had a flyby by a Coast Guard C-130, apparently on a SAR (search and rescue) training mission. They knew we were out here, so they deviated from their normal track and paid us a visit. Next time, we'll expect a supply drop! It seemed strange to see a plane way out here . . . we haven't even seen any jet contrails overhead.

Sister Sue and I called our Mom (in Florida) today on the HF. She was so excited, and it was a lot of fun. We were talking through one-way radio transmissions "patched" to standard telephone lines. An operator in Cedar Rapids had to key the system for us to change from "transmit" to "receive." On each end, we had to say "Over" when we were finished speaking and ready to listen to the other party. This was not strange for most of us, but it was certainly different for the folks at home talking on a regular telephone! It added a flavor of "techiness" and remoteness that enhanced the experience.

All the moms have consistently asked if we were seasick and if we're getting sunburned. Ours asked a funny question about the "signs" we've been seeing. . . . She didn't understand how there could be signs out here. We figured out she meant the references to passing a sign that said "Nowhere" or "the Doldrums" in my email messages home. I radioed back, "It's sarcasm, Mom. Over!" It was great to talk to her, and so nice of Rod, Tom, and Rockwell Collins to do this for us. And our friend (and Rockwell Collins communications engineer) Dave Graham back in Cedar Rapids, who has to explain to everyone how to communicate on HF, is a peach! He will deserve a present! The crew has really appreciated getting the chance to call home as well.

Later this afternoon, R.J. launched the skiff and took Bill and Kristin out to film some promo spots, or "teasers" from some distance away from the ship. I couldn't believe Bill took his big, expensive camera out there! They circled us several times, and shot some good footage. Unfortunately, R.J. lost his personal camera overboard. We said we'd look for it on the bottom in an hour or so when the vehicle went by the spot (not really—we could detect a trash can, but nothing as small as a camera). Elgen volunteered to give him some of his disposable cameras so he could have some shots of the trip, which was really nice of him.

After they returned and were safely on board, a rainbow appeared! Also, Captain Dave said he scored a hole-in-one on his golf computer game for the first time in all the years he's owned it. We will consider those to be good omens.

The midwatch made a duct-tape model of Kristin, complete with ocean-blown red hair, sandals, a camera, and various outfits. Today, it was wearing a bikini when she realized what it was. She took it down from Ops and is busily re-configuring it with a long red General Custer goatee and a Nauticos shirt, so it will look like Shawn. She's a good sport!

Hamburgers were grilled on the aft-deck barbecue this afternoon, and delicious corned beef for dinner tonight. Scotty is really a marvel! And it is interesting how new things appear, or things we thought we ran out of (like ice cream bars) reappear. And people are bringing out their hoards of snacks more and more often.

### March 26; Tuesday. Life at Sea on the *Davidson*.

Our morning ops briefing was filmed for the media team. Although they would have liked something dramatic and asked some leading questions to draw out some kind of controversy or issue, there really wasn't anything but good news. We have had a reasonable number of problems associated with operating a custom-built high-tech system at near 20,000 feet, but our team has anticipated and dealt with them smartly. The ops team is well organized, responsive, and proactive. The cooperation between crew and science team is outstanding, and the ship drivers are learning with every hour. One difficulty they were having was the ship's response to our winching in and out as we're trying to maintain sonar altitude. Moving nine or more tons of cable does tend to disturb the ship. So, last night the midwatch installed a vehicle altitude display on the bridge, so the ship drivers can attempt to adjust ship's speed to "fly" the vehicle with minimal winch movement. This has worked very well, and makes it easier on everyone, including the equipment. Now we are working to inch up the speed so we can cover as many miles per day as possible.

We did another Wombat Turn in under two hours, completing Line 13. So far, we have completed 7 lines out of 39, covering about 150 square nm out of 800. We have now done about 19 percent of our primary area. This has taken seven days so far, so we are right on schedule. As we have developed good ship coordination, are mapping faster than planned, and have developed a new and shorter turn procedure, we could pick up a lot of time over the next few weeks. Also, Tom feels that we have covered the areas we have searched very thoroughly, and are virtually certain to have eliminated them.

Life at sea on the *Davidson* has settled into a comfortable routine, despite it being quite unlike life at home. There are three populations of people on the ship (in one sense of dividing them): the on-watch ship's crew, the on-watch ops/science team, and the off-watch people. The only ones not standing an official watch are Tom D., Elgen, the media team, and the cooks. Of course, the latter work all the time (I don't know how they do it!) Tom is on call and around most any time. Elgen and the media team tend to observe a daily routine, interrupted as they respond to events. They do a lot of interviews and are making a great effort to talk to everyone and see everything. The ship is on a watch schedule independent of the ops team . . . the bridge watch rotates every four hours (four on, eight off), while ops rotates every twelve hours. So, the midwatch is on from midnight to noon, and my group covers the rest of the day.

Within the watch-section, there are enough people to rotate around, meaning no one is really on duty for twelve hours straight. For the first few days, we all tended to hang in Ops, plus we were doing maintenance, repairs, watching temperatures or monitoring equipment on the aft deck, so we felt like we had to be there. Now that everybody is well trained and things are in equilibrium, we are rotating people in and out every couple of hours. We keep three people in Ops almost all the time, and watch leader Tom B. tends to stay on duty throughout the watch (but takes breaks). When we're off duty, we have to be up and about, generally hanging around the wardroom, so we're available any time.

On watch, we cover two stations: one watchstander operates the winch control, and is primarily responsible for vehicle depth (and as a corollary is responsible for not driving the vehicle into the bottom). He/she also watches the MS-1000 forward-looking sonar, monitors vehicle operation, watches the aft deck through the security cameras, keeps watch on the level-wind and how it's wrapping the drum, makes sure the Klein sonar is working OK, and keeps the music playing for our entertainment. The other watchstander mainly monitors the Isis sonar display, analyzing and logging contacts for later detailed analysis. The watch leader is usually around and coordinates with the bridge, watches vehicle track, makes sure we monitor everything, takes a periodic tour around the aft deck, directs any maintenance going on, plans for the next watch, and administers verbal "dope-slaps" (reminders and corrections) as necessary.

The off-duty folks are often busy with one thing or another, but usually find time to watch a movie, read, or even nap. During major evolutions like launch, recovery, or when the vehicle is on deck, everybody has a job (including, usually, members of the opposite shift). If we anticipate such an event, we try to get certain people off to sleep early so they can be up for the extra time, but that doesn't always happen.

The days are pretty full with watches and routine work, which goes on 24/7. Scotty tries to make Saturday special with a fancier meal (usually steak), and he will barbecue on an outside grill from time to time. Everyone tries to make Sunday seem like a day off, but it's not much different than any other day. Entertainment consists of reading, movies, eating, and practical joking. Spence runs SEA School (which is pretty well attended . . . today Tom and Rod talked about their radio signal analysis), and some of us ride the rowing machine every other day or so.

I do so wish the ship would stop rocking for just one hour!

To: Pretzelmeister@snyder's.com
Subject: Emergency Pretzel Shipment Request

Hey, Pretzelmeister:

Help us!

We're being held hostage aboard a slave galleon at the Equator. Slavedriver Dave keeps us at the oars 24 hours a day, 7 days a week, rowing, rowing. He demands that we come back with an Electra 10. Back and forth, up and down. Day after day. Unless and until we find it, he'll keep us here.

We are only slaves. But among us is an educated one. Jeff Palshook, a nuclear physicist, and pretzel engineer. He will build the Electra . . . from pretzels.

Made strong by tie-wraps, made sleek by massage oil, and made impervious to the elements by duct tape. Then, on a moonless night while Dave slumbers, we will submerge it to the bottom of the ocean only to "discover" by morning for Dave's pleasure and satisfaction.

Please help us. We need a tri-wall container of Snyder's. Covertness essential. Do not attempt to e-mail us; we are denied all attachments. We suggest nuclear submarine. Jeff keeps one nearby which he visits regularly with borrowed scuba gear.

Hear our plea. Send us a signal. Something extraordinary, like a C-130 overhead. We'll know what it means.

The A-Team.

## March 27; Wednesday. Quiet Day . . . So Far.

We are marching along through very flat and featureless terrain . . . ideal conditions for detecting our target! Tom gave his daily ops briefing, and told us that we finished Line 11, and turned around in less than an hour and a half! However, our comp oil level continues to fall, and it's looking like a middle-of-the-night recovery. We'll take advantage of the opportunity to install stiffeners on the sonar heads (which Jay made in the machine shop last night). We have a small amount of noise on the sonar which Tom thinks could be due to cable strumming causing vibrations. This could be mitigated by stiffening the transducer mounts. The guys think the appropriate holes could be drilled and the stiffeners installed in an hour. We'll also reload the Cup Holder 6000.

We are now over 20 percent done with our area.

Last night we had a gale which generated winds up to forty knots. Today it is clear and sunny, but we still have a stiff breeze, which has created dramatic whitecaps. *Bowditch* also mentions that winds in the Doldrums can sometimes be strong for brief periods, so this is normal.

Everyone seems in good spirits. However, after two weeks, it is beginning to get old for all of us. We had some higher winds and seas the last day or so, and this ship really rolls, so we are all tired of it even if we aren't seasick, per se. It is tiring just standing, as you are always fighting to keep steady, and you always have to do everything with one hand, as the other one is holding onto something! Last night, Jon took a pretty dramatic tumble off his chair, right across the Ops room. No injuries, but it made us more wary of our balance. Julie put a nice knot on her head on a locker door, and has a dramatically colorful bruise on her upper arm. No worse injuries so far!

We got a nice message from home last night, which informed us that Nauticos has been selected as the "Calvert County, Maryland Technology Company of the Year." Great! The ceremony will be in June, after we get home.

Jeff led the SEA School today, and showed us his navigation (Monte Carlo) analysis. We all agreed he has the prettiest plots. As time goes on, Spence has planned topics on nautical lore, such as knot-tying and celestial navigation. Spence can still take a star fix, and we actually use that knowledge in our work since we're often dealing with data from times when celestial navigation was prominent. The media folks will have a chance to tell us about their trade, and we will also plan talks on our search system components. Handy skills such as welding could even be in the offing if we run out of other topics.

Spence writes up daily promos and posts them around, provides everyone with an assignment sheet, and generally coordinates things. It's a great way to fill our time with something useful, build some teamwork, and even develop useful skills. Hats off to Spence for organizing this great program!

We are gearing up for a 0200 recovery tonight, the first one in the dark. It could also be the first one in the rain; let's hope not. There's not much different to do for a foul-weather plan, except we'll rig a tarp to shelter the drillers who have to drill eight holes in stainless (should take them forty minutes). Then we bolt on the stiffeners, and should be ready for launch.

We have been looking at our mosaic so far, and have mapped out most of a large volcanic formation which Thompson's Ridge, Bitch's Bluff, and Ellis Escarpment border on the south side. The peak (near Mt. Vinson) is a huge caldera that would swallow up the whole of Dann's Depression. When we get the north side mapped out (if we get that far), we'll put together the entire mosaic. Since these features have never been seen by humans before, who knows . . . maybe these names will stick!

### March 28; Thursday. A Night to Remember.

Well, the midwatch met quite a challenge last night, and did a great job. At the end of our watch (just before midnight), we completed the line and began hauling-in to recover for a comp fillup and installation of brackets on the sonar projectors. At around 0300, NOMAD was near the surface, and the team was ready to do the first night recovery, when a heavy squall hit. The vehicle came up in driving rain and high winds, but the midwatch group captured it beautifully and brought it on board with minor bumps.

Jay and Jon stayed up to work stiffeners and cups, and Tom D. was there as well. The rain slackened as they worked on the system. Within forty-five minutes, Jay and company were finished, and we commenced pre-launch checks on the vehicle. Unfortunately, one of the HMI light solid-state switches failed, and even though we don't need the lights yet, it had to be replaced to prevent damage to something else. This involved de-pressurizing the comp and opening an oil-filled junction box. Shawn and Sue dove into the problem, and emerged forty-five minutes later covered in mineral oil, but ready to button up and test again.

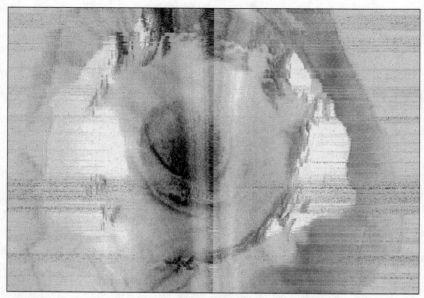

An undersea volcanic caldera, dubbed "Dann's Depression" by the crew, was imaged in 2002 by NOMAD. The sonar tracked directly over the center of this mile-wide crater; distortion of the image below the sled is evident. This and other features never before seen were mapped by the team while exploring earth's final frontier. On the crater rim lurks the dread "Hectapus" . . . (Courtesy Nauticos)

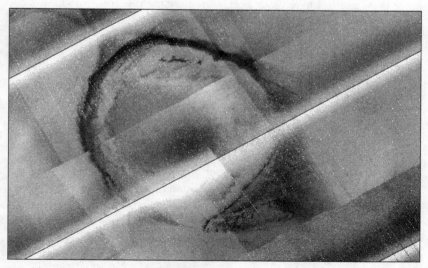

Another example of a caldera, this one spanning several sonar lanes as shown in this mosaic of images. The sharp ridges encircling the crater were several hundred meters high. (Courtesy Waitt Institute for Discovery)

After a bit longer than planned, and under drier conditions, NOMAD was launched back in the water and on its way down. One interesting experiment: Sue tie-wrapped a few light sticks to the frame, which are activated by shaking them (we use them for safety lights in case someone goes in the water). When the pressure increased a bit, and the sticks crushed, the lights came on! We could see them in the cameras clearly, and they glowed for hours.

It was 0530 by now, and I went below for a little rack time. When I came up at 0830, the vehicle was back on its way up! No sooner had we reached bottom and started working, than we started getting electrical ground fault alarms and losing power. After a few resets, we blew fuses in the bottle. So, up it came. This was suspiciously like the ground faults of yesterday at the same time . . . we are wondering if it's something on the ship's power.

NOMAD was recovered, the bottle opened, fuses replaced, the comp oil refilled, and cups reloaded in no time. It was back on its way down again, and just reaching bottom by the time I was back on watch at noon. Quite a night for the midwatch, with two launches and recoveries in twelve hours! We lost some time, which puts us slightly behind schedule now, but we are back in action and moving along.

We learned at our daily ops briefing that the ship is having some leakage from the propeller shaft seals. This sounds scary, but what it means is that twice a day they have to pump the water level down in Shaft Alley (otherwise the ship would fill with water and we would sink!) For reasons having to do with the piping arrangement of the ship, this involved securing toilets while pumping. We noticed that, and were wondering why. The seals can't be tightened while under way, so we'll deal with the leakage for now.

While on watch but off duty, we introduced Monty Python to Kristin. I brought a set of DVDs, and we watched some classic episodes including "Biggles Dictates a Letter," "Scaling Uxbury Street," "The Lifeboat Sketch," "Storage Jars," and "Cheese Shop." She really seemed to like it, or at least roared with laughter a lot. Maybe it's just that our threshold for entertainment is very low.

Anyway, we're back on Line 10. Tom V. logged one promising target, which was in the far field, so we'll get another (better) look at it on the way back day after tomorrow. You have to be patient out here!

### March 30; Saturday. More Progress.
We completed Line 9 last night, and are onto Line 8. The turnaround went very smoothly. The ground fault problem was traced to two leads in the slip rings, which were switched for two unused leads. (Slip rings are used to transfer

power and signals from the rotating cable drum to the fixed cables that lead to the Ops Center.)

The comp oil level is holding much better this time, so maybe we can complete some more lines before we have to refill it.

An ominous development . . . we are beginning to be concerned about our fuel supply. This ship does not have the experience operating for such a long duration, and even though we expected to have sufficient fuel for the full voyage we may need to refuel to complete the trip with enough margin to get home safely (and account for unknowns). The engineer has been sounding the tanks and checking consumption, and we will meet later to discuss this issue and our options.

Spence posted an updated Survey Progress Meter. He fills in the "thermometer" as we make progress on our search. The gradations are labeled as follows:

| | | | |
|---|---|---|---|
| 0% | C'mon, Get Going! | 80% | Must Be Along the Very Edge |
| 10% | Good Start | 90% | Nothin' But Sweet Spots Left! |
| 20% | Getting Better | 100% | Okaaay . . . Where Did It Go?? |
| 30% | In the Groove | 105% | TODAY Is the Day! |
| 40% | Cookin'! | 110% | We Love It Out Here |
| 50% | Halfway There | 115% | Won't Quit |
| 60% | I'm Optimistic | 120% | TP Is Running Low |
| 70% | It's Gotta Be Here | 125% | 'Splain It To My Wife |

Hopefully, we won't experience many of these stages!

We met about fuel later and explored options that we can exercise, including having a fuel barge meet us, refueling in the nearest port, or stopping early. In any case, at the rate we're going, we will be able to achieve our minimum mapping goal, which should give us an excellent chance of success (and would render the entire issue moot). However, by refueling, we would be able to extend and cover additional areas if necessary, while staying within our budget. We have a few weeks before we have to take action, but in the meanwhile we will investigate the options and set them in motion. The media team captured the meeting for potential dramatic material. There's always something!

### Nautical Term of the Day: **Marine Salvage**

"A science of vague assumptions based on debatable figures taken from inconclusive experiments and performed with instruments of problematic accuracy by persons of doubtful reliability and questionable mentality." — Capt. C. A. "Black Bart" Bartholomew

Black Bart met his demise in a diving accident.

It was a pretty uneventful watch, as the equipment continued to operate well and we continued to map miles and miles. We worked our way through the area around the center of the Renav area . . . would have been nice to be right on target! Still lots of Renav area to search yet. Mike was observed to be working on circuit boards and flying the vehicle at the same time. . . . Julie said he was really making bead necklaces.

Along we go, mile after mile.

### March 31; Sunday. Happy Easter!

We arose to find the ship decked out for Easter . . . balloons, plastic eggs, chocolates, etc. There was an egg for everybody on the ship. There was even one for Amelia. . . . Tom ceremoniously cast it to the deep. I guess Fred didn't get one. Thanks to Sue for all the goodies and hard work! I left little fuzzy chicks for the three "chicks" on board (they peep when you pet them).

The morning ops briefing found us on Line 6, having completed twelve and a half lines in twelve days. As may be recalled from earlier discussion, we are covering a nearly square rectangle, divided into 39 search lines. We decided to start in the middle of the box, on Line 18, and are working our way down to Line 1. We intend to return and cover Line 19 next, then continue north. The comp level is hanging in there at 22 percent! Those days of worrying about the level-wind seem long ago, but there is always some problem that rises to the top.

Shawn and Rod managed to fix the ship's gyro and autopilot . . . earning the sincere gratitude of the ship's crew. It's nice to be able to do something for the crew, as they have worked so hard for us. I'm convinced there is someone on this ship that can fix just about anything that might call for repair. We'll always want to sail with a radio engineer on board in the future!

The day seemed a little slower than usual, and there were more people out relaxing and catching some rays. It was a beautiful day for once, sunny, warm but not hot, a little breezy, with quiet seas. One thing that has been interestingly absent is fish. We hardly see any, only a few flying fish every so often. A number of us (not me) have tried mightily to catch some, and other than the mahi mahi that Scotty caught on the second day of transit, we have come up empty—very disappointing, and unexpected. On the other hand, there have been a surprising number of birds, even when we were mid-transit (hundreds of miles from shore). Some of these birds (albatross among them) live their lives out at sea, only coming ashore to nest.

Rod and Tom V. ran the HF radio for us again, and many of those aboard were able to call home for Easter. My sincere thanks to the guys that manned the radio in Cedar Rapids, giving up time on their Easter Sunday so we could have a treat.

Last night, during the midwatch, I stayed up to take in the sky a bit. It was very clear for once, and although there was a gibbous moon shining very brightly, you could still see a lot of stars, and many in the southern sky. Out here, as we are just about on the equator, the celestial poles are about on the horizon, and the sky pinwheels about those points in an unfamiliar way. Early in the evening, the Dipper points to the horizon, where Polaris is invisible. In the other direction, you find Leo near overhead, marked by the bright star Regulus. The most prominent constellation in our early evening sky is Orion, flanked by Sirius (the sky's brightest star) and Taurus, with the Pleiades a little farther along. It turns out that Venus shines very brightly after sunset, and Mars, Jupiter, and Saturn are visible higher along the ecliptic.

Later in the evening, the Southern Cross is visible well above the horizon, next to Centaurus and Scorpio. It was fun to see the Cross (officially known as Crux), pick out the star Alpha Centauri (famous for being the third brightest star, the nearest, and the one the Robinsons, the Robot, and evil Dr. Smith were headed for in "Lost in Space"), and all the other southern constellations I learned as a kid living in Venezuela. I was even able to find the Clouds of Magellan, companion dwarf galaxies to the Milky Way.

On subsequent nights, I arranged for the ship's navigation lights to be secured for a while, which improved the viewing substantially. On clear, moonless nights, with zero pollution (neither light nor smog), and an unrestricted view of the horizon, stargazing opportunities were unmatched. I had brought my *Burnham's Celestial Handbook* along (all three volumes), and regaled evening visitors to the fo'c's'le with astronomical arcana. I mentioned the names of some of the prominent stars, and the one that caught the most attention was Betelgeuse in Orion. Someone wanted to know the origin of the name, so I looked it up (I always wondered myself). According to *Burnham's*, the name is Arabic, and translates to "Armpit of the Giant." Hmmm.

Unsatisfied with this explanation, some further digging revealed that there are multiple sources with competing etymologies for the star's name. All agree that the name is Arabic and refers to its parent constellation Orion. Apparently, a European mistranslation into Latin during the Middle Ages led to the "armpit" interpretation, coincidentally (or not?) in keeping with its location in the constellation. Further enlightenment on this topic would seem elusive. . . .

On watch, things have been mostly quiet, but with some interesting or exciting events. The night before last, during a turn between lanes, the midwatch took the vehicle to video altitude (only a few meters to test the hi-resolution sonar and the optical gear. Everything worked fine, and we got our first view of the bottom in this area. We saw fish, sea slugs, crustaceans, worm trails, and all varieties of bottom-dwellers. There was an amazing amount of life, existing in total darkness at 18,000-foot depth, under pressures exceeding 8,000 PSI. There is so much to learn down there! One of the bottom features we noted with interest were numerous tracks in the sand that looked like Nauticos shells (our company logo). We know that they are made by a creature that likes to leave its excrement in spiral trails (Tom D. taught us this). So we call them "swirly turds."

There was a bit of excitement on the midwatch. I was hanging out with them (that's the best way to keep them from talking about you, but it doesn't always work!), when I noticed the ship was abruptly trailing off track. At the same time, Jeff (on the winch) noted altitude dropping rapidly. I watched in amazement as the ship track started to drift backwards, as the altitude continued to drop. Fortunately, Shawn assessed the situation immediately, had Jeff pull the pay-in stick to the stops, ran to the bridge and called for speed ahead. It turns out that in an attempt to fine-tune the ship's speed, with Spence trying to help, they lost headway, and the eight tons of cable being rapidly winched in actually hauled the ship backwards! Thanks to Shawn's quick action, we avoided "lawn-darting" the vehicle into the bottom, yet it did briefly get down to under 20 meters. This was a good example of how we have to be alert at all times, which is hard to do over such duration. But our team is doing it.

Another event happened this evening. We have a forward-looking sonar (the Simrad MS-1000), which helps detect objects under the sonar and looks ahead several hundred meters. After hours and hours of completely featureless plain, the MS-1000 began to show some strong returns, indicating a harder surface and rising terrain ahead. We all noted it and looked forward to some more interesting sonar images. However, as we watched, the MS-1000 started to show some dramatic sharp lines across the display, making me at first think the machine was broken. Jay, however, was clued in. He suggested to Tom B. that we rev up the diesel. Tom picked up on his concern immediately, and sent Jay and Tom V. down to the aft deck to the manual speed control on the diesel HPU and cranked it up to 1,800 RPM. This would provide more power to the winch, if needed. In a flash, they were back in Ops, and we watched the MS-1000 display anxiously.

Elgen happened to be in Ops at the time with his camera rolling, so he caught the entire event on film. As the line on the MS-1000 marched closer and vehicle altitude began to drop, it became clear that the cliff ahead was higher than the vehicle. Tom B. took quick action, speeding up the ship while having Jay winch in at the highest rate possible (helped by the revved-up diesel). Despite this, the sled's altitude continued to drop fast as the base of the cliff began to show on the sidescan. It was scary to see the bottom come up faster than we could winch in, and I once again began to have anxious thoughts about our half-million-dollar vehicle. All of a sudden, the cliff flattened out after a 200-meter rise and the vehicle was rapidly soaring over the plateau. Jay settled it back down, and we sailed along the top of the underwater mountain for half an hour until we had to take a 200-meter dive down the opposite side. Whew!

We made sure to mark the spot on the chart so the midwatch could look out for it on the next line. We dubbed it "Easter Crater." But in case (when we see the mosaic Tom will produce) we find it is not a crater after all, we will take advantage of the fact that it is already after midnight, Greenwich Time, and rename it "April Fools Crater."

### April 1; Monday. April Fools!

Astonishingly for our gang, replete with practical jokers, no serious gags were detected. April Fools on us!

This afternoon, while relaxing on the fo'c's'le, I reflected a bit on the benefit of being out at sea. You feel homesick, miss your friends and family, would love to take a walk or run, have a little privacy, take a drive, see some dirt, or any number of "normal" things. On the other hand, you are insulated from a lot of the worries of day-to-day life. Of course you have responsibilities . . . and the ones left behind will all be there when you return. But meanwhile, there is little you can do about them, so after a while you learn to relax. You focus on the task at hand, make sure you're responsible to your duties and shipmates, and if you can manage that and don't get seasick along the way, it was a good day. There are simple pleasures like certain foods, snacks you brought from home, sunsets, laundry day, the stars (like the Southern Cross), time to read, a chance to get to know people in a microcosm, and instant gratification as you learn new skills and accomplish tasks on a watch-to-watch basis. There are special kinds of fun, gags, lots of "in" jokes, plenty to learn, and of course, the chance to achieve something very dramatic. Having a chance to see (at least through sonar) features on the earth that no one has ever laid eyes on, or see images from the bottom with exotic deep-sea creatures swimming by, is a real gift.

### Nautical Lore of the Day: "Cold enough to freeze the balls off a brass monkey."

According to various sources, a "monkey" was a triangular metal plate with depressions in it to allow the stacking of cannon balls in a pyramidal pile. The cannon balls in the base tier of the pyramid would sit in the depressions of the monkey, and form a stable foundation for the layers above. This would stay put and not roll around in the seas. (Why they called it a monkey is probably another story.) Now, if the monkey were made of brass, and the cannon balls iron, they would contract at different rates when it got cold. If the brass contracted enough, one or more of the balls could pop off in a roll of the ship. Hence, "Cold enough. . . ."

Well, I was not sure this was true, and when I returned home a little research (including the reliable Snopes) confirmed my suspicion. Oh well, . . . as I have heard said, "It may not be true, but it is well invented!"

Today was a day of many meetings, with an Abandon Ship drill stuck in between. This morning we had our ops briefing, then another navigation meeting, and in the afternoon we had a media meeting. And of course, SEA School.

The ops briefing found us finished with Line 5, almost 40 percent of our main area. Comp oil is at 19 percent and holding. But we may need to recover the vehicle soon anyway in order to perform diesel maintenance and replace the hydraulic oil and filters. Some minor problems could use some attention, including the remote cable counter and a broken bolt on the alternator. It's nice when problems like this make the top of the maintenance list!

Last night we crossed a 300-meter ridge in the vicinity of Easter Crater. We'll look for it again this evening. We are getting info from Tarawa and other relatively nearby ports on fuel availability, which looks promising. Tarawa is "only" two and a half days away.

## *DAVIDSON* CLASSIFIEDS

**Just plain TIRED** after a long day at the office? Call "DancinFingers" Bruce for professional massage therapy. Bruce is having an OCEAN EXPLORER special this month, to sooth your aching "winch wrist," "NOMAD neck," and "diesel disc," or for a chassis alignment. $15/15 minutes or $300/300 minutes. By appointment only.

**Cribbage Lessons** at sea? Email guido@sanquentinfederalprison.com.

**Depressed?** Lonely? Jump from the stern. Be careful not to hurt yourself on the tow wire.

**Men's hairstyling:** Sue's Doos. Flat rate: 300 M&Ms. Saturdays at 10.

**Wanted:** Good, clean rags. Inquire at Wet Lab.

**NOTICE:** Boat runs ashore are cancelled until morale improves. That goes for Payday as well. The Captain.

**FOR SALE.** Used Fishing pole. See Paul.

**Hot Offer** from The Galley: Show'n'Tell. This week Scotty features Mum's very own homemade bread recipe requiring no measuring. And if that wasn't enough, then the secret of Mrs. Swistchew's Scottish Sushi, Scottish Pizza, or Scottish Chinese cannot be far behind.

**Winch and Gyro** Repair Service. Shawn, Talkie channel 1.

## April 3; Wednesday. Happy Birthday, Shawn.

The morning ops briefing found us about to start Line 2. We will do half of Line 1, then some southern extensions before moving north. There was a serious problem this morning . . . the winch control system went dead. Shawn responded by preparing the electric HPU while maintaining vehicle altitude through control of ship's speed. Troubleshooting revealed a blown fuse in the diesel HPU as a result of a corroded wire splice. The problem was fixed with no loss of data. Another great job!

We are seeing more terrain variations in spots, with a few 200-300-meter cliffs. Keeps people on their toes. Comp level is 19 percent, and holding.

Nautical Limerick of the Day:
There once was a man from Nantucket
Who at sea always carried a bucket.
When he was asked why,
He replied with a sigh,
"I never know when I'll upchuck it."

After the ops briefing, with everyone present, we had a surprise for Shawn. (Yes, Mrs. Dann, we embarrassed him to death, as you requested.) Thanks to Shawn's Mom, we were prepared for his twenty-ninth birthday. First, he received a letter from the Sperry Corporation Office of General Counsel, via "mail buoy," complaining about his "unauthorized repair" of the ship's Sperry gyrocompass. This was followed by a certificate from Nauticos, the Maintenance Improvisation At-Sea Award:

CITATION: For conspicuous action in the face of great danger, he courageously performed field repairs to the ship's master gyrocompass installed aboard the research vessel *Davidson*. Mr. Dann's dauntless spirit and indefatigable initiative was evidenced by his selfless willingness to bypass common safety devices, use hand tools in new and creative ways, and develop a circuit testing process using only his tongue to detect voltage. Using his own "no rules" process, Mr. Dann rapidly isolated the inoperative circuit board, effected repairs, and restored the gyro to service without the benefit of any formal training, certification, consultation, or even really knowing what he was doing. Nevertheless, as a result of his action, the *Davidson* gyro was returned to full service and the mission continued uninterrupted. His actions were inspirational, and were in keeping with the highest ideals of the Nauticos Corporation. Well done!

This, as well as the Sperry letter, was all in good fun, of course, put together by Spence and Sue, with the help of the rest of the midwatch. Sue also constructed a duct-tape cake (which had grease for frosting and a light stick for a candle). In the end, Scotty appeared with a real cake, baked in Shawn's honor.

### April 4; Thursday. Scotty's Angels.

The highlight of the morning was bread-baking lessons in the galley, led by Chef Scotty, and demonstrated by Julie, Sue, and Kristin. Covered with flour, they learned how to measure ingredients by the handful, make dough for forty, and keep donuts from rolling around despite the ship's rolling around. Of course, the entire episode was filmed. I'm entirely certain that there will be no film left by the time we make our discovery. The donuts and loaves of bread that ensued were delicious. Sadly, only the females on board showed an interest in baking (though everyone enjoyed the eating). In the end, the three intrepid explorers joined Scotty in an action pose . . . "Scotty's Angels!"

Jerzy made the most fabulous barbecued chicken on the charcoal grill. We all thought it was delicious. It has been over three weeks now since we left Honolulu, so a lot of "fresh" foods are in short supply (and not so appealing anyway). New things are appearing, like canned peaches and pies instead of fresh fruit. We did have some great watermelon today.

### April 5; Friday. Just Another Day in Paradise.

This has probably been about the most routine day yet. Our ops briefing had no news, just progress. We are working what we have come to call the Southern Extension, and the way things are going we hope to finish it before recovery. We are still assessing fuel, but it looks like a stop in a couple of weeks will be in order. We'll get another fuel estimate in a day or so.

#### Radio Term of the Day: **Ham**

What is the origin of the word "ham" in "ham radio?" One popular theory is that it is the combination of the initials of the last names of three Harvard students who supposedly had an amateur station in the teens. Their names were Hyman, Almay, and Murray, and they operated the little station with a call sign of HAM. However, Harvard has no record of little station HAM.

Another theory holds that it derives from what commercial operators called amateurs. They referred to them using the old telegrapher's insult of "ham fisted," meaning that they weren't of professional skill.

A third theory derives from the fact that Hugo Gernsback published a magazine called *Home Amateur Mechanic* in the early days of radio and it included many radio construction projects. Thus, when asked what sort of radio a person had, he might send back that he had one of those HAM radios (using just the initials of the magazine name in true CW shorthand fashion).

We understand that a group of ham radio operators will be setting up a station on Baker Island later this month. Those guys will go to great lengths for their pursuit. We found out the requirements for visiting Baker or Howland Island, U.S. Fish and Wildlife preserves. First, you have to have a Fish and

Wildlife agent accompany you. Next, you have to bring a complete set of brand new clothing (including shoes) to change into before landing. Any equipment must have new cloth straps or bags, and must be placed in a deep freeze for seventy-two hours prior to landing. These protocols are designed to prevent contamination of the island by seeds or other biological materials that might take hold on the sensitive ecosystem. There is no guarantee that they won't dump you in the surf trying to get over the reef. Once there, you are confined to a completely deserted island, about the area of the Washington, D.C., Mall. Have fun!

Jonathan led SEA School today, telling us about his passion for photography and giving some basics on the art. Jonathan is Nauticos director of media development, and photo-journalist for *National Geographic*, veteran of nearly forty articles in the magazine. Jonathan has traveled all over the world pursuing his images, and has plenty of stories to tell. They are all so fantastic, that they *have* to be true. He did a very good job, and helped us to appreciate some simple techniques for getting a good image . . . and keeping it. His talk was very entertaining, and there were enough questions at the end to go past the allotted hour.

## April 6; Saturday. The Steel Beach Salon.

The day began with a SEA School presentation by Kristin, adventure correspondent, who did a great job showing us how a correspondent puts together a piece. Kristin only found out that she was going on this two-month voyage to nowhere a couple of days ahead of time. We prepared ourselves for so long in advance, it seems hard to believe she could do it in such a short time. She wasn't told the straight story, though, in that there would be no supply ship, hence no snacks! Although she struggled with seasickness, a cold, and being thrust into the company of a bunch of sailors and engineers, she adjusted quickly and has been making the best of the experience. She has even begun to appreciate the benefits of being away from civilization for a while.

We all gathered in the wardroom lounge, to see Kristin on live TV. She was broadcasting live from a remote location (the ship's office) and did a lead-in to a hilarious video she and the media team put together of candid shots aboard ship. The theme was how hard the media team is working (including Kristin up in the bosun's chair "fixing" a crane, Jonathan at the ship's wheel doing a great impression of Mr. Howell from *Gilligan's Island*, and Bill telling Tom where to search, referring to *The Complete Idiot's Guide to Shipwrecks*). At the same time, they captured many shots of the crew and Nauticos team sleeping, exercising, playing guitar, relaxing . . . anything but working. It ended with a great scene of Jeff saying, very mysteriously, that we know where it is, but we're not telling. Finally, Kristin got dunked into the ocean in the bosun's chair, suspended from the crane.

The other member of the media team is Bill Mills, our videographer. He has been great to work with, and very eager to understand everything we're doing out here. It's not unusual to see Bill standing a watch in Ops, flying the vehicle for a couple of hours. Bill also had to make a quick adjustment to joining our team, hauling an immense amount of equipment across half the ocean, and trying to make it all fit and work in a difficult environment. I'm sure it's tougher when you are not already part of a group and have to fit in a new environment, but Bill has done well.

## *DAVIDSON* CLASSIFIEDS

### Personals 100
**SWF**, 21, NS, ND, All-American type, looking for strong, athletic, hunky guy for walks on steel beach, handholding at sunset, dinners at Scotty's. Discretion is a must. Leave message/pic in barbeque grill. I'll find you. BB105.

### Notices 150
**Get the News Now!** News with Paul Harvey is on 6350 KCY on AFRTS at 1900 daily in Radio.

**MARS Policy Change.** Effective April 1st, to serve you faster, Cedar Rapids MARS operator will be dialing from a list of random numbers to complete your telephone patch faster. Great way to meet new people.

### Wanted 200
**SEA School Wanted:** New Instructors. New Topic. Travel. Adventure. See Spence.

**Reward $5:** For the capture, torture, and keelhauling of the sick bastard who put the bucket and shackle on my fishing line. Scotty.

**Stargazers:** Heavenly tour-guide seeking gawkers. Nightly excursions. Astronomic storm activity scheduled. Call ahead for reservation. Dave J.

### For Sale 400
**Viagra & Scopalomine.** Turns out won't need either on this cruise. Will trade for fishing pole.

**Got Gummi Bears.** Will trade for M&Ms, 1 for 1 OBO. Sue, Nights on Ch-1.

**Electra Pool:** 20 squares w/ water views and clean surveys. Will sell/trade for more northerly locale. Jon T.

### Lost & Found 500
**Lost:** Journalist's notepad. See Kristin.

**Lost:** Battery charger. See R.J., Mel, Shawn.

**Lost:** *American Pie* DVD. See Shawn.

**Lost:** Sunglasses, wraparound, black cord. See Ron.

**Found:** One white sock, vicinity of laundry. Name it and claim it.

**Lost:** Lockheed Electra 10. Low hours, NR16020. See Elgen.

It was another equatorial day outside, hot, sunny and breezy. Sue opened the Steel Beach Salon, offering to clip all comers. Many of us got re-buzzed, and a few got real haircuts. Bryan had his yellow-dyed long hair cut into a Mohawk. Everybody not on watch was hanging out, playing music, sunbathing, relaxing in the hammock, and just taking it easy on a Saturday morning. Up in Ops, the endless work of surveying lines continued.

We made a "Spaulding" to mount in Ops above the monitors. It looks kind of like "Wilson" from the movie *Castaway*, complete with a blood-like hand print for a face, but it's made of duct tape.

## April 7; Sunday. Finishing the Southern Extension.

This morning found us continuing to survey mile after mile, no contacts, but good performance by the equipment. The ops briefings are becoming less interesting, as there are no problems to deal with. As we approach the halfway point of the survey, we are considering how to make best use of the remaining time. Even though we already have a perfectly good plan, it's good to reconsider as performance and environment changes. Tomorrow we should be finished with the Extension, and will haul up NOMAD for the first time in about ten days. We plan to change the hydraulic oil in the diesel HPU, refill the comp, and (of course) recharge the Cup Holder 6000. We'll relocate to the northern half of the original box and redeploy.

### SEA School: Discover the World of Ham

We're not talkin' 'bout no sandwich here. The radio guys are back to talk about the ham radio hobby. This is a loose-knit but highly dedicated bunch of radio nuts who not only provide themselves with endless entertainment, but also provide a vital service to governments, business and individuals by involvement in ARES (Amateur Radio Emergency Service), disaster response, and remote point communications. Find out how these guys spread their call signs "around the world" in a single night. And find out what to say when Mrs. Vinson yells, "Thomas, turn off that damn radio and come to dinner!"

The skiff was deployed today for more film of the ship, and a few others (including Sue and Tom V.) got rides. The sea was very flat with some long swells, and the wind was almost nonexistent. The sun was equatorially hot. We watched and waved, and were filmed looking pensively at the sea, no doubt. R.J. lost a fire extinguisher over the side this time . . . it's always something! We were wondering if we detected the implosion of the bottle on the NOMAD sonar. Tom said he'd check the recordings.

Tomorrow should offer some modest excitement, as we will retrieve the vehicle and try a new area. Now that we're in the middle third of the survey, I'm sort of expecting success any time. We have some very "sweet" spots up north to survey yet. . . .

### April 8; Monday. NOMAD Up, NOMAD Down.

Early this morning, the team completed the Southern Extension and, after nearly eleven days of continuous operation at depth, recovered NOMAD. The system was operating continuously for over 257 hours, and only came up because we were ready to relocate! Quite a performance. After a successful recovery, refill of the comp oil, and reload of the cup holder, the vehicle was back on its way down. We took the opportunity to change the hydraulic oil in the diesel HPU, and the captain was happy to give the ship a chance to drive at "high" speed (by this I mean twelve knots) for a bit to blow carbon out of the engines. They don't like running at slow speed continuously. By the time the noon watch took over, the sonar was on its way back down, and by evening we were searching the bottom again.

Earlier, while we were waiting for the vehicle to come up, a few of us were standing by the aft rail looking at the cable disappearing into the abyss, trying for a glimpse of NOMAD. All of a sudden, we saw fish! A school of some large (several feet long) fish that we couldn't identify were swimming along behind the ship. They must have realized we couldn't put a line in at that moment, as we were just setting up for recovery. Other than a few splashes in the distance, I have seen no other fish since we left the vicinity of Hawaii.

Someone noticed that there is an entire class of topics that we don't discuss anymore, prime conversational gambits just a couple of weeks ago. One of them was "the patch." That is, the scopolamine-based seasickness remedy. There are almost none on display anymore, although a little quarter piece will be evident on selected necks every now and then. Jonathan was saying how he suffered withdrawal symptoms when he stopped using it. I said what he needed was a "patch-patch," to help kick the habit.

Another topic which has waned in interest is the oil comp level, as it has held steady and not been a problem for some time.

### SEA School: **Practical Knots**

Enough from you flatlanders and computerophiles! Yammerin' forever 'bout ramp files, servers, hubs, nets, megs, gigs, ports, and dongles. How bout getting your hands on something REAL? Every seaman knows just about a handful of good knots that perform a myriad of useful tasks around the ship. So if you don't know a hitch from a bend, come on down. And plan on getting some salt on those city soft hands of yours. Download a mega-gob of Knot-ology.

About fifteen of us gathered under a tarp on the fo'c's'le (it was an equatorial day) to learn how to do bowlines, sliding hitches, clove hitches, and surgeon's knots. (Spence was surprised and a little worried that the entire deck division of the *Davidson* was present.) We also enjoyed a short lecture on line and rope terminology and construction, as well as safety in handling lines. We were all given a length of line, designated as our "buddy," which we are to carry with us at all times to practice our knot skills. You may be surprised to know that I, as a former Naval officer, am not very good at knots. Actually, I am really bad at knots. You see, submariners don't generally use knots as much as other sailors, and many of us had little occasion to practice. This was evident at the end of the session, as Spence took us on a tour of the ship and pointed out several poor jobs of securing equipment with lines. I was able to immediately identify many of the sub-par knots, as I had tied them myself when helping Jay secure some gear the other night!

Anyway, my "buddy" has been with me ever since, and I am learning! Hopefully, the deck division is up to speed, too.

This evening won the award for the most spectacular sunset so far, a 360-degree display. Lots of pictures were taken, adding to the already ample stockpile of sunset photos, while depleting film and disk space. Unfortunately, the old adage "red sky at morning, sailor take warning . . . red sky at night, sailor's delight" did not hold, as we were later hit with a deluge including sixty-knot winds. I guess we needed a fresh-water washdown of the after-deck, what with the earlier hydraulic oil spillage. The ship rode through it fine; we just stayed inside and watched it on the deck TV monitors.

Tonight we got going on Line 1N (formerly Line 19 in our original box), and will start working north. We are barely half done with our available time, and have about two-thirds of the minimum search area goal covered. So we should be able to exceed our coverage goal by a large margin. We are also hitting some of the highest probability areas on these passes. Everyone is optimistic.

We were all up in Ops when we passed Dann's Depression again, which we saw on the first line we did back in March. This time, we passed along the north side of it and looked obliquely into the crater, as there was a planned overlap of our search swaths. We again saw the Hectapus, still lurking in its lair. . . .

But still, after twenty-six days at sea and almost three solid weeks of deep ocean search, we had to admit "no joy." The elusive Electra was nowhere yet to be found.

Chapter **6**

# Unexpected Visit

### April 9; Tuesday. Unplanned Bottom Sampling.

We learned at the ops briefing this morning that we dove a little too deep last night. As NOMAD approached the end of Line 1N in the wee hours of the morning, some seriously strong returns suddenly appeared on the forward-looking sonar. Robert was on the winch, and started hauling in fast. Sue and Spence were watching the sonar, and Shawn was trying to decide the best course of action. Our operations are a compromise between staying close enough to the bottom to get good imagery, but high enough to avoid any obstacles that may appear ahead. Of course, a cliff of any height can loom, and we have no reliable prior survey data in this area. What we have is not detailed enough for operations at 80-meter altitude, and doesn't match well with what we find. Really, this area has never been of much interest to hydrographers.

By the time the 500-meter cliff appeared on the forward-looking sonar, at a range of only 200 meters ahead, it was already too late. Although increasing speed can aid in lifting the vehicle, Shawn correctly chose to hold steady and try to winch it over, since if you are going to hit bottom, the slower the better. As we are only moving less than two knots, you don't really need airbags, and our 1,500-pound vehicle is very ruggedly built to protect all the sensitive electronics, but touch-and-go's are not part of the program.

The bottom came up rapidly, and in a matter of minutes NOMAD crashed into the side of the underwater cliff, knocking rocks, mud, and sea critters into the abyss. All of this was seen on video, although the recorders were not hooked up, as we did not anticipate having anything to video just yet. So, no tape; sorry.

The sidescan sonar record shows the bottom closing in to zero altitude, and a very confused trace as the vehicle bounced off the cliff, turned on its port side, and was dragged up to the top. I'm sure the local biota were very surprised! After passing over the rim of the escarpment, the vehicle stabilized.

All systems were tested and checked out OK. The watch section settled down, and surveying quickly resumed, with only a few minutes' loss of data. Disaster averted. Now we will know to look for that cliff on the next line, and should be able to avoid a repeat. The bad luck of this circumstance was that it occurred at the part of the line next to the first line we surveyed, where we had not gotten good data in the very beginning. From now on, since we are overlapping lanes by 20 percent, we will at least be forewarned based on the data from the previous line.

Back on line, back to normal, and surveying away. Spence followed up his practical knot-tying class with a sequel: fancy knots! As he says:

> After a hard day of whaling, sailors of yore would take respite by gathering round the scuttlebutt, grumbling about the officers, and creating highly decorative and useful items from rope. Decorate your pegleg, make a gnarly eyepatch or just spin a new poopcloth for your parrot. Come and join Spence round the scuttlebutt, grumble about the officers, and learn some cool knots.

We kept Spence for well over an hour at each session with questions and remedial tutoring. We learned how to make a Monkey's Fist and a Turk's Head in the morning session, while the afternoon session (which included all of the women) quickly progressed to belt-making and elaborate macramé creations. No one showed any interest in poopcloths, or even asked about them.

## April 10; Wednesday. Hump Day.

We are reckoning that if we are out for the duration, this is the halfway point (known as "hump day" for being "over the hump"). Of course, we can be rewarded for success by getting home early. It is a submariner tradition to celebrate "halfway night" (halfway through patrol) with a special dinner, talent show, and other shenanigans. We are having barbecued steak tonight, so that's something.

We have been surveying steadily for three weeks now, and it's a good time to take stock of our progress. In Area A, Southern Portion (including Western Extension), we covered 363 square nautical miles (sq-nm), including 96 percent of the planned 350-sq-nm area. We missed two short stretches early in the survey, but we covered some additional area on the boundaries. Our overall rate of coverage, including all equipment down time and turns, was just under 1 sq-nm per hour. During the later stages of the search, when NOMAD was continuously deployed, we achieved 1.1 sq-nm per hour.

In the Southern Extension, worth 72 sq-nm, we covered virtually 100 percent and even some areas outside the boundaries, so our total coverage to date exceeded 435 sq-nm. We are well on the way to surpass our minimum goal of

600 sq-nm. Our rate was lower (0.8 sq-nm per hour) due to shorter lanes (proportionally more time lost in turns), as expected.

## Nautical Term of the Day: **Nautical Mile**

The circumference of the earth has historically been divided into 360 degrees, like a circle. Each degree has 60 minutes (of arc). It turns out that one minute of any circumference around the earth measures about 6,000 feet, and this distance was adopted long ago as the "nautical mile." A "knot" is one nautical mile per hour, a bit faster than a land (statute) mile per hour. (A statute mile is 5,280 feet.) This definition makes measurements on charts easier, and is still commonly used even in these days of the metric system. (In keeping with ocean technology tradition, I have mixed metric and English units shamelessly in this journal.)

Of course, that's not all. Any plane cut through the earth and passing through the center describes a circumference, known as a great circle. (A line along a great circle that passes through two points is the shortest distance between them on the sphere, hence, "great circle navigation.") But the earth is not a perfect sphere, so all of these circumferences are a little different, and as cartographers came to know this, there was dispute over the actual length of a nautical mile. Eventually, everything was standardized to absolute scales, and the current accepted value for a nautical mile is a little over 6,076 feet.

One very encouraging and remarkable fact was the increasing periods of deployment for NOMAD. The first time in the water, it was down for 18 hours. The second time 43 hours, and the third, 65 hours. After a fourth deployment of 71 hours, we had resolved all nagging problems and it stayed down for a record 257 hours, nearly eleven days of continuous operation. And it could have gone longer, as it was retrieved for operational and maintenance reasons, not for repairs. Great job by the ocean engineers! If we can continue that performance, our search efficiency will be at about the theoretical maximum.

Those of you reading journal entries back home have been brimming with questions, and a few of them have been forwarded to me. Here's a good one:

**Question:** Why don't you search the center of your target area? Once you have a center square complete, then search the perimeter using concentric circles to eliminate the need to do the Batwing [*sic*] Turns.

The search technique described in the question is usually done with squared-off turns (rather than a circle) and is called an "expanding square" search. It is very effective if you have a datum (i.e., a point that you last saw or expect to find something) and can maneuver freely.

We have several problems in using this approach for deep searches, relating to positioning and navigation. First of all, although we can easily control the motions of the ship and know its position (by GPS, thank you very much), the same cannot be said for the sonar sled (or vehicle, in our case NOMAD), trailing behind at the end of five miles of cable, three and a half miles below. When the ship turns, the vehicle responds in a way that can be hard to predict. The cable isn't straight, but falls in a curved shape called a "catenary," which depends on its weight, the weight of the vehicle on the end, the tension, the speed through the water, currents, drag, the rate of motion of the cable, and probably lots of other things. You have seen this with kite strings; the string droops a bit and can bend in response to winds. It's practically impossible to predict this shape exactly, especially when the ship is turning.

If we are moving in a straight line at steady speed, the system settles out and we can assume that the vehicle will trail almost directly behind the ship. (If there were strong underwater currents, this would not be true, but most currents of any consequence are near the surface and have little effect on the cable.) We can also estimate the "layback," or distance behind the ship, reasonably well, as long as the ship is moving at a steady speed and course. As soon as the ship turns, we can't say with any kind of accuracy how the cable-vehicle system will respond, and there isn't a good way to track it accurately enough. Remember, we'd like to know where our vehicle is to within a few tens-of-feet uncertainty, so we can be sure we're covering everything (and know where something is that we have found!)

It also takes a long while for the system to react. As an example, I just came off watch during which we were executing a turn. We began winching in the vehicle soon after I got on watch, and turned the ship minutes later. Nearly two hours after that, when I got off watch, the ship had reversed course and had been on its new lane for an hour; however, the vehicle was just beginning to turn around. We had a great loop in the cable, had hauled in 3,000 meters (to keep NOMAD from hitting the bottom), and really had no good idea where the vehicle was. However, we are confident that it will follow the ship and when the cable stabilizes, many hours later, it will be following the new line.

So, when we turn, we cannot control the vehicle position very well, and we cannot know where it is with any degree of certainty. The expanding box or expanding circle technique has us turning all of the time, and would be an impossible mess.

To add to the difficulty, we have to be very concerned about the angle the cable takes leaving the ship, so we don't put too much strain on the huge steel A-frame that holds it. If we do circles, we could be wrapping the cable around itself! And even though I said the ship itself could maneuver easily, that is not really so at slow speeds with nine tons of cable dragging behind, winching in and out—especially if there is a bit of wind and current. So we resort to simple, but effective "mowing the lawn," also known more formally as a "parallel lane search."

Spence was at it again today, with his first course in celestial navigation. Although this is fast becoming a lost art, it is still important to us as we work with old data they used that method to navigate. And any mariner should have a working knowledge of this technique, in the event that all other means are lost—or he is shipwrecked! Spence's talk on celestial theory was billed thus:

> Back in the days of sail, ships replenished their crew's roster by emptying the bars and jails the night before sailing. Captains barely managed to control these unruly crews, because only they possessed charts and knowledge of navigation. A mutinous crew would likely not be able to reach a safe shore, and therefore remained subordinate. Today, celestial navigation is rarely practiced because of modern satellites and computers. But Spence says that he can teach anyone the ancient art of celestial navigation. We'll just see about that. And watch your back, Captain Dave.

Spence had the wardroom decorated with the sun (made from a large yellow inflated rubber bumper, complete with a face and sunglasses), plastic Easter eggs taped all over the walls and ceilings to represent stars, and an orange for the earth. We learned about the earth's coordinate system, the celestial sphere, hour angles, declination, and how this all works out to become a navigation fix. Tomorrow, we learn how to calculate one, and if we advance, we will use a real sextant to take a sun line of position. At the end of class, we ate the earth.

April 12; Friday. More Q&A.
Every time I visit with the midwatch crew, something happens. (Maybe they're trying to get rid of me.) This night, as they were approaching the end of the line, and wary of upcoming geology, they decided to have the ship slow a bit and bring in some cable. However, the ship lost control for a few minutes, and as Jeff winched-in, trying to hold altitude, the ship started to be dragged backwards (this happened once before a couple of weeks ago). Joe put turns on the propeller (you could smell the diesels and feel the ship rumbling as they strained to push us ahead), but the ship kept sliding back, while Jeff kept winching in at full speed. Altitude of the vehicle was dropping, rock-like. After about a minute of this, with the vehicle down to seven meters, the descent was arrested and it began to inch up. Soon, things were back to normal. It is very tricky to make adjustments to the speed when the ship is going so slow, and the situation can get out of hand quickly. These incidents certainly serve to keep us alert.

Later, I stepped into the bridge and said, "Joe, looks like you hooked a big one on the end of that wire!" He said, "Arrgh, we needed a little excitement for the watch." I said I came looking for excitement, but I had a discovery in mind. He said, "Arrgh, we made a discovery that we couldn't drive the ship!"

Now for the mail:

> **Question:** Isis is an acronym, I assume, and not named for the goddess Isis. Maybe that question has been answered and I missed it.

Actually, we were wondering that a couple of weeks ago, and scoured the Isis tech manuals for anything that would enlighten us. Zilch. We were pretty sure it *was* named for the Egyptian goddess, especially since the icon on the computer has an Egyptian motif. *The Encarta® 98 Encyclopedia* says:

> Isis, in Egyptian mythology, is the goddess of fertility and motherhood. According to the Egyptian belief, she was the daughter of the god Keb ("Earth") and the goddess Nut ("Sky"), the sister-wife of Osiris, judge of the dead, and mother of Horus, god of day. Ancient stories described Isis as having great magical skill, and she was represented as human in form though she was frequently described as wearing the horns of a cow. Her personality was believed to resemble that of Athor, or Hathor, the goddess of love and gaiety.

Now, this does not in any way evoke thoughts associated with the Isis computer program. So, the mystery remains.

> **Question:** I had wondered about how long the ship could go on one fill of fuel, assuming its runs along the west coast of this continent were considerably shorter than this trip.

This is a good question, and we ourselves did not get good answers (as it turned out) before we left port. The real answer depends on a lot of factors.

The R/V *Davidson* carries about 55,000 gallons of diesel fuel (short of its advertised capacity of 63,000 gallons, probably due to ship modifications after it was acquired from NOAA). Now, you can never really "top off" the tanks, as the EPA will have their choice of your body parts if you spill a drop of fuel in a harbor. So you don't risk it, and you might actually have closer to 50,000 gallons in a full load. Normal transiting at around eleven knots uses about 1,400 gallons per day, which accounts for running the engines, generators, laundry, galley, and everything else on the ship. Now, no one knew how much we would use during surveying, and it has, in fact, varied between 700 and 1,100 gallons per day as the crew became more experienced, currents and winds changed or subsided, and we learned some fuel economizing measures. That fuel also is used to run our diesel HPU, which drives the winch, and we have nearly three dozen people on board using water and electricity.

There is a big difference if we are cruising along the coast, as opposed to being out here 1,600 nm from Hawaii and 600 nm from the nearest port. We need to plan on a fairly large reserve of fuel, as the consequences of running out of gas out here are somewhat more serious than running out of gas with your date. So the amount of fuel we are willing to use for operations is less. As you can see, the answer depends. But a simple statement is that if you burn 1,400 gallons per day, and have 50,000 gallons to burn, you can cruise about thirty-two days (leaving a 10 percent reserve), and cover around 8,000 miles.

> **Question:** I would like some technical information on the cable, which is such an important component of the system. You know, size, material, weight, strength, etc.

Well, the details of this, for those who work in our Hanover office, are on a one-page spec sheet found in the Rochester Cable contracts folder. But I will enlighten the general readership, as it is interesting (in a techie sort of way). I visited Rochester Cable in Culpeper, Virginia, when they were building our "wire." The company dates back to before World War II, and at that time was a critical supplier of cable to the U.S. Navy. (I'm sure it still is, but the company also supplies cable to the telecommunications industry, and for commercial marine needs. Our application is rather specialized.) Because the government was worried about U-boat or air attacks from Germany, they disguised some of the buildings of the factory as schoolhouses, and those facilities still are in use today.

We had our cable custom-built to carry both power and telemetry, and to be able to support its own weight as well as the weight of our vehicle. Power at 440 volts is sent along the 11,000-meter (36,000-foot) cable through three copper conductors. Telemetry is sent through three fiber-optic strands. These form the core of the cable. The electronics on each end of the cable are converted to laser light pulses by a custom-built de-multiplexing (demux) system made by Prizm Advanced Communication Electronics, Inc., a small company in Maryland that manufactures very high-end electronics. We can send all the data we want (control signals, vehicle telemetry, sonar data, and digital data from multiple video and still cameras) through a single fiber, leaving the other two as spares.

These components are sealed in plastic, and clad with a thin copper sheath, which is actually welded where it joins along its length. This all happens in a continuous line process, where the cable is zooming along at hundreds of feet per minute, wires getting wound, dies bending copper sheet, and joints being welded at a frantic pace. The core is then wrapped with layers of stainless-steel flat wire (extruded from stainless core metal as needed). The wire is pre-bent with the right radius to "grab" the core and wrap tightly. Alternating layers are wrapped in a contrary direction, and they are carefully bent such that the cable is "torsion balanced," so when it winds and unwinds it doesn't want to twist much. There are three layers of wire, with a plastic covering in between each.

The result is 11,000 meters of 0.68-inch diameter, stainless-steel armored cable, which weighs 0.609 pounds per foot, for a total weight of almost eleven tons. The working strength is rated at 20,000 pounds, only about equal to its weight. However, in water it weighs considerably less, which leaves room for our vehicle on the end, as well as dynamic loading. Of course, you can't put out all 11,000 meters (or it slides into the sea!); 10,200 is the most I've seen unreeled. This is considered adequate for working at water depths of 6,000 meters. Our cable cost about $280,000, and Rochester was very kind and patient to give us several months to pay.

> **Question:** How long does it take to raise the NOMAD 500 meters in order to avoid an underwater obstruction?

We can winch-in at a rate of about 55–58 meters per minute when at depth. The actual change in depth will be somewhat less than this, as the cable is trailing back at some angle, and the ship is slowed when you haul in cable. Practically, we can probably achieve 30–40 meters per minute by hauling in cable only. So the simple answer is that it takes about eleven minutes to clear a 500-meter cliff (starting at 80 meters altitude). However. . . .

We travel at a rate of about 1.8–2 knots, which works out to 55–60 meters per minute. The cliff that we scraped the other night rose at just about a 45-degree slope, so it rose in front of us at about that rate. If we start at an altitude of 80 meters, and the slope rises in front of us at a rate of, say, 60 meters per minute, if we haul in and change altitude by 40 meters per minute, we hit the cliff in four minutes (barely halfway up). We did a bit better than that the other night, and just clipped the top of the ridge as it was leveling off.

To avoid this, you need to react quickly and put on some speed, which effectively gathers up more cable and helps the vehicle up quicker. Our forward-looking sonar "sees" several hundred meters ahead, so it gives us some forewarning. Over the last couple of days we have been dodging periodic ridges (probably very localized volcanic formations). It takes alertness by the watchstanders, quick reaction (with the right decision) by the watch leader, and prompt response from the ship driver to clear such an obstacle.

Frustratingly, once you have made your choices, over the next five to ten minutes you can only watch the situation develop and hope you haven't found that 700-meter cliff. . . .

Point of interest: we recorded the deepest depth noted in our search area, 18,442 feet.

Joe told a story about navigating in the "old days" in coastal Maine (before he learned to say "arrgh"). And before Loran navigation was commonly used by fishermen. That would be *way* earlier than the introduction of GPS! There was a great fog and storm, and he was at sea and didn't want to venture into the harbor until conditions cleared up. But his captain (who probably did say "arrgh"), told him to "head north by north east for two cigarettes, then turn a point and a half to starboard." Sure enough, this method brought him right to the dock! It was his version of GPS navigation—"Geezer Positioning System."

Another old-time method of navigation Down East: If it's really foggy, carry a sack of Maine potatoes to the bridge. Take a potato to the starboard rail and throw it overboard. If you hear a "splash," go that way; if you hear "plop," turn the other way. Keep it up until the fog clears or you run out of potatoes. I am told one can use Idaho potatoes in an emergency.

### April 13; Saturday. The iPod Affair.

" . . . Copa, Copa Cabana. . . ." Arrgh! Can't get that song out of my head! But more on the "iPod Affair" later.

I woke up this morning to find that NOMAD was on deck, as the comp level had not held and had to be refilled. We must have developed a new leak. It was a very quick recovery and redeployment, and by late morning we were back on the bottom surveying Line 7N. Very little time was lost, and while on deck the midwatch took the opportunity to replace a leaky hydraulic fitting, and, of course, Jon reloaded the Cup Holder 6000. We observed that the port fin was severely cracked, but otherwise no damage was noted to the vehicle as a result of the "sampling" incident.

A funny thing happened on the way to the fo'c's'le. Today was a workout day for me (I know, it should be every day, but it isn't), and as customary I climbed up to Ops to fetch my iPod music player. (iPods were pretty new back then, and it became popular on watch as an alternative to a CD Walkman as our on-duty source of music. So I, quite graciously I must say, left it for the watchstanders to use.)

I got the iPod, chatted with Sue and the gang, got catcalls for a bad joke, and headed down a deck and forward to the fo'c's'le. After a bit of stretching, I sat on the rowing machine, turned on the iPod and went to select from the myriad of music I knew was at my disposal and chose . . . Barry Manilow singing "At the Copa Cabana"?! I selected this because, apparently, it was my only choice!

I had made the mistake of explaining to Shawn and Sue how my iPod works. It seems they couldn't resist playing with it and had managed to wipe its disk clean. Normal people would think, "Oh no, what will I tell Dave?" Did they think THAT? *No!* They thought, "How can we make a practical joke out of this situation?" Since they couldn't restore it the way it was, they simply re-loaded it with one song. You got it.

" . . . Copa, Copa Cabana. . . ." Arrgh!

## *DAVIDSON* CLASSIFIEDS

### Personals 100

Hey where are all the MEN on this ship? Are you guys gay? I'm still looking for my hottie to get a little equatorial mambo going. Too busy fishing or playing with your stupid laptop computer for a real relationship? I know you're there. Send me a sign, put a note in the grill. And PLEASE keep this quiet. And as for you BD2X4: The answer is NO, I'm not that type. You're a real sicko. BB105

### Announcements 150

**Wishing Well:** The *Davidson* Wishing Well is now in business. Located on D Deck, past the laundry room, port side. Stupid wishes: $0.25. Impossible wishes: $25.00 Visa/MC accepted. Ron

**Australia?** There is NO TRUTH to the rumor that the ship is calling in Australia next. However, the international exchange rate is $3AD = $2USD.

### For Sale 400

**Cribbage Book:** Just published. The holder of the *Davidson* Cribbage Peg, in his own words, humbly describes how he kicked butt on all challengers in the recently concluded *Davidson* Cribbage Tournament. Card strategies, psych techniques and illustrated card tricks included. Autographed by author. $149.99.—Scotty

**Deck Winch System:** Mechanic's dream. Needs brakes, hose fittings, heat exchanger, electrical wiring, electronic board repair, hydraulic leaks. Could use a good bath and coat of paint. Will remove Government Property ID. Best offer. Jay

### Lost & Found 500

**Lost:** Still looking for battery charger. R.J., Mel, Shawn

**Lost:** Chick sock, padded, white, crew. Sue

**Lost:** Seems like ALL the small line is disappearing from the ship. Apparently, there is someone who needs it more than the entire deck department. By the way, you ladies are looking jaunty in your fashionable nautical attire. If you'd like me to show you a few of my own special knots, just stop by the wheelhouse for a private lesson. Arrgh! Joe

The Deck Wishing Well, by the way, is a metal pan that Ron put under one of the air conditioning units. These units have not been used much, as the vessel spends most of its time cruising Alaskan waters, so their drains are all plugged and they leak condensate profusely, especially in this hot, humid weather. One day, someone threw a coin in the half-filled pan, and it became a wishing well.

### April 14; Sunday. Spaulding's Busy Day.

Today's ops briefing . . . more excitement overnight. The fan belts broke on the diesel HPU! One broke earlier in the evening, but Shawn discovered it in a routine watch inspection. So he had the watch keep an eye on the remaining one (they are used in pairs). Sure enough, it soon broke, but everyone was ready and the diesel was shut down before it overheated. They quickly switched hoses to the electric HPU (not a fun or easy job at all), but one of the ship's generators shut down while trying to run it. This caused a "brown-out" on the ship, and so the electric HPU was shut down before it turned into a black-out (a big problem with a vehicle and five miles of cable out). We have had problems with the ship's power from the beginning.

Meanwhile, the diesel was repaired and placed back on line. No survey time was lost, since it happened during a turn, and no damage was done to anything. Unfortunately, we have to admit that we can't depend on the electric HPU as a backup, although we could use it for an emergency recovery if we were careful.

We have been discussing refueling and making plans, and now is the time. So we are planning to complete Line 8N, then head west to . . . Tarawa! The bad part is, it will cost us five or six days, eating up the five-day contingency budgeted in our schedule. The good news is that we will get a little break, and a few spare parts (like extra belts for the diesel). Fortunately, everything else has gone so well that we're ahead of plan for coverage, and still expect a successful outcome in the two weeks of searching we'll have remaining.

I gathered as much information as I could about our destination. Tarawa is the nearest port to our location, about 600 miles (and a bit over two days) away. We're hoping to make a morning landing, refuel, and depart by evening, so we will waste as little time as possible. Should be a chance to get ashore for a few hours for many of the crew, and maybe get a few souvenirs.

Tarawa is located in the Republic of Kiribati (pronounced "KEE-ree-bass"), an island group in the western Pacific Ocean, consisting of an archipelago of some thirty low-lying coral atolls surrounded by extensive reefs with a total land area of 800 square kilometers. Kiribati gained independence from the United Kingdom in 1979, and has an elected president and a legislative assembly. The capital of Kiribati is on the island of Tarawa. Kiribati includes three administrative units, sixteen atolls of the former Gilbert Islands, eight atolls of

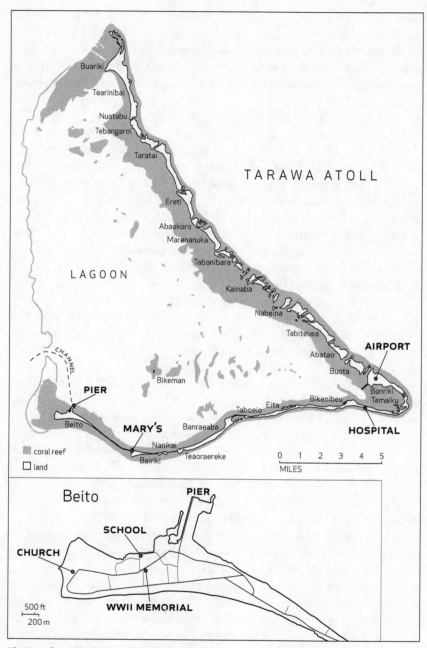

The Pacific atoll of Tarawa, Republic of Kiribati.

the former Line Islands (including Christmas Island and Fanning Island), and eight atolls of the former Phoenix Islands. Kiribati has few natural resources, and its economy is very small. The islands are not self-sufficient in food. Tourist facilities are not widely available.

According to our information, Tarawa is heavily urbanized. It contains more than 30 percent of the nation's population and is severely overcrowded. If you are a traveler, Tarawa should not be your destination; go to one of the lesser populated "outer" islands instead. This doesn't sound promising!

Some of us were interested in the shopping. A reasonable variety of basic food, household and hardware items are said to be available. Supply fluctuates with the arrival of ships bringing cargo. Fresh fruit and vegetables are often difficult to obtain and very expensive when they arrive. Few vegetables are grown locally. Rice is used extensively. The fish is always fresh, plentiful and inexpensive. Bread is baked locally but if you are a "whole grain" fan— forget it! Prices for most grocery items are a little more expensive than in New Zealand or Australia.

Tarawa is famous for the 1943 U.S. Marine invasion during World War II. The island was defended by 2,600 imperial marines, the best amphibious troops in the Japanese armed forces. With the importation of 1,000 Japanese workers and 1,200 Korean laborers the island airstrip of Betio had been transformed into one of the most formidable fortresses in the world. When the U.S. Marines landed on the morning of November 20, a critical miscalculation of the tides resulted in the first wave being stranded on the reef surrounding the atoll; few survived the initial attack. By the end of the day, 1,500 of the 5,000 assaulting Marines were dead or wounded, but a beachhead had been established.

Over the ensuing three days, the Marines moved inland and fought off waves of Banzai suicide charges. Japanese resistance was fanatical because, according to the Bushido Code, each isolated soldier or group of soldiers was obliged to either fight to the death or commit suicide unless ordered otherwise. In the end, only seventeen Japanese surrendered while only 129 Korean laborers had survived out of a total of over 4,700 troops and construction workers.

Owing to our tight schedule, we won't have much time to explore the history or the culture. But we will have to get there. So, Spence had a new SEA School idea:

## SEA School: **Navigate to Tarawa**

If shooting sunlines is now merely child's play, and you're ready for the big leagues, join the navigating team that will guide (or misguide) the *Davidson* from its survey departure point to the channel entrance at Tarawa . . . a 3-day tour. (Remember where the Skipper and Gilligan ended up!) Our team of intrepid navigators will be using only the sun, stars, moon and planets to fix the ship's position daily just like the old geezers did. Your actual course and speed recommendations will be sent to the Captain daily at noon. You too can be waiting pensively on deck for first a sniff and then a glimpse of land . . . if you're good enough. So, if you'd rather shoot stars than sleep, then this may be for you.

More on this later. Meanwhile, Julie and I had the idea to take some pictures of Spaulding on a typical day on the *Davidson*. Spaulding, our duct-tape version of Wilson, the "sidekick" volleyball from the movie *Castaway*, had become our regular mascot. He was photographed all over the ship, and we made a slide show of his antics. It was a hoot!

Tonight we are hauling in the vehicle and heading for a gas station. We are taking the opportunity to grease the cable, done by installing a special clamp with hoses to pump in grease as the cable is drawn in. The stuff is real sticky and makes a big mess, but will help preserve the wire. We have a long work list of items we plan to do on the few days off, although none of them is essential to continued operation.

### April 15 (16); Monday (Tuesday). Crossing the Date Line.

Well, today was an unusual day on the *Davidson*. First of all, we didn't have the vehicle out for the first time in weeks, and the watch routine was suspended. The diesel HPU was shut down, which made for an eerie change in the noise level around the ship. Not that it was quiet, mind you. We had different combinations of faces at meals, and by evening it was almost deserted as everyone was down for a rest.

However, SEA School went on.

### SEA School: **The ABCs of Welding**

You probably noticed that the days of wooden ships have passed and we now live in an era of steel. This gives rise to a new kind of seagoing tradesman, the shipfitter, or welder. While it takes years to acquire the skills and experience needed to become a professional welder, it takes just a few minutes to "sorta get the hang of it." So, welcome to Welding Kindergarten. And if this is your first welding class, then get ready for some arcing and sparking fun. And to go in your scrapbook along with your first finger painting, if it's not too heavy, you can take your precious masterpiece home for your mommy to admire. So what era comes after the era of steel, you might ask? According to some, it would be . . . duct tape and tie wraps, duhhh.

The other highlight of the day was crossing the International Date Line at 180 degrees longitude. So our day went from Tuesday the 15th to Wednesday the 16th, same time. Another way to say this is we changed from +12 hours GMT (Yankee Time Zone) to –12 hours (Mike Time Zone). By international agreement, GMT (Greenwich Mean Time, centered on Greenwich, England) is designated the Zulu zone. Time zones are counted eastward by the letters A to M (Alpha to Mike), skipping "J" (so as not to confuse it with "I"). This makes twelve time zones going east from Greenwich. Going west, they are labeled N to Y (November to Yankee), making twelve in that direction. The wrapping of a straight timeline around the globe must have a "seam" somewhere, and by convention that occurs in the middle of the Pacific . . . the International Date Line. I find it remarkable that, with all of the conflict and disagreement in the world, a convention of global timekeeping was able to be established at all.

An excellent book on this fascinating topic is *Plotting the Globe* (Praeger Publishers, 2006) by Avraham Ariel and Nora Ariel Berger. As noted on the book jacket, Ariel and Berger "transport readers to faraway lands and ancient cultures that span more than 3,500 years of exploration" as they tell the story of man's efforts to organize our notion of timekeeping. The debates (and occasional battles) over establishing meridians, parallels, and reference points continue even today, driven by commerce, politics, and our ever-growing sophistication in measuring the shape of the earth and its geography.

Tradition holds the Crossing of the Line to be entering the Realm of the Golden Dragon. (The counterpart for crossing the equator is becoming a Shellback.) These mock ceremonies are a maritime tradition, and (in the case of the Shellback) can be quite elaborate. I guess that, since the equator is a natural boundary, it seems more significant than the man-made date line. In any case, we made everybody certificates, signed by the captain and Tom (as "Chief Assistant to Neptunus Rex"), which certified as follows:

> Know all men by these presents: and to all pirates of the yellow seas and other derelicts of far eastern seas, Greetings:
>
> Know ye: On the 15th Day of April, 2002, at 1630 hours, within the boundaries of my Dragonic Realm, there appeared the Good Ship *Davidson*.
>
> Be it known: that the said renowned vessel crossed the 180th meridian in latitude 1° 16.7' north, and all her officers and crew have been duly inspected and found qualified by my Venerable Court. It is therefore my privilege to proclaim, with all the authority of my sphere of influence, that: <name>, having been found worthy, has been granted membership in my domain, the Silent Occult Mysteries of the Far East.
>
> And be it further understood: that he is now a member of my August Retinue and is therefore entitled to all the Rights and Privileges accorded such personages.
>
> Disobey this order under extreme penalty of our Royal Displeasure.

At the moment of crossing, a number of us gathered on the flying bridge to recognize the event. We took a group photo, with several of us holding signs that indicated "Tomorrow" (ahead), and "Yesterday" (behind).

On to Tarawa.

## April 16 (17); Tuesday (Wednesday). Hot Tubs and Star Shots.

Over the last couple of days, R.J. rigged up a real treat for us—a "hot tub." It has been really hot and sultry for a while, and we stare all day at water we can't swim in. So R.J. (with help from Bruce, I'm sure) fashioned a box about 4 × 4 feet, 2½ feet deep, lined it with a large blue plastic tarp, sealed the leaks, and ran a hose into it from the fire main. The fire main draws on seawater, so there's an endless supply. He runs the hose full blast into it, and just lets it overflow onto the weather deck, near an overboard drain. As the ship rolls, it sloshes out and refills, always keeping near full. It's a hot tub! It is so relaxing, especially after a workout, and the warm seawater feels very nice.

Spence had the idea that he and I (with part-time help from many other folks) should navigate to Tarawa using only the ship's course by compass, speed by engine setting, and the sky. No GPS or other electronic means, other than using the clock for accurate time. This is more or less equivalent to the state-of-the-art of navigation around the time of World War II, and it's useful as an exercise because we often deal with data from that era. It's also fun in a nerdy sort of way.

I found that being an old-time ship's navigator is a full-time job (and I wasn't standing watches during the transit). A lot of it involves "shooting a fix," using a sextant to measure the altitude (height above the horizon) of a star, sun, moon, or planet, and using tables of orbital data to calculate a ship's position. The sextant works by projecting an image of a part of the sky onto another image of the horizon, with an adjustment to move the projected image in altitude. You adjust until the image of the star just touches the image of the horizon, and read the angle between the projected images off the dial. You can measure reliably down to one arc-minute (1/60th of a degree) using this instrument. We used one that Elgen brought, as the ship doesn't even carry one (the crew relies exclusively on GPS).

The basic principle is simple. Through astronomical observations, we know very accurately the positions of the stars, sun, moon, and planets at any time. We can project the location of a particular object onto the surface of the earth at any particular moment, known as the Geographic Position (GP). If we are at that exact position, that object would be directly overhead (that is, at an altitude of 90 degrees). If we are away from that point, the altitude will be lower, and we can use the observed altitude (measured with the sextant) to compute our distance from that GP. If we plotted the GP on a globe, and drew a circle around it with radius equal to that distance, we would be somewhere on that circle.

In practice, since we have some idea where we are in the world, we only need to draw the part of that circle that passes near our position, which is a "line of position" (LOP). If we do this with three or more objects, we get several lines, all of which should pass through our position, and when we plot them, we get a fix. Of course, there are lots of details to correct for, and the computation itself is a bit arcane, and time consuming.

The daily routine a celestial navigator follows starts before dawn:

*0500.* Shoot morning stars before sunrise at nautical twilight, as soon as the horizon is visible, and try to get a star position fix. This takes about forty minutes, and ends when the sky brightens too much to see stars.

*0600.* Calculate the fix (this took me a couple of hours, although a *real* navigator with more practice could do it in under an hour).

*0800.* Based on dawn star fix, estimate the ship's position at 0800 using best guess at course and speed (called "dead reckoning"). Estimate the current (set and drift) by comparing the course steered with the "course made good" (actual course) between fixes. Estimate new course to next "waypoint," accounting for current. Make the 8 o'clock report to the captain, including position, estimated currents, recommended course, distance to next point, time to arrive at waypoint, hazards expected along the way, and any other useful information.

*1000.* Shoot sun (lower "limb" of the disk, usually), resulting in a single LOP (line of position). You do this with a filter in the sextant so you don't fry your eyeball. Although you only get one line, this is usually more accurate than a star LOP, since the horizon is easily visible.

*1200.* Shoot a series of sun altitudes to determine the time and maximum altitude at Local Apparent Noon. The height of the sun at noon depends on your latitude, so this tells you that valuable piece of information.

*1500.* Shoot another sun line. If you keep track of your distance traveled since the morning sun line, and advance it in position to the afternoon one, and drag along the noon sighting as well, you get three lines together for a fix. If it's visible at any time during the day, you can also shoot the moon (so to speak).

*1800.* Just after sunset, when the moon, planets, and stars come out (but you can still see the horizon), shoot as many as you can (seven is nice).

*1900.* Compute and plot the LOP's, get a fix, and dead-reckon your track until morning.

As you can see, it's a busy day . . . then it starts again! We worked our way through the 600-mile transit, and managed to keep our position to within a few miles and gave good course recommendations to the captain. And we found Tarawa!

**Question of the Day:**

What is the bottom of the ocean like where you are searching? What if it's silty and the plane is covered?

Well, this is a great question, with lots of answers. Here are a few: We are in an area of intense volcanism, on a line of several volcanic peaks (including Howland and Baker Islands). In between, the water depth is over 17,000 feet, generally flat, with occasional ridges and dotted with volcanic craters and smaller "cinder cones." These features rise generally less than 50 meters, but sometimes as much as 500 meters above the abyssal plain, which was formed when the massive volcanoes in the area erupted long ago and filled the area level with lava and ejected material. This stuff has settled and is reasonably hard. Up close, as seen in video cameras, the bottom is peppered with nodules of manganese metal (about the size of golf balls), and lots of creatures. Fish, squid, worms, and shells of all sorts are everywhere, although many of them blend in with the bottom pretty well. These creatures are not known at shallower depths, as they must live in total darkness at almost 9,000 PSI pressure. There is almost no silting in these areas, as there is no nearby land mass to create silty runoff; other wrecks we have found in these conditions are barely dusty.

Speaking of sea life: after weeks of nothing, we came upon a region of the sea which was teeming with life above and below the waves. The seas had calmed a lot, so the surface was very smooth and the swells were gentle. First, we saw whales! At least a half-dozen small whales were cruising along, spouting away, a few hundred yards from the ship. Almost everyone not asleep went forward to watch them from the fo'c's'le, a show that lasted about forty-five minutes. Just about the time they disappeared, we noticed a gathering of hundreds of birds nearby. Soon, they were diving at the surface, snapping up little fish by the dozens. The fish were confined to a fish "ball" near the surface, presumably by some larger fish herding the school from below. So they were caught between the predator fish below, and the birds above.

We maneuvered the ship to drive right through the spot, and saw a dense mass of fish (almost like a slithering creature itself) pass under the ship and astern. Those who were aft quickly manned the fishing rods, and sure enough Mel pulled in a small tuna. It was not very long, but quite fat. When Scotty cut it open, it was stuffed with little minnows! I guess it tried to eat one too many. . . .

After a time, numerous fish balls formed around us, some quite large. We also saw squadrons of flying fish skimming over the water. It seems we were passing through some kind of convergence zone, where the currents and temperatures were attractive to the local fauna.

## April 17 (18); Wednesday (Thursday).
## Adventures and Misadventures on Tarawa.

Well, we had quite a day on Tarawa, and I can't begin to relate everyone's experiences. Up until now, we have all been confined to our little *Davidson* world, where everyone pretty much is part of everything. Once on land, however, small groups ventured out independently, or in a few cases stayed on board and worked the fuel problem. So I can only report some events second-hand, and a few events are best not reported at all!

This morning at around 0400 we made landfall by radar about fifteen miles from the island. It was a beautiful night, with brilliant stars. The lights on the horizon which appeared over the course of the next few hours seemed very much out of place.

Sunrise found us running along the south side of the island about five miles away, and by 0800 came in sight of the pilot boat maneuvering toward us. The pilot came on board to guide us through the passage in the reef. Sue, Jeff, Carl, and I watched the proceedings from the flying bridge, while a lineup along the foc's'le waited, and another group was at the aft rail. After so long we were all anxious for a close view of land.

We were greeted by a large pod of dolphins performing synchronized jumping in groups. There must have been two dozen frolicking along beside us. A few of them, at least, were spinner dolphins, as we saw one pirouetting in the air ahead of us.

We arrived right on time at 0900 sharp, and cleared customs in an hour. By talking to the officials who came on board, I learned the following snatches of the local language:

| | | |
|---|---|---|
| Please | – | "Taiaoka" |
| Thank you | – | "Coraba" |
| Hello | – | "Mauori" |
| Goodbye | – | "Sabot" |

And, of course, beer is "beer." I have no idea if these are spelled correctly, but I have been told that the Kiribati alphabet has only fourteen letters.

I also learned that the people here on Tarawa (the capital) mostly support administration and commerce. The other islands are fishing economies. As the nation spans over 1,000 miles with hundreds of islands, there are small airports everywhere that fly twelve-passenger planes between them. Most of their goods come from Fiji or Australia.

Our agent departed, ostensibly to arrange the fueling. Tom sent everybody ashore who wanted to go (actually, I think the media team and a few others were on the dock before the brow was over). There was nothing I could do to help, as Tom, the captain, and the engineer (Mel) were working it. Tom asked me to be on the lookout for souvenirs, and Tom B., Shawn, and Sue needed to find a hardware store. Everyone who hadn't already split gathered on the pier, and then set off on foot toward town.

We knew it wasn't far, and in five or ten minutes we reached an intersection (which as it turned out, was the center of town). We found ourselves in a truly third-world setting. The main street was packed dirt (with some evidence of long-ago attempts to pave it), densely lined with one-story cinder block or open-air thatched buildings which served as hardware stores, fabric stores, food shops, brothels, bars, and general goods stores. It is hard to describe what we saw. I have looked at pictures we took, and I see lush tropical foliage and quaint-looking colorful huts with hand-painted signs. But the photos didn't show the garbage, litter, and squalor, nor did they record the smells and oppressive heat. On the other hand, the people were very friendly, could all speak some English, and waved and smiled to us as we walked.

Cars and flatbed or pickup trucks trundled by, along with numerous small busses. For some reason, almost all traffic moved in one direction, even though the street was easily wide enough for two-way traffic, and the occasional car swimming upstream suggested that it was not a one-way street. We couldn't tell if a car would stop if we were in its path, and we were careful not to test any theories on the matter.

There were several destinations in mind: a bank, the post office, a souvenir shop, and a beer. In small groups, we explored. My first stop was the bank; I had brought no cash with me, not expecting to need any until we returned to Hawaii. The bank was one of the newer, and certainly more modern, buildings. It was actually air-conditioned! It was only a five-minute walk from the main intersection (we discovered later the town only extended a short distance beyond that before it degenerated to just huts).

Elgen had loaned me $50, but I thought I'd try to obtain a cash advance and prove that one could show up on an island in the South Pacific with nothing but plastic and survive! Well, I was unpleasantly surprised. While everyone else was changing dollars for Australian currency (the local standard), I gave them my USAA MasterCard for a cash advance. Some time passed, which I did not count as unusual, having occasionally tried to get a non-ATM cash advance at an American bank. Behind the counter, there were several women bustling about, writing the transactions down in little books with carbon paper, and figuring the exchange with calculators. The money was dispensed from a drawer. There wasn't a lot of security. After a longer while, by which time I was regretting making things too complicated, the teller came back to the counter and told me that the bank in Australia said she should cut up my card and send it to them! I was too stunned to protest. Apparently, either there was a mistake, or they were just too suspicious of a cash advance in Tarawa. I didn't try to fight them, as I figured it could be easily replaced. So I relented, watched them cut it up, and had the Elgen-loaned $50 changed into Australian money.

(I later discovered that Lynn back home had some concern that our MasterCard had been compromised and had the card cancelled and reissued. She saw no reason to mention that to me. So, the system worked!)

That mission barely accomplished, some of us continued down the road. The shops became interspersed with residential huts, mostly with thatched roofs. Some of the plain block buildings were identified as "Nite Clubs," and we realized we were in what passed for the red light district. We saw a general goods store, and it was interesting to see the inventory, mostly from Australia. Fish were being sold on the street, but not much else. We saw another fabric store (they seemed to have a serious infestation of them), and looked at some of the cloth (we were told it was from Fiji). They were astonished when I thanked them in their own language, and seemed to appreciate it.

We had been encouraged to go see the World War II memorial, which I assumed would be a museum, but in fact was an obelisk in front of the town assembly hall. It was dedicated to the Marines who landed there in 1943, and contained a 200-year time capsule.

Farther down the street was a Catholic church, the only edifice taller than two stories, and a bit farther a school, with kids in class singing together. We spied some war ruins just off the main track, followed a path which led to a couple of blasted gun turrets, and investigated. The lagoon beach was just on the other side, and one of the guns (which were quite large, greater than five-inch muzzle diameter) was lying in the sand half underwater. The other was in place.

We decided to head back via the beach, hoping for some mitigation of the stench. The island (called Betio) was one of the larger of the chain found inside the Tarawa atoll, and was contained in the lagoon, so there was no ocean surf. The lagoon water was very still and shallow for a long ways out; you could see the nearer part of the reef off in the distance. The beach was alive with crabs of all sorts, including hermit crabs everywhere. However, it was also slathered with waste of all sorts, as it became clear that this part of the lagoon served as garbage dump and toilet for the community. In fact, we realized that the small groups of people standing in the lagoon were "using the facilities" as they saw them. We didn't spend much time on the beach.

We turned inland, and found ourselves on the other side of the school grounds. It didn't seem a problem to walk on the grounds and, as a recess seemed to be in progress, we walked right through groups of children playing. Of course, back home we probably would have been arrested, but here the kids waved and smiled and were eager to show off their jump-roping skills.

Back on the street, we realized the air smelled so fresh compared to the beach!

Having seen the entire town, and not run across one thing that seemed worth buying (except fabric), we decided to head back to the intersection where we knew in that direction we could get a beer. On the way, we bought some fabric, said to be from Fiji. This may have to serve as our souvenirs . . . in fact, later we sent some others to the same shop, and we all bought something there. They were very nice, as they should be, since they probably did a month's worth of sales in an hour or so. In fact, between the fabric, fuel, postal stamps, and beer we bought, the minister of finance is probably working his calculator at top speed, figuring out new interest rates to curb inflation.

They sell XXXX and Victoria Bitter, both from Australia, by the boat-load here, and for about $1 U.S. you could get a large can. Discarded beer and orange soda cans seem to be the predominate source of litter in the streets and surrounding grounds. I paid for the beer, and said "Coraba!" in my best Kiribatan . . . they were amazed! As I turned away and said "Sabot!" They were astonished!

Another mission accomplished. We had been off the ship for an hour now, had seen the entire town, and had two hours left. We decided to go to the post office and buy some Kiribati stamps. This was Jon's idea, and since he is clearly the entrepreneur and eBay genius of the group, we pursued it with gusto. Besides, we had a fistful of Australian dollars and little else to bring home at that point.

Jon, by the way, having learned a smattering of Kiribatan from the Jourdan Institute of Western Pacific Language Studies, said "Mauori!" ("Hi!") to everyone he saw. But he said it with a Tennessee accent. Most everyone responded with a smile, so I guess he had it right. Of course, we could have been told the wrong thing, and "mauori" could really mean "dog poop," and that would also explain the smiles. Come to think of it, with the number of scraggly dogs everywhere, those could be interchangeable and equally useful salutations.

So, we crowded into the post office, which was the only other modern, air-conditioned building in the town, and were amazed to find a huge collection of very colorful and artistic stamps. Clearly, the Kiribati government has not been idle in its efforts to keep abreast of global developments in postage stamp design. We bought sheets of them (again, to the astonishment of the clerks), without intending to mail anything! Earlier, Jon found out they were behind in other ways . . . he tried to get some postcards postmarked, and discovered that they had not been able to advance the date on their ink stamp to 2002, because it was rusted stuck on 2001. They also had no way of making change, and were happy to take U.S. dollars on a 1-to-1 basis (ignoring the 1.6-to-1 exchange rate, in our favor). They didn't seem to have any envelopes, so we had to stuff the stamps into our wallets. Oh, and if you want to buy a post card, you have to go to the bank, which is the only place they are sold.

In the post office (and earlier on the street), we ran into Harold, one of the ship's deck seamen, who chatted with us animatedly and bought $20 worth by himself. Harold is perfectly nice, but has not said more than about fifteen words in the last month. Even when the news got out that he had become a grandpa the other day, he said as little as possible in acknowledgment of any congratulations. Here was this same person, chattering like a magpie. After ten minutes of this, I finally said, "Harold, I've seen you every day for five weeks, and I believe I've heard you speak more in ten minutes that the prior total." He said, well, he was off the ship now. Curious.

Back at the original intersection, we spied a bakery in the other direction, so we walked over. Inside, we found a half-dozen of our group. We bought some cheese bread (which was excellent), and, having shuffled the membership in each little group, set off a ways further down the street.

There were more "houses" . . . which were, actually, a little nicer looking than the ones in the other direction. Dogs, chickens, and piglets (tethered by one foot, which they kept trying to pull off) were everywhere. Sue reported that the inventory of the hardware store mainly consisted of stacks of blue tarp, and they didn't find anything they were looking for (like hose clamps and fan belts). Hopefully, the shipment from home will come, which should have most of the items we need.

We walked a bit farther, and saw another World War II Japanese bunker, this one clearly damaged by cannon shell hits. As we maneuvered for a picture, the rain started—and picked up. As we sheltered under a tree, it grew steadily in intensity, and the tree became a poor umbrella. About the time we were way past damp, we saw Julie fifty yards away waving to us . . . she and a few others had found shelter in a small three-vehicle carport that served as the parking complex for the ministry of justice (clearly Julie, the lawyer, was a Friend of the Court). There was only one vehicle present, and there was even a wooden bench, so we all took turns sitting and standing under the carport as the rain fell harder and harder. Pretty soon it qualified as a first-class deluge! And it kept up. After forty-five minutes, there was no sign of stopping, and pools over a foot deep were collecting in the dirt road in front of us.

That was the cue for the kids to come out with their "boogie boards." Dozens of barely clothed children appeared with small pieces of thin plywood and large cans. They sat the cans on the boards, and pushed them along the water, skimming like a boogie board. We would have been more impressed if they had actually stepped on the boards, but they seemed to be having lots of fun. Meanwhile, the rain continued to fall in buckets. We had an hour before we were supposed to be back to the ship, but I was wondering if the puddles would get so deep that the ship could come and pick us up! So we huddled, getting cold (after being so hot earlier), and waited.

In the meanwhile, others of our group, including the media team, had split immediately and were nowhere to be seen. We were worried that they were caught out in the mini-monsoon on the skiff or somewhere unsheltered. We later discovered that they had run into an Australian gentleman who was on the island installing software for the country's pension plan system (it was hard to imagine that they had a computer, much less a system, much less a plan of any sort). He directed them, via overcrowded bus, to Mary's, an establishment across the causeway connecting to the next island in the atoll. So that group was having fish for lunch, sipping beers, watching the rain fall outside . . . although they did report that the place began to flood, and they had water sloshing about their feet. But that's all I know about that story. . . .

Then there was Comm-Tom and Rod-io, who had managed to hook up with the minister of telecommunications via HF radio, and had applied for a ham radio license via satellite fax, and were off getting permission to operate their radios from Tarawa.

Back at the ministry of justice, the rain finally stopped after over an hour, and we ventured out. At this point, we'd seen all there was of Betio, and had about forty-five minutes to get back to the ship (as we were hoping to be refueled and getting ready to leave). But, we figured we had time to grab a beer for Tom, who we assumed was still stuck on the ship. So a few of us went back down the dirt street, now sloshing with puddles that could drown a dog. Sue decided to duck into a fabric/hardware store (this is a recurring theme), and while waiting for her I was grabbed by a guy with a broken-in-half cigarette asking for a light. I didn't have one, and acted apologetic, and he bear-hugged me! My first thought was that he was demented, and then I wondered if he was a pickpocket. But one look in his eyes confirmed the former guess. I managed to disengage myself, and hurried down the street looking for the other guys and the bar, and found them with . . . Tom! He was sitting on a picnic-type bench at a bar with an XXXX. It turns out that the refueling was going so poorly, he figured he was getting nothing accomplished and took a break. So we sat with him for a while and caught up with the latest news.

It seems that nothing about the fuel was as advertised. First of all, it was not 80 cents U.S. per gallon, as our paperwork promised. It was 80 cents Australian per liter. That worked out to nearly $2 U.S. per gallon. As we were looking for 30,000 gallons, the difference was notable. Besides that, the trucks they use to move the fuel had both broken down several days ago, and there was no hope of repairs for weeks! So, as of 1500, there was still no fuel to be had, although they were working on a plan to pump it via the dock's fire hose. There were issues of fittings that Mel (our engineer) was working. Everything was progressing on Island Standard Time.

So, we walked back to the ship. On the way, we were accosted by the cigarette guy I encountered earlier, who wanted to give us another hug. We managed to sidestep him. The rain began to fall again, only more of a drizzle, which persisted for the next few hours. In the rain, Tom D., Tom B., Shawn, Mel, Captain Dave, and a few others labored to get things moving. We wanted fuel, but we also didn't want it contaminated, so it had to be checked, and the hoses had to be flushed. Then the hose wasn't long enough.

Captain Dave had had enough, and said, "If we can't get the hose to the ship, we will get the ship to the hose!" We got everybody back on board (except for Scotty and a working party who were getting groceries), and got under way for a twenty-yard voyage. Basically, we cast off, backed the ship while still keeping at least one line on the pier, executed a reverse 90-degree turn, and tied up again around the corner of the pier—all for want of a hose. Between Spence directing on the pier, and Dave and Rod working on the bridge, it went smoothly. R.J. called for help with the forward lines, and Tom B. and I were nearby, so we worked with him. He was strangely silent through the whole evolution . . . we found out later that he was so drunk he didn't remember the incident. But you couldn't tell by his actions! (This explains my earlier reference to R.J. running the ship "tight.")

About that time, Scotty and party returned with a busload of groceries. Actually, Scotty himself was no better than a sack of Irish potatoes, as he had succumbed to the evils of drink (Irish and a sailor . . . doubly cursed!) Fortunately, Kristin and Carl were part of the working party and managed to rescue the situation. Kristin took care of the payment (having to return to the ship for more cash), and managed to herd the goods and gobs back to the pier. Once we were tied up, eggs, bananas, sodas, lettuce (which I will probably not sample), and other stores were loaded noisily.

It was now dark, fueling had not started, and the harbor pilot announced that he would not be available to escort us out of the harbor until the following morning. We had also learned that the next day was a national holiday, then would come the weekend, so we were in despair of being stuck in "paradise" for days. They were at least working, as a mixture of fuel and seawater was being pumped into fifty-five-gallon drums, in the process clearing the fire hose lines of water. It made me wonder what would happen in the future if there was ever a fire.

Finally, by 8 PM, fuel started flowing into the *Davidson* tanks! Meanwhile, the local police boat had slipped its lines and anchored just off our port bow, presumably in an effort to discourage us from stealing away in the night. Not that we would dare trying to negotiate the reef opening in the dark without a pilot. We were stuck until morning, at the minimum.

At least two of us were not disappointed. Comm-Tom and Rod-io had snagged a Kiribati ham radio license, and had moved their equipment down to the pier, rigged an antenna up to the fo'c's'le, and were busy talking to the world. If you know anything about hams, you know that they crave making contact with people from different countries, and measure their worth by how many "QSLs" they can collect. "QSO" is radio-talk for a radio contact; QSL is confirmation of same. When this occurs, the parties send each other a QSL card that confirms the contact (and if they are nice, a self-addressed envelope with a couple of "green stamps," which is radio-talk for dollar bills, for the party that has taken the trouble to get to a remote and desirable site). The objective is to collect QSLs from as many countries as possible (there are over 300 defined by the hams). Since a signal received from a long distance is called a "DX" (an early telegraph term), the event is known in ham-speak as a "DXpedition."

As one can imagine, it is very difficult to obtain a QSL from such a remote place as Kiribati. So Tom and Rod-io were popular guys, in their circles.

When I stepped out on the pier to see how they were doing, they were deep into Morse Code, talking to Oman. I said "hi" to Tom and he looked at me vacantly and said "dit-dit-dah-dit-dah-dah . . ." They were making one contact after the other, for a while more than two per minute. They kept at it all night, and by dawn had made contact with 571 fellow hams in fifty-nine countries! Over the nearly ten hours they kept at it, they averaged about one contact per minute! Tom says he has prepared his wife to get sacks of mail from his new friends all over the world. By the way, our opinion of hams was elevated when we were told that rock singer Joe Walsh ("Rocky Mountain Way") is an avid enthusiast, and is a friend of Tom's.

Once we figured out we were there for the night, a few got permission to leave the ship for another meal at Mary's, while the rest of us stayed on the ship, having exhausted the offerings of Betio. While fueling was proceeding, a gathering of kids lined up along the pier to fish, and in the lights of the ship we could see hundreds of little fish swimming by (along with the garbage and filth). Occasionally, a larger fish (like a blowfish) swam by, and, more interestingly, a number of white octopi.

When I reflect on our short visit to Tarawa, I find it amusing that our pre-visit list of things to do included checking in with the local Rotary Club and seeing if there was a Kinko's. It was also ironic that part of clearing customs included observing strict rules about sanitation.

## *DAVIDSON* CLASSIFIEDS

### Personals 100

**Captain Jerzy.** Thank you, my love, for the wonderful tour of your ship, the USS *Saratoga*. I just loved your magic soup and that cute little cabin boy, Scotty. Best wishes on your around-the-world cruise, and I'll remember our sunrise together. Lisa

**Adios.** Thanks, *Davidson* boys. I'll be saying "so long" because I jumped ship in Tarawa. You guys really know how to show a girl a nice time with your knot-tying, fishing, sonar . . . geez! I'll be looking to hitch a ride next time with some "yachtie hottie" with a real Jacuzzi. And you can have your grill back for all those fish you've been catching, losers. BB105

### Wanted 200

**Good Woman:** Must be able to sew, clean, cook, dig clams, split wood. Also must have own boat. Submit resume and pic. (Of the boat, ya flatlander.) Joe

**I'll pay ye $5AD each** for every photo you may have of me wicked identical twin brother who was seen drinkin' wee beers and chasin' wee lassies and shootin' wee pool games last week in Tarawa. The poor boy's still on parole, and he just don't need no unwelcome photograph landin' in front of da judge. Scotty

### For Sale 400

**Tetracycline**—Good for what ails ya. Clears up all forms of gastrointestinal bugs, skin infections, and most of the social diseases. $50AD a pop.

**Australian $$:** Will pay any amount for Australian coins. None of your business why. Ron

**Business**—A retail marine fuels business for sale in Tarawa. Complete with a proven business plan. VERY PROFITABLE this year. Owner will consider investment or retirement property for sale or trade in Oahu.

### Lost & Found 500

**Lost:** Yo. My floppies. Two 3-1/2 inch, off-white w/ "Sue" CLEARLY marked. A priceless shell reward is offered, no questions. Sue

**Still Missing:** The chick sock. Never mind, you can keep it. Sue

Strange, isn't it? Write the editor if you can come up with a way to help Sue hang onto her stuff. Seems like the entire "Lost" column was owned by her at one time or another. Maybe someone's not getting enough attention, hmmmm?

April 18 (19); Thursday (Friday).
"Red, Right, Returning to Reality"—Bill Mills.

Well, fueling was completed, customs arrived on board promptly at 0530, the pilot showed up, and we were under way by 0700. As we followed the buoys to sea, I wondered again why the red buoys were on the right, green on the left. The convention I always learned was "red, right, returning" (to port). It turns out that only the United States and a few other countries follow this rule; the rest of the world has it the other way. I had little experience entering foreign ports as a submariner, so I just never knew. That's what prompted the quote by Bill above.

The crew was slowly recovering from their day on the "town." Some had taken the typical sailor approach to liberty, and were paying dearly for it. Scotty said to me, "Dave, can we just cancel today?" I told him it was worse than that . . . not only could we not cancel today but (owing to crossing the date line) we would have to do today over again tomorrow! He said at least he wouldn't be hung over.

I asked Joe if he got ashore. He said, "Arrgh, I stepped on the pier to see how the radio guys were doing, and they were talking to a guy from Alaska. Then I went back aboard. That was enough shore leave for me!"

Reality was a bit unpleasant, as with only a few hours of stillness and quiet we lost our sea legs. Everybody was stumbling around, and the fumes from diesel burping up the vents didn't help. Everybody who could, took it easy . . . fortunately, the "hot tub" and hammock were placed back in service.

One treat was packages from home. We managed to get our deliveries in time, including some camera gear and other odds and ends we needed for the operation, as well as some personal goodies. Back home, Carla and Lynn— along with anyone else who helped—deserve kudos for a great effort. It was critical to have their support, working with the ship office and the agent in Tarawa to arrange for fuel, deliveries, and payments. I know it was very busy and frustrating, and out here we can't really appreciate how much work is involved. They and Colleen also help keep the families, investors, and friends informed, and help them with any problems. Kathleen Liedy and Steve Abdalla have been keeping track of project finances, and they all have to keep the rest of the business finances in order. Joe Crabtree keeps the bulk of the technical business moving ahead. We can't do it without all the folks at home.

Anyway, our box included the last two Sunday issues of the *Washington Post*, and a tape from my son Eric with the April 10th Orioles vs. Tampa Bay game (I'm watching it as I write, and as we're in the ninth inning now, there is quite a gathering watching the excitement). Carla sent the ladies a special box, which they opened together gleefully. It was fun to have some physical connection to home. It was also interesting to read Dave Barry's March 31 column, which had a reference to Amelia Earhart being lost in the Dallas airport.

## April 19 (20); Friday (Saturday). Painting and Planning.

Today we worked very hard to get ready for the next deployment and last third of the mission. Anyone who was not busy with computers or mechanical systems on the vehicle was painting the equipment. The Navy will be happy to know everything is being covered in a nice gray epoxy, and looks great. Joe said in all of his years as a commercial sailor, this was the first time he's seen a charter crew painting their equipment. Jon (who is an investor, so I guess he had a motivation to protect his investment) worked like a dog, and was rewarded with a sunburn; he and Rod painted the diesel. Julie, Jeff, and Kristin worked together on the winch, and Spence was everywhere.

We had a navigation team meeting to assess our approach to the last third of the mission, but we all felt our original plan should be completed as originally envisioned. Here is a summary of where we are:

## SURVEY PROGRESS
Updated 4-19-02

In Area A, Southern Portion (including Western Extension), we covered 367 sq-nm (square nautical miles), including 97 percent of the planned 350 sq-nm area. (This has been updated, because we picked up one missed area from Line 18 when we returned to Area A later.) Our overall rate of coverage, including all equipment down time and turns, was just under 1 sq-nm per hour. During the later stages of the search, when NOMAD was continuously deployed, we achieved 1.1 sq-nm per hour.

In the Southern Extension, worth 72 sq-nm, we covered virtually 100 percent and even some areas outside the boundaries, so our coverage was 93 sq-nm. Coverage rate was 1.0 sq-nm/hr.

We returned to Area A and searched eight lines in the Central Portion, designated 1N-8N. This portion was worth 136 sq-nm, and we covered 100 percent of it. Area coverage was 151 sq-nm, and the total to date is 611 sq-nm. Our rate increased to 1.1 sq-nm/hr. We have met our coverage goal in twenty-six days of survey, and have fourteen days remaining of the planned forty-day search. If we are able to complete the remaining search at the rate we are achieving, we will cover over 900 sq-nm total, a remarkable accomplishment. Of course, we hope to quit early owing to a discovery!

NOMAD continued to perform at near perfection, although I doubt we will break our record earlier in the mission of 257 hours of continuous operation. During the Central Portion of Area A, NOMAD operated for almost five days (111 hours) before needing a comp oil refill, which was accomplished during a turn with a loss of less than 2 hours' downtime. So far, we have logged 600 hours of survey, with less than 20 hours (3 percent) maintenance time. This is superior performance, and you all deserve congratulations for your efforts.

NOW, LET'S FIND IT AND GO HOME!

The other statistic not mentioned above is that we're searching at better than 1-meter resolution, which means we're practically guaranteed to see our target if we hit it with the sonar, and we are using 20 percent to 40 percent overlap between lanes to account for any errors in navigation or weaknesses in detection at long ranges. (The 20 percent figure is based on the nominal range of the sonar, 750 meters, but we do get data out to 860 meters, although it is less reliable). We are running two frequencies simultaneously, 50 and 500 KHz. We also have a forward-looking sonar (the Simrad), which not only helps us avoid cliffs, but helps fill in any weak areas directly below the sonar. All of the data is being saved in digital format, and Tom reviews it all in raw form after the real-time operators have had their pass at it. Then he creates mosaics. Ironically, we heard from an associate that one of our competitors has been gossiping that his sources tell him we are having "massive equipment problems." I guess that tells us his sources are not particularly reliable!

We are very optimistic that the target is in the area we laid out in the beginning, and we should be able to cover the rest of it in the next two weeks. If it's not there, I'll be very surprised.

The sea does not give up her secrets lightly.
—Author

# Night of Heroes

April 20; Saturday. Back in the Western Hemisphere.

This morning we crossed the International Date Line again, heading east, which technically puts us in west longitude. This makes sense if you consider that we are west of the Prime Meridian, which passes through Greenwich in London. Anyway, we get to enjoy Saturday again, not that the weekends matter much out here.

We spent the day making final preparations for deployment, as we expect to be in the operations area by late this evening. We are also preparing ourselves to resume the watchstanding routine that became so familiar for so many weeks. The visit to Tarawa was a welcome break, but also a chance to forget good work habits. The first deployment would be a crucial test of our ability to quickly regain our edge and return to the disciplined search process that had become our standard.

Many changes were made to NOMAD during the five-day interlude, mainly with the expectation of having something to photograph. These included: adding a 35MM film camera, adding a Benthos pressure bottle to contain electronics for the camera, adding strobe lights, adding a battery for the strobes, re-locating one of the HMI lights and brackets, and adding a K-990 video camera. We also found (we think) the comp leak, and pulled the sonar board out to fix the leak detector indication. I was nervous about the latter, as everything important was working, so going into the pressure bottle was asking for trouble.

My job was to determine how all of these equipment modifications would affect the weight balance of the vehicle. As we have no active control of the system's attitude, any imbalance will lead to a constant roll or pitch, which affects the pointing of the sonar. As a former submarine ship's diving officer, I knew just what to do. Of course, we shouldn't mention the incident surrounding my first dive as diving officer on the submarine USS *Kamehameha*, when I miscalculated the trim of our boat 60,000 pounds heavy. That's *thirty tons*!

When we tried to dive to 68 feet (periscope depth), we dropped like a stone; or rather like a metal tube filled with too much water. Despite frantic pumping of ballast tanks to sea, were unable to control depth until we reached 400 feet! After being whipped by the captain, I figured out the mistake: when we left port (Charleston in the winter), the water temperature was about 38 degrees. But we dove in the Gulf Stream, where, just off shore, the temperature rose to 68 degrees! Warm water weighs less than cold, which made our ship less buoyant, to the tune of 2,000 pounds per degree for our particular vessel. Hence, the thirty tons. This story is told in embarrassing detail in my book *Never Forgotten* (Naval Institute Press, 2009).

Fortunately, no one heard this story on our team, so I was given the job with confidence. After calculating all of the moments (or twisting forces, based on estimates of the weights of the equipment and their precise locations on the frame), I installed two lead bricks on the starboard side. This, as we later discovered, balanced the roll pretty well and reduced the four-degree down pitch we were experiencing by a degree or so. So it was a success this time.

At 2000, our watch section met to review launch procedures, even though we had done it many times before. We also reviewed recovery procedures, just in case. Such is Tom Bethge's meticulous preparation for each event . . . and a good thing, as it turned out.

Launch proceeded very smoothly, interrupted only by an intermittent problem with the forward-looking sonar. Bill set up his filming equipment, and had the deck lit as though it were daylight. Tom B. was in charge, and in communication with Mike up in Ops via "talkie." Jon, Tom V., and Kristin manned the port tagline, while Julie and I manned the starboard. The taglines help stabilize the vehicle as we raise it from the deck; they run through steel loops on each side of the nose of the vehicle and are tied to the deck on each side. The line handlers tended the other end, allowing the vehicle to move aft and down without (hopefully) swinging side to side. Line handlers also carry a knife to cut their line if it becomes snagged.

Bragg manned the A-frame hydraulic controls, and Jay ran the winch hydraulics. Jonathan served as the still photographer and Bill's "gaffer." A few observers (Elgen and Tom D., and a few of the *Davidson* crew) were on the E Deck rail, watching from above. Everybody on deck was dressed in steel-toed shoes, hard hats, work gloves, and life jackets. As it was night, we all clipped on fresh light sticks and activated them. This is in case one of us falls overboard, and serves to attract sharks.

The launch was a well-choreographed evolution. It started with vehicle checks on deck of all systems: sonars, lights, and cameras. We routinely perform a number of "housekeeping" checks, including bolt tightening, checking for stray tools, and checking for loose or unclipped tie wraps. Jay topped off the comp oil reservoir. Then, everybody donned their gear and took position, tag lines attached.

Julie (the Diesel Queen) started the diesel, and returned to position on the tag line. This time, since things had been moved around a lot in five days, we had to take up slack in the cable. To do this, Julie held the cable up over the vehicle, while I grabbed it with both hands and maintained as much tension as possible (those gloves were later discarded, as the grease on the cable is nasty!) Jay slowly took up the slack while Tom checked the wrapping through the traction sheaves.

Ready for launch. We unhooked the straps which tend the overboard sheave, hanging from the top of the A-frame. When tilted back, the sheave will guide the cable (and vehicle) into the water. Then we removed the safety net from the aft deck opening, where the vehicle will go over. Bragg raised the A-frame to vertical, so the sheave was directly over the vehicle. Next we tightened the tag lines, three of us pulling on each side, and removed the tie-down straps holding the vehicle on the deck. Now NOMAD was loose, and could slide across the deck if there was a severe roll.

Jay hauled in on the winch, and lifted the vehicle just off the deck, while Bragg eased the A-frame aft and we hung on to the tag lines with all our might. By these actions, the vehicle moved aft and overboard; then Jay lowered it into the water. Meanwhile, Tom was directing everyone by voice and hand signals, as well as directing the ship as it lined us up for the best seas and speed to deploy. As soon as NOMAD was in the water and away from the ship, we reattached the safety net, and the deck crew collected the tag lines and straps, making them up neatly for the next time. Jay shifted control to Ops, and winching down continued from there.

Fortunately, last night it was fairly calm, although VERY muggy. We were all hot, thirsty, and sweaty, but NOMAD was in the water and on the way down.

I headed up to Ops, as I had the first watch. Mike and Tom B. were there when I arrived. No sooner had I sat down, when Mike commented, in his typical calm and quiet voice, that comp was going down quickly. It was to 20 percent and visibly dropping. Tom secured the dive, and started hauling in—FAST! Then he had the vehicle systems secured. We had a catastrophic compensating system leak, and were in danger of getting seawater into the sensitive electronics.

I ran down to round up the launch team and make preparations for emergency recovery. Good thing we discussed it in the briefing. By the time I got to the Wet Lab, the team had gathered and was already redonning their gear. The lead line handlers become hookers for recovery, so we got out the long yellow poles and attached them to the tag line hooks. We were ready within minutes, and were waiting for the vehicle when it surfaced.

We got the starboard hook on right away, but before the port tagline could be hooked, the system spun to starboard in the ship's propeller wash. We called for extra bodies on the starboard line to haul in and straighten NOMAD . . . then the port line was hooked. We winched the vehicle up and on deck smoothly.

The problem turned out to be simple, but potentially devastating. One piece of plastic tubing popped off (presumably because of the propeller wash from the ship during launch), letting all the comp oil out. Thanks to Mike's alertness, and Tom's quick action, there was no damage. We simply had to reconnect (more securely!) the tubing, refill comp, run vehicle checks, and redeploy.

Meanwhile, the deck crew was preparing for another deployment. While we were waiting, we got some stiff brushes from the bosun's locker, some detergent, and gave the aft deck a wash-down as it was very slippery from all the spilled oil.

Redeployment went as smoothly as it had the first time. Bill was pleased, as he got shots from two locations of essentially the same scene with the same people dressed the same! By 2330, it was all over. Whew! We were glad to turn over to the midwatch with everything under control, the vehicle on its way to the bottom, and all systems operating perfectly. And we were happy to get a "sea shower" and go to bed.

## April 21; Sunday. Runaway Cable!

The ops briefing this morning was short and sweet. We are halfway through Line 9N, with all vehicle systems working fine. Comp is 29 percent and holding steady. The biggest discussion of the meeting was about the hot tub water supply.

> Quote for the day:
> Champions are not those who never fail; they are those who never quit.
> (Supplied by Debbi Lange)

I posted the above quote on the wardroom wall this morning – little knowing what was in store for us this day.

We were 200 meters from the end of Line 9N at 1924 (7:24 PM), with 8,924 meters of cable out. Twenty minutes later, we were just about to call the turn when Bill (who was on the winch) realized he had no response to his joystick. He reported this, and to our surprise Jay immediately leapt up and headed for the aft deck. I looked up at the security monitors and saw the image of the winch and reel, and looked for Jay.

When Jay reached the vicinity of the winch, he saw hydraulic fluid spewing from a broken hose, under 3,000 PSI of pressure. His first thought was to secure the diesel. With no pressure, the cable started to pay out . . . and the drum started spinning, faster and faster! Apparently, the "fail-safe" brake that is supposed to prevent this circumstance . . . failed. Jay restarted the diesel and ran to the side of the drum where the manual brake was located, as the drum continued spinning. According to those in the vicinity, the machinery was screaming, as the reel was revolving ten times faster than designed. Jay kept cranking on the brake with a hand wrench, standing right next to the spinning drum. Bill had run to get his camera, and Tom B. had left to take charge of the situation aft. In an instant, Tom D. joined me, and we both stared helplessly at the security monitor, watching Jay in an apparently futile attempt to set the manual brake. Designed for keeping the drum secure during shipping and maintenance, it was never meant to bring a wildly spinning reel to a halt with a dozen tons of cable and equipment hanging into the seas. But it was our last hope.

Meanwhile, NOMAD settled to the bottom barely thirty seconds after the initial casualty. It was dragged a bit, and turned to starboard, but Tom D. had the ship stop to keep from tugging on it and take some strain off the winch. The still-working instruments showed it came to rest ten minutes later. The weight of the cable pulled the ship backwards at three knots as it settled to the bottom. Tom and I watched the monitor, transfixed, as the drum continued spinning out of control. The cable payout display frantically clicked off tens of meters in moments as more and more of the cable left the ship. I looked at Tom, and said, "We've lost it, haven't we?" He didn't comment, but remained fixed on the monitor. We were taking all of the actions possible, and it remained only for a few more minutes to tell the scope of the unfolding disaster.

Time seemed to creep along, even though only seconds had passed. I began to have visions of the scene in the movie *The Abyss*, in which an umbilical with crane tending an underwater habitat plunged into the sea during a storm. Our situation was not dissimilar, as tons of steel cable were rushing to the bottom with apparently nothing to stop it.

I turned back to the monitor. My next thought was of Jay, standing next to the spinning drum. The bitter end of the cable was attached to the drum, the winch system, and the ship. When the spool ran out, something drastic was going to break . . . and Jay was standing right there! As I opened my mouth to order Jay to "GET OUT OF THERE – IMMEDIATELY!!" I saw in the camera that the drum had stopped spinning. Jay had managed to engage the manual brake, and it held . . . our last chance. . . .

Tom worked to manage the ship to slowly drift backwards and lay the cable down in front of the vehicle. The vehicle was holding steady on the bottom, not being dragged any further. So, things were stable—for the moment. We had a little time to collect our wits, make a plan, and begin damage control.

Jay left the aft deck and walked into the galley. He drew a glass of water from the fountain. He sat down and took a sip.

Sue walked in, with one of our cameramen in tow. "Jay, why are you shaking?" she asked, knowing the answer, of course.

"We had a little . . . hose break . . . a hydraulic hose break," said Jay, haltingly. "It's a little exciting." He paused. "And the wire starts going out . . ." Jay nods his head slowly. " . . . and out. . . ." He nods again and looks at Sue, smiling vacantly. " . . . can't stop it!" He nods again. "It's exciting."

Jay exhibited his heretofore unappreciated mastery of the understatement. He had just risked serious injury or death to save NOMAD and the cable . . . exciting indeed! His cool head, quick thinking, and technical competence allowed him to quickly assess the situation and take action, averting calamity . . . at least for the time being.

Everyone from both watch sections was up by now, looking for a way to help. The broken hose was replaced, the hydraulic oil refilled, and the diesel restarted. We were ready to winch in within thirty minutes. However, the winch wouldn't move. Our technicians concluded that the "fail-safe" brake had jammed and the hydraulic motors were possibly damaged. By about 2200, the team on the deck had secured the cable by wrapping it with interlocking straps attached to a securing wire, a device called "Chinese Fingers," and was working to relieve the stress on the winch. This would allow us to remove the brake and relieve the jam.

I called Lynn and Carla at the office on the Iridium satellite phone. This device could put us in instant touch with home, and was brought by the National Geographic team for an emergency. It was hideously expensive to use, but this certainly qualified as an emergency. I explained to her what had happened, and asked her to call the Navy and Coast Guard to see if anyone could help. We didn't know if we would be stranded for days, or if someone would suffer a serious injury and require a medical evacuation. I ended the conversation by saying, "I will consider this night a success if all my team comes home alive and with all their limbs."

Lynn immediately understood the gravity of the circumstances. The desperate details of the matter were clear enough, but she also heard it in my voice, even through twelve thousand miles of satellite communications link. She knew me to rarely overreact to a crisis, to try to hold my emotions at bay until the problem was understood and a resolution was clear. This time, my voice exposed my anxiety, my fear of the worst that could happen.

Of course, Lynn had her own fears to manage, but set them aside and began making calls. She would do what she could to find help, though it would be days away at best.

By 0300, the situation was far from resolved. The motors had been damaged, and would not turn the winch at all. Unfortunately, we carried only one spare motor. We called Dynacon in Texas on the Iridium phone for consultation. They said one hydraulic motor should be sufficient, though of course at reduced capacity, but we would have to boost the hydraulic pressure up to maximum. This we were reluctant to do.

Meanwhile, the ship was stuck, essentially anchored to the bottom. We discussed the last resort of cutting loose the cable and dropping everything on the bottom for future recovery. This was a drastic measure, as nearly a million dollars of equipment would be left at nearly 20,000 feet depth, 1,700 miles from port. To return to the site with a system to recover it would probably cost about as much as the equipment was worth!

Still, we had to consider this, since if we could not recover the cable we were stranded at sea. The trick with cutting the cable was to do it safely. Mel and his engineers prepared acetylene torches and a plan for safe release of the tons of cable dangling below us. The plan did not sound safe, as it involved two crew members in a small boat floating behind the ship where the cable plunged into the sea. When the cable is cut, tons of force are straining to be released, and all of it goes when the cable parts. I didn't want anyone to be at that spot, so I figured I would insist on being the one to wield the torch when the time came. This would have to involve a short training session for me on how to use an acetylene torch.

In spite of all that had happened, at night, at sea, and in an emergency, we had suffered no injuries . . . yet. As the night wore on, this became my primary concern.

We had not despaired of retrieving the system, however. There was some promise that one of the hydraulic motors was not severely damaged, and could work if cleaned up and rebuilt. One problem was getting all of the metal shards from the broken motors cleaned out of the hydraulic system, which meant pulling and flushing all hoses, and shifting to the electric HPU (which although inadequate for operations, should allow us enough power to slowly retrieve the system). Hopefully, the rebuilt motor would work, and the undamaged replacement motor would continue to function.

Mel, the ship's engineer, said it couldn't be done. The better of the two damaged motors was in such bad shape it looked unrepairable; the other was destroyed. But there was nothing to do but try. Rod, who grew up on a Kansas farm and had experience making old equipment operate under dubious conditions, volunteered to help. So Rod and Jeff began working under Shawn's supervision to rebuild the motor. Julie, Kristin, Jon, Carl, and Mike gathered clean hydraulic fluid from all sources, and recycled used oil by filtering metal shards through t-shirt fabric. Sue and Spence flushed hoses. Robert wrestled with the long, heavy hoses to shift them to the electric HPU. Jonathan was in Ops, monitoring the still-operating vehicle systems. Everybody was busy with something, and the aft deck appeared in the security monitors to be infested with ants. The ship's crew was pitching in also, primarily Mel and his gang, with Ron standing by as always to lend a hand.

It was wonderful to see the unbridled enthusiasm and persistence of this group! In spite of the gravity of the situation, there were still smiles and the satisfaction of working hard to accomplish a difficult job.

Joe was driving the ship now, and doing a fine job station-keeping so that we wouldn't drag or damage the vehicle. NOMAD was as happy as a clam, alive and pinging (although it was in danger of remaining a clam for sometime if we could not get it off the bottom!) Mother Nature was cooperating, as well, with a beautiful, calm night and gentle swells. If one of the ever-lurking squalls were to come near, the situation could become critical in a moment.

I realized at that point there was almost no chance of continuing the mission. But if we could get the cable and system safely aboard, I would count it as a major victory of the day. Then we would consider the future.

### April 22; Monday. Night of Heroes.

*0620.* Over the course of the night, Rod and Jeff worked to rebuild the aft hydraulic motor, our remaining hope of lifting NOMAD off the bottom of the ocean. They tinkered with it for a couple of hours, comparing it to the other (destroyed) motor, and cleaned it meticulously. A radio engineer and a Renav analyst rebuilding a hydraulic motor! Rod insisted it could be done, drawing on his experience on the farm in Kansas as a kid. Mel helped, but he gave it a 10 percent chance of working. I gave it less than 50-50.

Shawn and Jay installed the motor. The launch team assembled. Another briefing, and we were ready to give it a go.

Throughout the long night, my immediate role had shifted from participant in the watchstanding routine to the leader of the expedition. The outcome, financially, medically, and otherwise, was my responsibility. So I stepped back from the recovery team and stood with Tom D. to observe the proceedings from the vantage of the E Deck. We had done all we could to prepare for this last-ditch effort, and all I could do was trust the team to perform and the repaired motor to work.

The electric HPU started and came up to pressure just fine. Shawn manned the winch control at the local station and gingerly pulled the joystick. The HPU whined as the winch turned, jerked, and seemed to lock up. My breath caught and my heart thumped off time, as Tom B. slowly uncranked the manual brake on the drum, and Shawn carefully winched in. The cable moved a couple of feet. Tom and Shawn locked eyes, and Shawn nodded perceptibly. Tom made a hand signal, and very quickly a ready team assembled at the cable to remove the Chinese Fingers. This scared me the most, as they were rapidly unwrapping the straps, in a hurry to move away from the cable in case it slipped. If the rebuilt hydraulics failed and the cable slid overboard, they were in danger of having an arm caught. As we saw the night before, with tons of tension on the cable, it goes fast, and we would not be able to stop it from pulling someone off the deck and underwater. They knew that from the briefing, and tried to be careful, but quick. After a few tense minutes, it was removed without mishap, everyone was clear, and I breathed a sigh of relief.

It was time to haul in, and Shawn carefully began to draw back on the stick, using local control. The winch responded, and the drum began to turn! Slowly, but quick enough at one-quarter speed (fifteen meters per minute), the system began to haul in the cable. Steel began to inch off the bottom. The counter showed 8,783 meters out; hauling in started at 8,930 meters, so we were already making progress. After a few minutes, with everything going as smoothly as could be expected, Shawn increased to 21 meters per minute, one-third the maximum speed we get with the diesel HPU and good hydraulic motors.

*0635.* 8,578 meters out, and winching in at 23 meters per minute. We had moved the local control station to be directly in front of the reel so Shawn could watch the level-wind and wrapping, and react immediately if anything seemed wrong. By 0700 we were still coming up, to 7,934 at 33 meters per minute. Looking better.

As we winched in, we were picking up cable from the seafloor. So, we were heaving in a steady weight of about five tons (the weight of length of cable dangling to the floor at 5,600 meters). When we began to lift NOMAD at about 5,600 meters of cable out, we would add about a ton . . . a critical moment. Then, the weight would become progressively lighter as we reeled in more cable.

*0707.* Things are looking better, and Shawn has increased speed, at 7,705 meters out and hauling in at 36 meters per minute.

*0733.* The sensors on NOMAD began to twitch, indicating vehicle motion . . . the sled started to pitch down on its nose and in a few minutes reached 50 degrees from vertical. The cable was at 6,680 meters, coming in at 45 meters per minute. The pitch continued to change, as we began to drag the vehicle slowly along the bottom on its nose. All sensors were working perfectly, so we could "see" the process from the vehicle's point of view, at least by instruments.

*0750.* NOMAD began to move more rapidly! We were still dragging it along the bottom, but now on its skids. 5,953 meters of cable were out, but coming in at 33 meters per minute.

*0800.* 5,663 meters out at 39 meters per minute.

*0802.* NOMAD left the bottom! The sonar was indicating a bottom return, and we were able to lock on it and measure vehicle altitude. After a few minutes the added weight began to tell on the system, as the winching rate slowed. But still moving! Nearly thirteen hours after the initial casualty, NOMAD was on its way home!

*0819.* 5,000 meters at 35 meters per minute. NOMAD was coming up. The ship, now free to maneuver after a long night of station-keeping, turned into the sea. Every meter increased the chances that we would get the system to the surface. The HPU and hydraulic motors were doing great . . . but something could fail at any time, possibly causing a repeat of the events of the night before.

*0850.* 4,000 meters at 38 meters per minute.

*0914.* 3,000 meters at 42 meters per minute. There was considerably less strain on the system as the scope of cable shortened, down to about 4 tons, so the winch moved faster.

Another critical time was passing. With half of the 11,000 meter cable out, if we had to cut it, we would have two short lengths (of little value to us as they cannot be spliced). With each meter in we were lengthening the recovered segment. Also, with NOMAD off the bottom, even if the system seized at this point, we might be able to tow it to a shallower, more accessible location. As each minute passed, our options widened and our chances of success improved.

*0938.* 2,000 meters at 33 meters per minute. Shawn finally relented and let Sue take over on the stick for a few minutes so he could take a break. After three hours with his hand on the joystick, afraid to make any quick movements and monitoring equipment with constant attention, he was certainly tired. I talked to Lynn briefly on the Iridium phone and gave her an update to pass to the folks at home. I tried to tell her about Rod and Jeff, sweating, covered with oil, teasing apart the damaged motor as though it were a delicate watch. But the words would not come.

*1006.* The recovery team assembled in the Wet Lab for yet another briefing. We normally bring the vehicle on board carefully and slowly, to avoid any damage to sensitive electronics. This time, we would bring it to the deck as quickly as possible. The winch system had performed well at a steady haul, but as the vehicle surfaced it would feel dynamic forces and we would have to change the speed at the last moment. A failure at that point could send the entire system reeling back down into the abyss.

We doubled the tag lines, and added extra people to each. Fortunately, the weather remained calm.

*1017.* 570 meters, at 55 meters per minute pay-in. The recovery team as-sembled on deck.

Tom and I stood on the third deck and observed the proceedings. It was a nice, sunny day, with calm seas and beautiful sky. Some birds flew by. Tom B. was in charge on deck, and was watching the water anxiously for a glimpse of the vehicle. When he saw it and signaled, I felt that we were going to make it.

NOMAD was watching. We had turned on the cameras and recorders, and one camera was pointed ahead. Through these eyes, we saw a dim blueness, bright-ening each minute. A hazy darker blue shape took form . . . the hull of the ship! As NOMAD rose from the deep, the hull image cleared, and the rudders and slowly spinning ship's propellers came into view.

A splash of foam, and NOMAD broke the surface. We all saw it from above, as NOMAD watched from below. A cloud of mud washed off its skids as the water splashed over them. Sunlight, blue sky, and a sharp horizon came into NOMAD's view, the picture clearing as seawater drained off the camera lens. "There we go!" said Tom B. on audio. "Alright, take your time. . . ." The vehicle camera dunked underwater again, but immediately resurfaced, with more foam, and then cleared. The propeller wash had spun NOMAD off to the side, so only ocean and the vehicle frame was visible from the forward-pointing on-board camera.

Tom encouraged the hookers . . . they could scarcely afford a miss! "Take your time . . . OK, back the pole out . . . good catch!" One line was on! "Take your time . . . take your time . . . that's alright. . . ." The second hook had missed, but Tom was positive as he urged them on to another try.

"Tighten up on your line . . . there we go . . . OK!!" NOMAD began to swing around as both tag lines were attached and the line teams took in the slack. Another splash on the NOMAD camera . . . then clear . . . and the hull reappeared! The letters D-A-V-I-D-S-O-N panned by, and then the camera stabilized on "SITKA, AK," written underneath, white block letters on the blue stern.

Tom signaled to resume winching in, and the scene from NOMAD climbed up the stern of the *Davidson*, to the lip of the aft deck, and over the rim revealing the hard-hatted, life-jacketed figure of . . . Tom Bethge! In the background, the view showed the rest of the crew on the aft deck and even Tom and me up top!

"Boom in . . . boom in," Tom called, hand signaling. NOMAD swung smartly over the edge, and hung over the deck . . . almost safe! Tom grabbed a skid as it swung toward him, the tag line tenders heaving to steady the vehicle. Tom gestured to winch out, for the first time in fourteen hours, and Shawn gently lowered the sled to the deck of the *Davidson*. Tom raised his fist to halt the winch. "Good! All set!"

There was a pause. Tom lowered his fist and looked down into his gloved palms as if thinking, "Look what I found!" Another moment passed. . . . Then the deck erupted with cheering and clapping. NOMAD's camera framed Elgen, standing center stage one deck above, pumping his fist in triumph. The ship gave a mighty blast of its whistle.

What a moment! Almost a million dollars of equipment snatched from the deep!

We all shook hands and congratulated one another. A solid night of hard work by a determined group of people. Like the heroes in Debbi Lang's quote, they never quit. They are champions!

For today, that will have to be as good as finding Amelia. Now, we consider our options.

## April 23; Tuesday. On the Way Home.

There were some last-ditch efforts to figure out a way to get replacement parts to us. Rod and Tom tried to bring the hams to the rescue and, in fact, a group of them were planning to be on Baker Island in the next few days and were more than willing to bring us parts. Unfortunately, it would be impossible to get the parts to them in time, would be extremely expensive, and would cost us a week of idle time. We also could not be sure of such an extensive repair made at sea, as the winch system would probably require a complete overhaul, including a fresh supply of oil. We decided it was better to call off the search at that time, go back to Hawaii, regroup, and make plans for a return trip to finish the job as soon as possible.

We headed for Hawaii at ten knots. Nothing more was urgent, so I went to bed for a "couple of hours," and woke up at 11 PM! I wasn't the only one. I felt like I'd been beaten with a stick, more from the tension than fatigue. The disappointment of having to quit when things were going so well had not quite sunken in yet . . . all I could think about was getting home and getting started again for another try.

There was much work to do to break down all of our gear during the week-long transit to Honolulu. We made plans for a barbecue and crew appreciation party on Saturday, which included drinking the champagne we brought on board to celebrate a discovery.

May 16, 2002

## For Immediate Release

In March and April, a team of ocean explorers led by the Nauticos Corporation joined the crew of the R/V *Davidson* to conduct a deep sea search for Amelia Earhart's lost Lockheed Electra. The team was supported with equipment and in-kind services by a number of sponsors, including the U.S. Navy (through a cooperative research agreement with the Naval Meteorology and Oceanography Command), Rockwell Collins, Konsberg-Simrad, and James Cameron—Earthship Productions. The $1.7 million expedition was funded largely by Nauticos, with significant support from private investors. The expedition was led by Elgen Long, former pilot and Earhart researcher, author (with wife Marie) of the book *Amelia Earhart, the Mystery Solved*. Operations were managed by Tom Dettweiler, veteran of numerous deep ocean discoveries, including the *Titanic*, the Japanese submarine *I-52*, and the Israeli submarine *Dakar*.

The search was conducted with a deep-sea sonar system developed by Nauticos called NOMAD, which is towed near the bottom at the end of a 11,000 meter (36,000 foot) steel-armored, fiber-optic cable. The team planned a sixty-day expedition, with forty days of days search time, and an objective of at least 600 square nautical miles. However, six weeks into the mission, after twenty-seven days of survey, the cable winch hydraulic system failed, ending our operation. To that point, the NOMAD system had operated flawlessly, covering about 630 square nautical miles of ocean bottom at 18,000 foot depth at better than 1 meter resolution.

National Geographic filmed the operation, and a NG Channel special will be aired soon. Nauticos is working on plans to make repairs and return to the site near Howland Island in the central Pacific, and complete the search in the near future.

# Interlude: Where in the World is Amelia Earhart?

The disappearance of Amelia Earhart is possibly the greatest aviation mystery of the twentieth century. It ranks with such enigmas as: Who shot JFK? Where is Jimmy Hoffa buried? What really happened at Area 51? In each of these cases, there is an important historical event or serious scientific question at its foundation, and each has a simple and straightforward, but unsatisfying, answer. A lack of primary evidence, or the perception that there is evidence that cannot or will not be revealed, feeds the notion that there is something more to the story, something dramatic, something duplicitous. Delightfully unsavory details must exist that, if revealed, would prove a massive cover-up, a conspiracy designed to insulate the public from the terrible truth.

To many, the Amelia Earhart tragedy is really not a mystery. She ran out of fuel, crashed in the ocean, and sank. End of story. However, this is not very satisfying to most people. Amelia and Fred disappeared without a trace. Other than a few fleeting radio messages, there is no primary source to narrow speculation. No wreckage, oil slick, or floating debris of any sort was ever found. When one knows almost nothing, almost anything is possible.

On the other hand, there is no lack of anecdotal material from which to draw any number of theories. Many South Pacific islands along Amelia's flight path have an Earhart legend as part of local lore. There is a real appeal to the idea that Amelia and Fred found their way to an island (or were captured and taken there), mainly because, otherwise, how can they be found? This is what is known in the underwater search business as "The Drunk and the Lamp Post Syndrome."

A man walks out of a bar and finds another man, a drunk, on his hands and knees under a lamp post.

"Can I help you?" the first man says.

"Yes," says the drunken man, with a slur. "I lost my car keys. Can you help me find them?"

"OK," says the first. "Where did you last see them?"

The drunk, still on his hands and knees, looking around the lamp post, vaguely waves a hand. "Over there, across the parking lot," he says.

"Well," says the first, "Why are you looking over here?"

Says the drunk, "Because the light is better!"

The ocean depth near the shores of Howland Island, where Amelia was last heard from, is nearly 20,000 feet. Almost no one can search there. But anyone can search an island. The "light" is much better!

Over the decades, a huge body of folklore has arisen about Amelia and Fred. Believable accounts from apparently credible eye-witnesses abound. Physical evidence, including shoes, map cases, airplane parts, and even bones have been produced. Blatant hoaxes have been perpetrated, yet many versions of the post-disappearance Amelia story have ardent supporters.

I will try to give the reader a flavor of this body of lore, and some appreciation for the wide-ranging (and sometimes bizarre) legends that surround the disappearance of this famous and inspiring woman. In doing so, I am guaranteed to raise the hackles of proponents of various theories by not believing their particular version against the backdrop of all the other mutually contradictory scenarios. I am also not qualified to expertly refute every alternative theory, nor am I interested in trying to do so.

In fact, for the most part, I welcome the proliferation of explanations and encourage the people pursuing them. I am convinced, based on solid evidence and rigorous analysis, that Amelia and Fred crashed her Electra in the ocean off Howland Island . . . but what if I'm wrong? Or, what if, somehow, Fred and/or Amelia managed to escape the sinking wreck, and floated for days, alive, fetching up on some deserted island? Stranger stories of survival against all odds have been recorded. So, I welcome the efforts of others to try to solve the mystery in their own fashion, and cover ground (however barren) that our search team has no interest in. It helps make the quest for Amelia a richer and more interesting endeavor. If some other theory, however implausible, turns out to be true, proving it will save the rest of us further time and money spent on a fruitless quest.

My only real complaint about other Amelia search groups is that many of them seem to be offended that we are searching in the ocean where she was last heard from, and not helping them with *their* search. Some proponents of one island theory or another demand that Nauticos drop what it is doing and turn all efforts to searching a reef off of some Pacific island, or a jungle somewhere in the region. Or, quite often, claimants have "secret information" they will share that will prove us wrong . . . but I have to pay, sight unseen, to hear the conclusive evidence that contradicts what we know!

And, of course, I have to explain to one prospective sponsor after another, "Whatever happened to Amelia Earhart's shoe?"

One can loosely group the various "theories" about Amelia's disappearance into three categories: The "crashed-and-sunk" theory, the "island" theories (of which there are many variants), and "everything else," which includes a few intentionally comical scenarios, and a few so bizarre as to be comical anyway.

The crashed-and-sunk scenario was the version of her disappearance that was generally held at the time by those on the scene, and is the version that Elgen Long and the Nauticos team subscribe to. There are many others who believe this, and some have even written extensively about it. One example is *Amelia Earhart: Case Closed*, by Walter Roessler and Leo Gomez (Markowski International Publishers, 1997). This book pre-dates Elgen and Marie Long's *Amelia Earhart: The Mystery Solved* (1999) and arrives at the same basic conclusion, that the Electra went into the water off Howland Island. In fact, Roessler has staked a claim for credit pre-discovery, asserting that he said it before Elgen (and once approached one of our sponsors with this position).

I read Roessler and Gomez's book, and think I can safely say they did not publish any analysis. It is a useful collection of research information, though much of it irrelevant to her loss. For example, they include a lot of information about a problem with the propellers that may have led to the ground-loop incident in Hawaii on Amelia's first attempt. (That problem was fixed before the subsequent flight.) They contend that Amelia was tired, which affected her judgment, and so spend a whole chapter talking about time-zone lag. That is almost certainly true, but does not help anybody find her. Also, they contend that the plane probably stayed intact when ditched (which is interesting in itself) and probably sank very quickly (which is also important), and I'm glad they think so. They support that premise by saying that there would have been floating debris if the plane broke up, and provided a six-page detailed item-by-item listing of every item on the plane—but on a flight the year before! Hopefully, this would give us clues to what we might find in the plane, and for that it is valuable. But again, it has no bearing on the *location* of the plane.

Shortly before we departed on our 2002 expedition I received in the mail a self-published pamphlet by retired Marine Corps Major Bowen Weisheit entitled *The Last Flight of Frederick J. Noonan*, with a subtitle (in smaller letters) *And Amelia Earhart*. Weisheit, a flight navigator instructor with two hundred combat flight hours in the Pacific during World War II, paints a detailed scenario of the final flight based on the thoughts, decisions, and actions of Fred Noonan. He suggests that part of the problem was Amelia herself, as "the pilot . . . wandered off course in random circles," confounding Fred's attempts to accurately navigate. Weisheit predicts a splash point off Howland, and describes in detail the probable events of the ditching.

As the news of the 2002 Nauticos search spread, we received other self-published analyses of the final flight. One was a hand-drawn chart in a letter from "Senior Citizen" Ed Smart, sent in 2007, with a postscript "Good luck on searching." Another analysis sent to Nauticos was from Frank Wolfe entitled *Amelia Earhart's Last Flight: "Circle of Sound Theory,"* which included a cover letter saying, "If my conclusions are substantially the same as those provided by Elgin [sic] Long, you can take comfort in the fact that two honest researchers agree. . . . There will be no charge for my efforts, I want to see you find that airplane." His attached hand-written note said, "If this study is of value—fine. If not, just trash the theory." I think these folks were intrigued by the problem, and just wanted to support anyone who was willing to try a search.

Contrary to those who freely volunteer their ideas are those who want to sell their information. This is not in itself unreasonable; after all, Nauticos purchased the archive from Elgen, realizing that he had put a huge effort into its collection and if we wanted to use it, some compensation was in order. But, we knew what we were getting. More commonly, the seller does not want to reveal what he knows, unless he is paid up front. One petitioner claimed that he had information unknown to anyone else, and asserted, "I am 100 percent certain that I know the answer. I have information which blows the whole thing wide open. Even better is that it is in such detail that I cannot see anyone even trying to refute it." He goes on to criticize Nauticos for preparing to "risk huge sums of other people's money . . . without taking the trouble to find out if they could be wrong." This fellow proposed that, after having heard his information, we would only have to pay his fee if we could *not* find the Electra near Howland Island. But his refusal to offer any detail of even the nature of his claim was very suspicious. My team and I concluded that either the fellow was convinced of some anecdotal evidence, or was a charlatan. Further communications from him became increasingly vitriolic, reinforcing our opinion.

Another subscriber to the crashed-and-sunk scenario, one who has actually done something about it, is Dana Timmer. Dana, a venture capitalist, small plane pilot, and sailor, set about to raise funds for a search and teamed up with Elgen to develop a plan to locate the Electra. Elgen's agreement to work with Dana expired before Dana could raise the expedition funding, and subsequently Elgen chose to team with Nauticos. That did not stop Dana's efforts, however, and in November of 1999 he launched a search in the area off Howland, working with our long-standing colleague Mike Williamson. Williamson and Associates had supported our successful discovery of the Israeli submarine INS *Dakar* earlier that year (see *Never Forgotten*, by yours truly), and has other discoveries to his credit, including the Gold Rush–era steamer SS *Central America* (see *Ship of Gold in the Deep Blue Sea*, by Gary Kinder, Atlantic Monthly Press, 1998).

Dana's team conducted a search covering several hundred square miles of area in the vicinity of Howland Island, but returned without any evidence of the Electra. As of this writing Dana's team has not returned to the site. Members of Dana's team approached us about working together prior to their expedition; later, I met with Dana and further explored working together in some capacity. In the end, it didn't make sense for Nauticos to team with Timmer because he did not have any information, means, or expertise that we needed, but he did have obligations to investors that we would have to absorb. I imagine he felt the same way about us. So, we shook hands and parted company, at least for the time being.

Dana Timmer and Mike Williamson deserve credit for launching the first deep-sea expedition to find Amelia Earhart's Electra. I hope someday their map of the ocean floor can be added to ours and together will be useful to future geologists and ocean scientists.

There is a massive body of lore associated with various island theories. There are a number of reasons that these scenarios are advanced. In most cases, there exists some kind of "legend" about a white woman flyer or a silver aircraft that has been handed down through word of mouth. There is usually some reason that this information was kept secret and not reported at the time. Some examples include: association with pre-war spying on the Japanese; discoveries made by soldiers during wartime who were told to keep their knowledge secret; observations by islanders who didn't know what they were seeing or had no way of reporting the information until much later; or even a U.S. government coverup, designed to protect the president himself. The fact that Eleanor Roosevelt had a personal relationship with Amelia, and President Roosevelt ordered government assets to be employed to support Amelia's flight suggests to some that something was up. Any hint of conspiracy triggers our very human "associative learning" instinct (see Chapter 4), and any suspicion that there are documents still under wraps lends credence to the idea of a coverup. The existence of anecdotal evidence combined with a suspicion of secrecy fuels many (though not all) of the island theories.

Another factor supporting the idea that Amelia and Fred did not go down near Howland Island is the possibility that the July 2, 2013 GMT, transmission from Amelia was not her last. The Coast Guard immediately began a search when Amelia did not arrive, and tried every means available to tease further communications from the airwaves. The search was joined soon by the U.S. Navy, and before the day was out Amelia's disappearance was world news. A number of signals of various types and quality, including clear voice transmissions, were documented at the time or reported later. Some of these signals hint at calls for help from Amelia herself, claiming to be castaway, or through some kind of analysis point to an island origin.

The body of analysis and speculation concerning what has come to be known as "post-loss transmissions" would fill a small library. One could group most reports of these transmissions into three categories:

*Signals heard during the day or so after July 2, 2013* GMT, *on various frequencies, in voice or Morse, that were not identified.* There were many vessels and aircraft searching for Amelia over the ensuing days, and many of them were transmitting on her frequency. Some of these transmissions were mistakenly suspected to have originated from Amelia. Some well-meaning folks, trying to help, heard a signal, copied some fragments and reported them to the Coast Guard, the Navy, or the newspapers. Some of these reports were probably not fully understood and were distorted in the record.

*Hoaxers, publicity hounds, and nut cases, who derive satisfaction from confounding legitimate efforts or who just want some attention.* Sadly, this nearly always happens in such cases, and we have seen such behavior associated with other searches at sea. One notorious example was a California-based amateur (ham) radio enthusiast Walter McMenamy, who (with the backing of fellow hams) reported picking up a number of signals from Amelia with sufficient content and technical detail as to be credible, even though it was *incredible* that such signals could be heard so far away. It wasn't until 1959 that McMenamy confessed to the elaborate hoax. A tiny minority of the ham community gave the rest a black eye as a result of those events.

*Inadvertent signals.* Quite a few hams back then used a receiver known as a "regenerative" receiver. These receivers had a very wide selectivity, so a person could hear signals tens of kilocycles removed from 3105 (the frequency that Amelia was expected to be transmitting) and not know it. Also, these receivers could readily radiate a low-level signal back out the antenna. If a person was listening to 3105 (or a nearby frequency) with one of these receivers and was located within a few miles of any commercial receiving station, the commercial station could possibly hear this signal, which would fit the common "post-loss" description of a weak, unsteady, or wavering carrier. This type of receiver, a National SW-3, shows up in the photos of the Howland Island ham station. That model was very popular with hams and short-wave listeners of modest means in the 1930s.

Less than a week after Earhart's disappearance, a radio program called *March of Time* broadcast a reenactment of the dramatic event, complete with Amelia's desperate messages and the *Itasca's* fruitless calls. People hearing bits of this broadcast, including radiomen intercepting the short-wave relay from California to Hawaii, were convinced they were hearing Earhart herself. A little-known cast member of this program by the name of Orson Welles would be inspired by the effectiveness of this and similar shows to fool the world the following year with his Mercury Theater broadcast of *The War of the Worlds*.

Though one could probably assign every report of a signal to one of these categories, there is no way to prove it in most cases. On the other hand, no "post-loss transmission" has been shown to be more than speculative. Commander Thompson, commanding the *Itasca*, searching for Amelia during the days following her loss, said, "We are calling Earhart frequently and consistently on 3105 kilocycles and, undoubtedly, amateur and other stations mistake us for Earhart's plane." He did not place stock in any of these reports.

By far the most serious and doggedly pursued island theory holds that Amelia and Fred managed to fly to the nearest island to Howland-Baker, now called Nikumaroro, and ditch there. (Nikumaroro was formerly known as Gardner Island, and is part of the island nation of Kiribati, which includes Tarawa. It is about 350 miles from Howland.) This idea is supported by a group called Tighar (The International Group for Historic Aviation Recovery). Founded in 1985 by Ric Gillespie of Wilmington, Delaware, Tighar (pronounced "tiger") has a number of historic aircraft finds to its credit, including several rare World War II planes. The nonprofit group has a small army of volunteers. A visit to its extensive Web site (http://www.tighar.org) describes the organization as "the world's leading aviation archaeological foundation. A full-time professional staff guides an international membership of researchers and supporters in the non-profit organization's efforts to find, save, and preserve rare and historic aircraft."

Ric is serious about pursuing this theory, and in the twenty years since the project was inaugurated (in 1988) Tighar has raised over two million dollars and conducted five expeditions to Nikumaroro, the most recent in July of 2008 (commemorating the seventieth anniversary of Earhart's disappearance). Though, in some ways, Tighar and Nauticos are rivals, and some of each of our supporters have been known to cast aspersions against the other group, we are really not in competition. In fact, Ric and I have a good relationship, and Ric has visited my office and proposed that we work together to merge our research archives and preserve them. I think this is a good idea, and I hope to be able to work it out in time (after overcoming issues with sponsors first).

Ric and I basically agree on almost everything about the Amelia final flight, except for what happened after the 2013 GMT message. I could not pretend to do justice to the extensive body of work that Tighar has done on this, so I invite anyone who is interested to look at their Web site. To summarize: Tighar believes that Amelia had about four hours' flying time of fuel remaining at 2013 (contrary to the analysis I earlier described by Fred Culick). This would give them just enough range to reach Nikumaroro. According to this scenario, Amelia, having been unable to find Howland, decided to use her remaining fuel to fly south looking for Nikumaroro. It is there that she and Fred ditched on a reef, and somehow were able to make the weak transmissions that were reported to be heard after 2013. Shortly thereafter, a storm and high tides washed the aircraft wreckage off the reef and into shallow water, so when the Navy flew over the island in their search a week later they did not see anything. Fred and Amelia, having taken shelter in the dense bush inland, were not able to signal the searching aircraft. The pair remained castaway on the deserted island, surviving for a while on provisions from the ship *Norwich City*, wrecked there eight years earlier.

Tighar cites a number of pieces of circumstantial or anecdotal evidence to support this scenario. Nikumaroro happens (by coincidence) to be directly on the line 157-337 degrees that Earhart was flying when she last reported at 2013 GMT. Thus, they suggest that it was a "contingency plan" of hers to seek this island if she could not find Howland. (There is no evidence that she had such a plan, and flying an additional four hours and 350 miles would only degrade her navigation accuracy further, making it harder yet to find a small island. Nikumaroro was deserted and had no landing strip, fuel, or provisions. A dubious plan, I would think.) The additional fuel needed is supported by an analysis, which, again, contradicts Culick.

One of the most intriguing and publicized clues that Tighar points to is a set of bones found by colonists who inhabited the island for a few years beginning in 1939, shortly after Amelia's disappearance. These bones, a partial skeleton, were collected by British authorities and discounted as evidence of Amelia after a doctor (with no forensic training) pronounced them to be the bones of a short, stocky, Polynesian male. The bones were discarded. However, in the 1990s the report of this analysis, which included measurements, was re-evaluated by modern forensic anthropologists who concluded that the bones were most likely from a white female of northern European extraction who stood approximately 5 feet, 7 inches tall.

Other artifacts were collected, most famously a woman's shoe that was of a type worn by Earhart. All of this is described in a book published in 2001 called *Amelia Earhart's Shoes*, by Tighar members Thomas King, Randall Jacobson,

Karen Burns, and Kenton Spading. King was kind enough to send me an auto-graphed copy, with a letter including "Best wishes . . . even if you are searching in the wrong place."

Ric published a comprehensive summary of historical research called *Finding Amelia: The True Story of the Earhart Disappearance* (Naval Institute Press, 2006). He does not argue for any particular theory in this book, but rather "presents all of the authenticated historical dots and leaves it to the reader to make the connections." It includes a DVD with reproductions of documents, reports, and studies. Regardless of who turns out to be right, Ric Gillespie and Tighar can be credited with mobilizing a serious and enduring investigation into the Earhart mystery and have made a welcome contribution to the body of knowledge about the famous flyer.

Other island theories abound, all based on circumstantial evidence, some much thinner than others. One popular and dramatic idea was that Fred and Amelia were spying on the Japanese, but were captured and eventually executed. The basic scenario is that the secret flight plan included an over-flight of Truk Island in the Central Carolines, north of the direct path to Howland. Their un-official mission was to observe airfields and fleet servicing facilities in support of intelligence gathering in the tense environment that preceded World War II. Because of this detour (adding nearly 300 nautical miles to the direct route), and weather problems along the leg to Howland, Amelia ran short on fuel, got lost, and stumbled across Mili Atoll in the southern Marshall Islands, then controlled by the Japanese. They were taken prisoner, transferred to Kwajalein (also in the Marshalls), and then to Japanese Pacific Headquarters in Saipan, landing themselves in the famous Japanese jail (known as Garapan Prison) that Elgen and I visited in 2007.

A good summary of this theory is found in the Tighar Web site, under "Common Earhart Myths." "This popular fantasy began with the wartime Hollywood film *Flight For Freedom* (RKO, 1943, starring Rosalind Russell and Fred MacMurray). Allegations that Earhart and her navigator had been cap-tured by the Japanese were investigated and found to be groundless by both U.S. Army Intelligence and the United Press as early as 1949. In 1960, with the capture of a genuine spy flight in the news (Francis Gary Powers' U-2), radio commentator Fred Goerner popularized renewed charges that Earhart had been imprisoned by the Japanese. His book *The Search for Amelia Earhart* (Doubleday, 1966) became a bestseller. Since then, a small library of books and articles has expanded the legend, but there remains no evidence, either written or physical, that it has any basis in fact."

A number of others have offered support or variations of the "captured by the Japanese" theory, including Thomas Devine, former Army sergeant and veteran of the Saipan invasion, who makes a case that Secretary of the Navy James Forrestal personally visited Saipan after the island was captured by the Americans to oversee the destruction of the Electra, which had been hidden in a hanger there. Other reports included a twist—GIs finding a safe that contained all sorts of Amelia Earhart's personal items, which were taken away from them by their superior officers.

Another conspiracy theory suggests that in 1979 the aircraft carrier USS *Constellation* visited the Phoenix Islands (east of Nikumaroro) and performed some secret task. According to one correspondent, "Knowing what was in the Phoenix Islands in 1979 would only open a Pandora's box of lies created by the leaders of our country during the time frame that they occurred." This individual was interested in our endeavor because he wanted to know "what they did with the wreckage which was seen that day and I would find it appalling that it was secretly dumped in an obvious location to be found years later."

Many people ardently believe that a conspiracy of some sort was afoot, and there are secret documents yet to be released by the government. One can find lots of speculation about this, and many hints that some kind of nefarious connection existed between Amelia and the highest levels of the administration, and that she was known (or even arranged) to be alive somewhere. For example, according to Dave Horner (author of *Shipwreck*, 1999, Sheridan House), a May 25, 1938, article in *Pacific Islands Monthly Magazine* reported that the Jaluit Post Office in the Marshall Islands had unclaimed mail addressed to:

Miss Amelia Earhart (Putnam)
Marshall Islands (Japanese)
Ratak Group, Malaelap Island (10)
South Pacific Ocean

The return address was "Hollywood-Roosevelt Hotel, Hollywood, California." Margo DeCarrie, Earhart's personal secretary, lived in that hotel after Earhart disappeared. Of course, the primary document itself is lost (if it ever existed). Horner, supporter of our 2002 expedition, and originally planning to cover our search efforts, has become convinced by the weight of anecdote, and talked of writing yet another book about her winding up on an island, based on yet-to-be-located secret documents. (Regardless of our difference of opinion, Dave and I remain friends and personal supporters.)

I will mention just one more of the many island theory versions, as it increases the geographical scope of these mutually exclusive scenarios. Australian David Billings believes that Amelia flew to the vicinity of Howland,

and essentially agrees with our scenario up to the 2013 GMT message, except Billings asserts that she was much farther west of the island. Realizing this, she turned around hoping to find a safe landing spot in Rabaul (on the island of New Britain, east of Lae), missed that, and finally ran out of fuel and crashed in the jungle after covering nearly 5,000 miles. The inspiration for this is evidence from an Australian Army reconnaissance patrol in 1945 that discovered wreckage of an aircraft with radial engines. The patrol noted an identifying tag and other characteristics that Billings contends correspond to Amelia's Electra. These assertions are documented in the New Britain Project Web site, http://www.electranewbritain.com/. Billings has the advantage that his endeavors are relatively inexpensive compared to island excursions or deep-ocean searches, and over the years he has conducted seven expeditions on the ground to search for the wreckage. He most recently was seeking funds to conduct an aerial magnetometer survey, though the Electra, made mostly of aluminum, would produce an exceedingly weak magnetic signature.

It is interesting to note that the island theories, for the most part all mutually exclusive, encompass locations over a range of 2,500 miles in longitude and 900 miles in latitude, spreading over 1.8 million square miles (over half the area of the continental United States).

Last, we come to the category of other theories, which includes some truly extraordinary Amelia Earhart lore. I like to refer to the group of us (myself included) who have pursued the quest for Amelia (or her aircraft) as "Ameliacs," though some deserve the obsessive overtone of the moniker more than others.

The best known of this genre is the incredible story of Irene Craigmile Bolam. As Ric Gillespie says, this one "raises the bar for extraordinary claims." The tale began in 1965 when Joseph Gervais, a retired Air Force officer, met Bolam at a Long Island, New York, cocktail party and became convinced of her resemblance to Earhart. Obsessed with this revelation, he teamed with author Joe Klaas to publish the book *Amelia Earhart Lives* (McGraw-Hill, 1970), claiming that she was, indeed, Amelia Earhart. The gist of the story is that Earhart was captured by the Japanese, but later repatriated under an assumed identity, sort of like a "witness protection program" caper. Bolam not only denied this, but sued, and the publisher withdrew the book. Undaunted, Klaas and screenwriter Tod Swindell have endeavored to prove their point by forensic analysis. After Ms. Bolam died in 1982, there were a number of studies commissioned to "prove" the physical connection. In 2002, an Amelia Earhart symposium was held in Oakland, California, that was a "Who's Who" of conspiracy theory Ameliacs. Featured with individual lectures in the program were Gervais, Klaas, and Swindell. Jon Thompson (veteran of the

2002 Nauticos expedition) volunteered to attend the conference, and was moved to ask how to account for the several-inch difference in height between Earhart and Bolam. The answer: Ms. Earhart's femurs were shortened, as "it was common in those days to change identities with such surgical procedures." Impressed by the forensic "evidence," another Air Force officer, Rollin Reineck, entered the fray and published a book entitled *Amelia Earhart Survived* (Paragon, 2003). There is an interesting summary of these claims on the Tighar Web site. Enough noise was made that the National Geographic Society arranged for a criminal forensic expert to study photographs of the two women in 2006; he concluded that they were not the same person, which did not surprise most of us.

Also straying from the mainstream are those who claim they can deduce the fate of Amelia and even the location of her plane by thought alone. The reader may not be surprised to learn that I have received mail from more than one group with similar claims. One is called Psi Tech, and they claim to be "Founders of the Remote Viewing Industry." This may be the most credible claim on their Web site, http://www.remoteviewing.com/. If one is willing to wade though some of the material on this site, it seems that through the techniques of "remote viewing," one can link directly to the "collective unconscious," also referred to as "the Matrix." Through this process (for which Psi Tech offers training courses), one can solve just about any mystery.

Apparently, this has already been done (or can be hired to be done) for Amelia's last flight. The results are on the Web site . . . the reader is welcome to launch an expedition to go search there.

Finally, we turn to one of my favorite sources of current events, the *Weekly World News*. The February 20, 2001, edition reported "AMELIA EARHART FOUND ALIVE!" The cover featured a picture of an elderly woman wearing goggles, said to be 103 years old and living on a tiny island in the South Pacific. An interview with an Australian treasure hunter who took a polygraph for the *News*, but promised not to disclose Ms. Earhart's whereabouts, revealed that she had a "spiritual reawakening," and was happy to live out her days as a hermit.

In an apparently blatant self-contradiction, the same periodical published a story in the July 16, 2002, issue reporting "AMELIA EARHART'S PLANE LANDS . . . WITH A SKELETON AT THE CONTROLS!" According to this account, the plane landed unexpectedly on Howland Island a few days before, witnessed by twenty-five "rock-solid eyewitnesses" who happened to be present, along with military personnel, on the otherwise uninhabited U.S. Fish and Wildlife Preserve. The plane was piloted by a skeleton, the skull of which can be seen clearly in the cockpit on the included photo. The plane was whisked away to "an undisclosed location." Accompanying this article, on the front page, is "Tragedy at 20,000 Feet: Dwarf Stuck in Toilet 2 Hours!"

So, I end this Interlude with a recap of the relevant principles that should guide us in our quest for objectivity:

*Consensus about the wrong answer is still wrong.*

And:

*False associations are easier to swallow than logical reasoning.*

On the other hand, it is true:

*In a disaster, it is the improbable that is most likely.*

So, I say to all the Ameliacs, "Keep searching!"

The research vessel *R/V Davidson* during operations in the central Pacific in 2002. The 175-foot-long ship would be the home of the search team for seven weeks at sea. (Photo by Jonathan Blair, courtesy Nauticos)

The NOMAD sonar sled was built by Nauticos and can image a mile-wide swath of ocean floor down to a depth of 20,000 feet. (Photos by Jonathan Blair, courtesy Nauticos)

Mike Davis (left) and Shawn Dann, working on NOMAD. Days from technical support or spare parts, the crew must be as self-sufficient as possible. (Photo by Jonathan Blair, courtesy Nauticos)

Safety drills were a regular part of the ship's routine. Julie Nelson enjoys the aftermath of an exercise with an impromptu flare display. (Photo by Jonathan Blair, courtesy Nauticos)

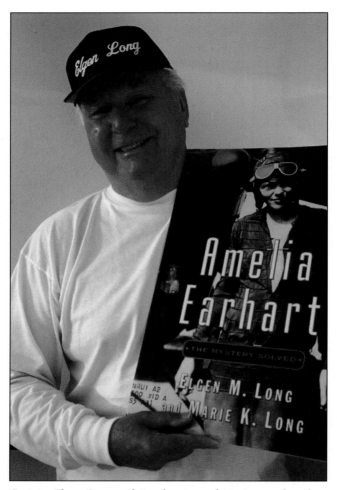

Captain Elgen Long, pilot, adventurer, historian, and author. Elgen was a great shipmate and key source of research, advice, and experience during the expeditions. (Photo by Jonathan Blair, courtesy Nauticos)

Captain Joe Litchfield, First Mate on the *Davidson* in 2002 and Mate on the *Mt. Mitchell* in 2006, pictured ashore at the Salty Dog Saloon near his home in Homer, Alaska. About the search for Amelia, Joe says, "It just got into my soul." (Photo by author)

In 2006, the expedition sailed on the R/V *Mt. Mitchell*. Longer that the *Davidson* at 231 feet, she was able to easily accommodate our crew and 80 tons of Oceaneering search equipment. She is seen here just off shore of Honolulu. (Photo courtesy Elgen Long)

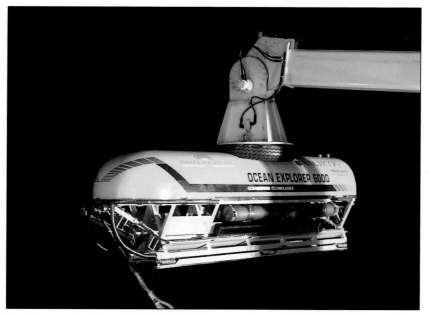

The Oceaneering Ocean Explorer imaged over 650 square-nautical-miles of ocean floor in 2006. (Photo by author, courtesy Waitt Institute for Discovery)

Why are these women smiling? From the pier at Honolulu, Lynn Jourdan (right) and Charlotte Vick bid farewell to the crew for the seven-week expedition in 2006. (Photo by author, courtesy Waitt Institute for Discovery)

Operations Assistant Bethany Jourdan (left) compares equipment with Student-at-Sea Marika Lorraine just prior to departure from Honolulu in 2006. (Photo by author, courtesy Waitt Institute for Discovery)

Sue and Jeff Morris view the scene on the aft deck with concern as repairs are made to critical equipment during the 2006 expedition. (Photo by Bethany Jourdan, courtesy Waitt Institute for Discovery)

Rain or shine, day or night, operations proceeded around the clock. It was with particular urgency that the sonar was recovered at the end of the 2006 expedition to begin an emergency medical evacuation. Larry Tyler focuses on the job at hand. (Photo by Bethany Jourdan, courtesy Waitt Institute for Discovery)

Teacher-at-Sea Carla-Rae Smith mans her station despite rough weather and a bout of sea sickness. The ever-rolling decks led to the sage advice, "One hand for you, one hand for the ship!" (Photo by author, courtesy Waitt Institute for Discovery)

Third Mate and Medical Officer Amanda Becker was put to the test during a medical emergency in 2006, and proved to be a real asset to the crew. (Photo by Tom Vinson, courtesy Waitt Institute for Discovery)

The Education Team films a demonstration of the shrinking of Styrofoam cups when exposed to sea pressure. (Photo by author, courtesy Waitt Institute for Discovery)

The control room on board the *Mt. Mitchell* in 2006. This station was continuously manned during search operations. (Photo by author, courtesy Waitt Institute for Discovery)

Rod Blocksome conducts an all-night "DXpedition" on Tarawa in 2006. (Photo by Tom Vinson, courtesy Waitt Institute for Discovery)

Tom Vinson coaches the team in preparation for a transit of the International Space Station and communications with astronaut Bill McArthur. (Photo by author, courtesy Waitt Institute for Discovery)

A happy islander displays Tarawan white octopus during our visit in 2006. (Photo by Sue Morris, courtesy Waitt Institute for Discovery)

The guns are now silent, but they were deadly to the invading U.S. Marines in November of 1943. Other relics of the battle that cost nearly 3,500 American lives, as well as those of over ten times as many Japanese soldiers and civilians, can be seen around the island. (Photo by Marika Lorraine, courtesy Waitt Institute for Discovery)

The tropical beauty of Tarawa was marred by waste and sewage evident throughout populated areas. (Photo by Tom Vinson, courtesy Waitt Institute for Discovery)

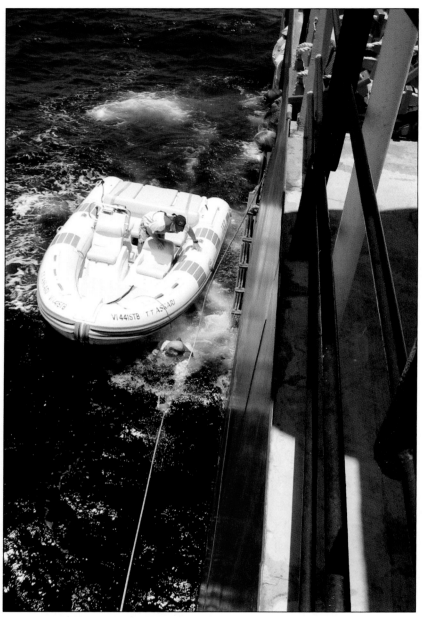

Man overboard! A crewman from the skiff of the *Askari* plunges into the sea during an attempt to transfer personnel in rough weather. (Photo by Sue Morris, courtesy Waitt Institute for Discovery)

Identical twins Sherrie Hubler (Assistant Cook, left) and Shirley Mira (Housekeeper), natives of Palau, were beloved members of the 2006 crew. But their sudden seizures led to an aborted mission and dramatic medevac. (Photo by Marika Lorraine, courtesy Waitt Institute for Discovery)

The twins were brought ashore at Tarawa for evacuation via air ambulance. They continued to experience seizures at random intervals and durations throughout the ordeal. (Photo by author, courtesy Waitt Institute for Discovery)

"Doc" Pam Geddis leaves the *Mt. Mitchell* to accompany the twins during their evacuation. (Photo by author, courtesy Waitt Institute for Discovery)

The ever-present cloud deck and endless horizon treated the *Mt. Mitchell* crew to beautiful Pacific sunrises and sunsets. (Photo by Carla-Rae Smith, courtesy Waitt Institute for Discovery)

The author "shoots the sun" while Operations Manager Captain Spence King looks on. In 2006, we sailed from Tarawa to Honolulu using celestial navigation techniques. (Photo by Rod Blocksome, courtesy Waitt Institute for Discovery)

# Expedition 2006

April 5, 2006; Wednesday, about 2 AM EST.
Cape Porpoise, Maine.

Lynn Jourdan kept the phone by her bedside while the expedition was under way. She knew from hard-won experience that a problem could occur at any time, day or night. She wanted to be able to help if she could. The phone jangled, waking her from a sound sleep.

It was Charlotte Vick, calling from Honolulu. She just blurted it out. She was frantic, but clear—Charlotte is always clear and direct in a crisis. Two people on the ship were sick, having seizures. A medical evacuation was under way. She was trying to call back to the ship, but was getting no response. She knew nothing more, but needed an alternative ship contact number from Lynn.

Lynn was startled, frightened, and beginning to panic. She had more questions than Charlotte could answer. Charlotte promised to call back as soon as she knew more.

Seven hours earlier, April 4, 2006; Tuesday, 12:18 PM YST.
Near Howland Island.

The equipment was performing well, and the team was working together. Morale was high. We had searched far and deep for the elusive Electra, and though our toil had not yet been rewarded, we were confident. I hung up the radio telephone, having just given a status report, and getting the go-ahead for the next phase of the search. Our team knew that competence, diligence, and patience were usually rewarded, eventually.

I sat back and took a deep breath, considering how to break the good news—bad news to the team. We can keep searching (good), but we can't go home yet (bad). Spence appeared in front of me, breaking my train of thought. I had never seen such a serious look on his face. Spence said, quietly but firmly, "You are needed in the women's berthing. We have an emergency."

He didn't know much yet himself. I was on my feet in an instant, heading for the ladder.

Down four levels, "Girl's Town" was one of the few spaces I had rarely visited, in deference to the privacy of the residents. But I knew exactly where it was, and flew down the ladders. My heart raced, but I knew nothing, so I didn't speculate. I would find out soon enough. I reached the C Deck, and looked down the passageway. Through the door into one of the bunk rooms, I could see a cluster of figures on the deck. I hurried down the passageway.

About 2:30 AM EST. Cape Porpoise, Maine.
Lynn sat in bed waiting for Charlotte to call back. She held her little pet Sheltie, Luna, so tightly she squeaked. Two crew members with seizures . . . why two? Could it be toxic fumes or a deadly virus, and could it be contained? The ship was days from real help.

Two crew members—who were they? Would there be others?

Lynn waited for the phone to ring.

Insanity: doing the same thing over and over
again and expecting different results.

—Attributed to Albert Einstein

Chapter 8

# The Expedition Begins . . . Again

Lines were cast off, waves, hugs, and tearful goodbyes were rendered, and in general there was much excitement and fanfare as the Research Vessel (R/V) *Mt. Mitchell* left Pier 19 in Honolulu to begin the second Nauticos Amelia Earhart search adventure.

An hour later, the ship returned.

A nasty stuck rudder forced *departus interruptus* on the frustrated crew. For several hours, we waited while repairs were made. Then we waited for the Coast Guard inspection. Then we waited for the union line-handlers to make an appearance. Thanks to cooperative agents and harbor masters, we finally ran out of things to wait for.

The second departure was with less fanfare, although with more success.

So it began (again) on the morning of February 28, 2006. An inauspicious start to what had already been a trying and frustrating endeavor. It had been almost four years since we returned from the first trip, and not a week passed during that time that we were not in some way working to launch the second mission.

Part of the problem, of course, was funding. But a lot had happened since we returned in April 2002, which offered delays and distractions, diverting our focus from returning to sea as soon as possible. Primary among these diversions was the reality that we had a business to operate, a staff of fifty to keep gainfully employed, and a lot of serious work to do for the U.S. Navy and our other Nauticos customers. Having expended over $400,000 of company cash and dedicated significant time from key staff members to the project, it was imperative that we make sure important balls were not dropped and people were busy on tasks at hand. In spite of the fact that people had been at sea for many weeks and needed a vacation with some time at home, the team turned-to and made sure we pitched right in with those who had been left behind.

Our investment in the Amelia project was significant, and while we came home empty-handed, the publicity was positive and good for business. Our family and staff welcomed us home with fanfare. We didn't have time to reflect on failure.

We also had to wrangle with Ocean Services over the issue of fuel. We were promised a ship with sufficient capacity to conduct the chartered mission, and the documentation made available to us validated that commitment. Unfortunately, owing to modifications of tanks on the *Davidson*, and probably some internal disagreement about tank capacities, we did not depart Honolulu with sufficient fuel, requiring the side trip to Tarawa. This was not an entirely straightforward issue, as no one knew exactly how much fuel we would consume during our very unique deep-ocean survey operations. After some back-and-forth, we negotiated a settlement that satisfied all parties. We promised ourselves we would ask even more questions about fuel in the future.

I tried to visit and brief as many of our investors and sponsors as possible. A number of them were local to our Maryland office, but others were scattered about the country. Trips to San Francisco, Seattle, and Los Angeles covered some bases and gave me a chance to follow up with some of the Hollywood contacts who were following our progress. Of course, their enthusiasm had waned dramatically compared to what it was before our departure. I remember one of the executives at a well-known media organization asked as we sat down to brief him, "Well, what happened? Did anyone lose a limb?" While I had been working to keep everybody safe, some parties were apparently hoping for dramatic injuries to add spice to the story!

We also briefed the staff at National Geographic, who were disappointed with the outcome, but promised to make a mini-documentary anyway. We actually produced our own short piece, thanks to Jonathan Blair, that told the story of the 2002 expedition quite well. This was helpful in attracting additional funding, and was a video I was proud to show.

Thanks to all of this activity and some other exciting business opportunities, 2002 was a blur of travel for me. California (twice), Hawaii, Mississippi (where the Naval Oceanographic Office is located), Japan (for a conference), Seattle, Memphis, Kansas City, Seattle and California (again), and even Cyprus in the Mediterranean! Folded into all of this was an exciting undertaking. Prior to departing on the Amelia expedition, we had received some overtures about selling the business. Having led Nauticos for sixteen years, and struggling to manage growth and success, often without adequate capital, this was an attractive opportunity. After returning from the 2002 mission, over the ensuing year we negotiated a merger of the Nauticos Corporation with the publicly traded company Oceaneering International, which took place in April 2003. Terms of the deal included keeping all of the staff at their existing positions and salaries, with our general manager (and veteran of the 2002 expedition), Julie Nelson, remaining in charge of the group. For my part, I was able to form a new company, Nauticos LLC, and retain the rights to the Amelia Earhart program as well as other "Ocean Discovery" projects. With enough cash to pay off debts and investors, and move to our new home in Maine, I set about to raise expedition funds to continue the search for Amelia.

Things then moved along pretty quickly. I had some funds earmarked for a new expedition, and some commitments from partners and investors of the 2002 trip. Part of the agreement with Oceaneering was that, for a period of time, Nauticos LLC would be required to hire them for any ocean expedition (essentially, using my old team supplemented by the resources of the bigger company). In return, they offered a discount on the service. We found a suitable ship in Seattle (the R/V *Mt. Mitchell*, another former NOAA vessel). This ship was newly refitted, and the owner, Global Seas, was eager to put it in service. An excellent price was negotiated. When I added up the available funds and the rock-bottom price of $1.3 million for the mission, I had a shortfall of about $500,000.

Again, to the road: California, Florida, New Orleans, Maryland . . . and on the phone, looking for support. Over the years, my list of people we had talked to in some serious manner about this project had grown to nearly two hundred, and had ranged from movie stars, to their agents, to billionaires. Everyone was interested, and my opportunities to meet with fascinating people were some of the pleasures of the endeavor. Few, of course, would actually invest in what was perceived to be a risky program, but along the way we had garnered a fair amount of support. I knew it was only a matter of time and persistence.

During 2003, in October, we held a project technical review in Cedar Rapids with the Collins Amateur Radio Club (CARC) team, Crawford MacKeand, and Nauticos. Our two-day session covered probability analyses, antenna models, electronic noise estimates, radio sea-wave propagation, and other technical topics; we also discussed operational plans for the next expedition and educational opportunities. As always, Rockwell Collins and CARC were wonderful hosts, and the session was very organized and productive. We left Iowa feeling certain we were on the right track, and determined to pull together the funding for the second expedition.

At the end of the month, the break I was looking for materialized. One of our supporters with the means to help was a billionaire founder of a Fortune 500 corporation. (To respect his privacy, I will refer to him as "Sam.") We had many conversations prior to the 2002 mission, and he had referred me to a colleague who became an ardent supporter and investor. Although Sam did not throw any financial backing behind the 2002 mission, he wished me luck and followed our progress. I took heart in his comment to me of January 2000, "My enthusiasm remains boundless," in spite of his reluctance to commit any tangible help. In October 2003, I sent him a letter describing the circumstances, our needs, and asked for a chance to meet. He responded immediately, and barely a week later Jon Thompson and I were briefing Sam in his corporate office.

When we left the meeting, Sam shook my hand, and said he was convinced that, if anyone could find Amelia Earhart's plane, "Dave Jourdan could." Jon and I were elated, and we channeled our enthusiasm into work on detailed plans for the Amelia Earhart exhibition that we hoped to launch sometime in the near future (once we'd found the Electra).

Sam knew we needed $500,000, and he proposed that this be provided to the project in the form of a sponsorship, with advertising and promotional benefits going to his corporation for the duration of the program, including future exhibitions. This turned out to be a lot more complicated than I expected, but I was willing to do what was necessary to make it work. Counting on these funds, we started making plans for a January 2004 mission.

At this point, Sam himself bowed out of the process, and, as was proper, turned it over to his corporate staff to negotiate and execute. Unfortunately, the corporate staff did not share Sam's enthusiasm, and although we entered negotiations and I did what I could to accommodate their desires, it became clear that the corporate staff was trying to push me to the point that I would back away from the deal myself. At least, that's what it seemed to me. Time passed, and the schedule slipped; by January we were still in discussion and I had moved the departure date to the end of February. We were in danger of losing the ship to another prospective job. At one point, I wondered whether the company really wanted to complete the deal, at which time the corporate board held a meeting and decided, no, they really didn't. I tried to appeal to Sam personally, who had not been involved in any of the proceedings. On February 3, he replied, "I delegated this analysis and decision to our Marketing professionals and while I do not know the details, I support the position they have taken and do not believe there is a satisfactory mutual opportunity." I could understand his position, but I was *very* disappointed. With mobilization less than four weeks away and trucks shipping equipment to Seattle due to roll in barely two weeks, I had no alternative but to shut down operations.

Disappointed, but undaunted, our team picked up the pieces and set about to find alternative sources of support. I decided to pursue some new approaches that would not only support the mission financially, but also achieve some of the media and educational objectives of the program. That summer, we decided to try an "Internet auction" to raise a portion of the expedition funding and support the educational and science components of the mission. We used eBay to advertise a few tourist slots on the mission, available for sale. The packages were complete with airfare, lodging at the Royal Hawaiian Hotel on Waikiki Beach, private staterooms, and other special attention. We set the price high enough that it would make a difference if anyone bid. As it turned out, no one was willing, and the auction fizzled. Later that year, I was approached by a media company interested in making a film about Amelia and the search. They convinced me they could raise expedition funding, as well as support all of the media and educational objectives, and we entered into an agreement in February 2005. This, too, fizzled, as the media company was unable to deliver. In June 2005 that deal was terminated, just in time for the call from Thomas Lee of the Waitt Institute for Discovery (WID) on July 7.

At first, it just seemed like yet another call from someone interested in what we were doing. I am always polite to callers, and usually send them a packet of information, just as a courtesy. This call seemed innocuous . . . until I Googled the name. I had never heard of Ted Waitt, but his name popped right up as founder of Gateway Computers, and through his foundation he was judged to be one of the top philanthropists in the country. His Web site promised support of a wide range of scientific and educational endeavors, with emphasis on exploration and historical discovery. One of the mottos was "Helping good people do good things." I felt that I had finally met a partner that would share my values and had the wherewithal to back the endeavor.

Lee, as it turned out, was a summer intern of WID, and was following up on a "word-of-mouth" referral. I immediately sent a package of information about the project, and was invited to visit their offices in La Jolla, California, on July 21. There I met Ted himself, as well as the president of the Institute, John Heubusch. My note of thanks for the meeting said, "I admit I was not prepared for the scope of Ted's vision, but the more it sinks in, the more exciting it seems. I would greatly welcome the opportunity to help realize this, Amelia and beyond." Among our ambitions at Nauticos was to leverage a successful Amelia Earhart discovery to create opportunities for other exploration ventures. This promised to be a big step in that direction.

The process of due diligence began, and I shared with WID all of our business plans, analysis results, operational plans, and 2002 mission results, all under the umbrella of an intellectual property confidentiality agreement. I met with Heubusch at the beginning of August. I made sure he understood that, although we were keen to support educational and scientific activities, we also aimed at generating revenue from the project to pay for the work done so far and to fund future activities. John assured me that we would work to satisfy all of the stakeholders in the venture, and that they, too, would seek income from the project in order to fund future research.

The Institute would plan to fund the next mission, and ensuing ones. In exchange, Waitt wanted to control all of the media rights and activities, under the framework of an agreement providing for certain rights to Nauticos. Impressed with Ted's vision, promises, and resources, I was more than willing to become a part of this program. I was even prepared to, as I stated in a message to John, "subordinate my vision to Ted's, as I believe in what I have heard and can accomplish much more as a part of your team than I can as the leader of my own. Don't have any concern at all about my loyalty to the cause or need for personal publicity. . . . I always promoted the team above myself."

As the weeks passed, our team enlightened the Institute people on the roots of the project, the marketing, exhibition, and media prospects we had developed, as well as the science and educational goals we were pursuing. I compiled a detailed listing of all the stakeholders, including investors, sponsors, and volunteers. I described the extensive archive we possessed, representing over three decades of research by Elgen and Marie. I answered questions about competition, other Earhart theories, and made available all of the legal research we had conducted over the years. As August closed, our team had drafted an operations plan, and was working with John on a business agreement.

By the end of October 2005, our agreement was signed, funding started to flow, and we set our sights on a February 2006 mission launch. Besides the obvious primary goal to locate the Electra, our seventy-eight-page operations plan listed a number of subordinate objectives. We were keen to improve our techniques for deep-ocean mapping, including the experimental Bat Turn of 2002; we planned to develop a state-of-the-art sonar analysis laboratory; and we would develop a communications system to take advantage of the latest in global satellite communications technologies.

Besides the technical aspects of the mission, we would also establish a public relations program to be prepared for a successful outcome, develop an education program anchored by a teacher and student at sea, and fully document the mission for future media outlets. I was frustrated in my desire to share the progress of the exploration through live Web casts and daily dispatches, as Ted and John were keen to keep all under wraps until we had some news to report. I was also unable to justify a science project, as the Institute was unwilling to complicate matters further in an already challenging program. Satisfied that we had established a credible program with more than enough to do, I pledged our team to do our best to make the mission a success.

Having come to agreement and set our goals, I was eager to introduce Elgen and key members of the team. So, in December, a group of us trooped out to La Jolla and met with Ted. Our plan was to present to him the basis of our analysis, and why we wanted to search where we were proposing. Ted met a number of us, including Elgen, Spence (our operations manager for the mission), Jeff Morris (our lead sonar analyst), and Sue Morris. Ted gave us a stirring speech about his vision, and listened to our presentation.

Spence continued to refine our operations plan. I was very proud of the final product, which I believe was one of the most thorough and informative documents ever produced for such a mission. It included a brief background of Amelia's last flight, an overview of our analysis and 2002 efforts, clearly stated objectives, a summary of organizational participants, command and control protocols, manning, and responsibilities. With so many participants, many with no at-sea experience, it was very important to make the plans, tasks, and communications very clear. The plan also discussed shipboard safety, ship's routine, facilities, schedule, and travel advice. A short "primer" on deep-ocean survey was included, as well as an archaeological "research design" for the investigation of the aircraft wreck site, should we find it. Spec sheets, confidentiality agreements, even packing lists rounded out this valuable document. We printed copies for all participants, and made it "required reading" for anyone working on the project.

Meanwhile, a problem was brewing. In August 2005, Hurricane Katrina devastated the Gulf Coast, including extensive damage to offshore installations, pipelines, and oil rigs. Suddenly, the demand for vessels that could carry ocean salvage equipment, and the equipment itself, skyrocketed. The economics that favored a low-end price the year before were blown away with the storm. Though we were conservative in our initial budget projections with the Institute, the pricing for the prospective 2006 operation was considerably higher. The budget for the mission ballooned to over $2 million, half for the ship.

However, WID was willing to foot the bill, and these concerns were relegated to distractions. It was time to focus on the task at hand: launching the 2006 expedition. In order to meet a scheduled departure from Honolulu on February 28, we needed to mobilize the ship in Seattle for a February 15 departure. That meant rolling the equipment out of Oceaneering's warehouse in Maryland at the beginning of February. So we had just a few weeks to make all final charter and contract arrangements, as well as personal preparations for up to eight weeks away from home and work.

There were many similarities to the 2002 mission mobilization, as the ocean search equipment had to be trucked from Maryland to Seattle for installation on a research vessel there, followed by a transit to Hawaii where the balance of the charter team would join up. In 2006, however, things were *much* more complicated. Most important, Nauticos was not really in charge, as the Institute wrote the contracts with Global Seas (the ship company) and Oceaneering (the equipment company). Our operations manager, Spence, generally held sway in all operational matters, but was always in danger of being overruled. We were also bringing more equipment and more people. The Oceaneering suite included a sonar system called Ocean Explorer, which was a bit more elaborate than NOMAD; also, they were bringing a Remotely Operated Vehicle (ROV, also known as a robotic vehicle) with cameras, lights, and manipulators (robot arms) called Magellan. This vehicle was the size of a small car and needed its own 11,000-meter cable spool, maintenance van, and support equipment. The *Mt. Mitchell* could not accommodate all of this gear on one deck, so a multilevel installation was devised that required a custom-built $20,000 sheave to redirect the run of the deep-ocean cable. By the time all was installed, eighty tons of equipment rested on the stern of the *Mt. Mitchell*.

A team of eight technicians from Oceaneering International accompanied the search equipment. Oceaneering's roots are in the offshore oil and gas industry, and the main office of this worldwide corporation is in Houston, Texas. A division called Oceaneering Technologies (OTECH), located in Maryland, develops and operates unique marine systems, and has over thirty years of subsea search and recovery experience. Notable OTECH projects include work on the RMS *Titanic*, salvage of the Civil War submarine *Hunley*, and recovery of Gus Grissom's space capsule *Liberty Bell 7*.

This Oceaneering operation was self-contained, with an integrated display and analysis lab in a deck-mounted van. Oceaneering company rules did not allow our Nauticos team to operate that gear, so we decided to take the data feed from the Oceaneering van and set up a separate analysis lab in one of the ship's spaces. This allowed us to have better access to the information streaming up from the ocean floor, and employ more sophisticated computer tools in the analysis. But it was an added complication and, in the end, more people were involved.

One notable absence on this trip would be Tom Dettweiler, accomplished ocean explorer, sonar analyst, and operations manager. Tom had left Oceaneering during the first year after Nauticos Corporation was sold to the bigger company, and in a surprise move took a position with Odyssey Marine Exploration, a treasure-hunting company based in Florida. The lure of gold, and (probably more important) the opportunity to lead an operations team pursuing a rigorous at-sea program was enough to attract Tom away from the stable but conservative Oceaneering. Fortunately, we had two capable substitutes: Spence King and Jeff Morris. Spence had the experience, talent, and leadership to serve as operations manager, and I had every confidence in him. Tom had recruited Jeff many years before to assist him in his work with the U.S. Navy, and became Jeff's mentor as the young underwater archaeologist honed his skills as a sonar analyst and helped develop new computer tools for display and processing. Jeff was also an accomplished historical researcher and assisted Nauticos with gathering background on many projects, suggesting new ones, and supporting the Renav analysts in their work. Along the way, Jeff and my sister Sue developed a relationship that led to marriage in October 2000.

There were others who had not been on the 2002 mission. We now had an education team on board, including a teacher (Carla-Rae Smith) and a student (Marika Weiner). Carla-Rae was teaching physical science and math to sixth graders when she got a call asking if she'd join our team, replacing our original candidate Sallie Smith, who had to stay home with her ailing mother. Sallie had hoped to go on the 2002 mission, but media restrictions and lack of funding forced us to curtail that effort. Despite the double disappointment, she continues to support our program. We missed Sallie, but were extremely pleased with her replacement. With a masters in chemical engineering, an MBA, and a masters in Education, Carla-Rae was more than qualified to teach eighth-grade science, as well as to be our "Dean" of SEA School. The latter assignment earned her the delightfully multiple-punned moniker, "SEA-Rae." Her main mission objective was to gather materials to help the public experience our adventure and to teach the science behind it all.

Marika Lorraine Weiner had this project in her blood. As Elgen's granddaughter she had heard stories about Amelia for as long as she could remember. She had just earned a bachelor's degree in journalism, and so we considered her qualified to represent the student perspective. When Marika returned home from our expedition, she would resume her job at KRCG in Columbia, Missouri, as their investigative reporter.

WID sent management representatives John Heubusch and Pat Sullivan (who was a former Secret Service agent for presidents beginning with Nixon, rising to detail leader for presidents Bush and Clinton). At our suggestion, the Institute also sent two other members of their organization to help them gain experience in ocean operations. Laura Walters was an experienced sailor and diver, with a background in archaeology, who was slated to fill a number of roles for the Institute, including "Historical Coordinator," deck hand, and dive assistant. Her eclectic résumé included performing as an "aerial ballerina" for a circus troupe, a qualification that we could not figure out how to apply aboard the *Mt. Mitchell*. Mike Dessner had experience with the fishing industry in Alaska, and was to work as a sonar operator for other WID missions. We welcomed Laura and Mike on board, and assigned them sonar watches and other shipboard tasks to help prepare them for a future in ocean exploration.

We had been seeking a volunteer doctor to come along, just in case; at WID's invitation, Dr. Pam Geddis filled that bill. Pam's medical specialty was orthopedics and neurology, and she performed pre-operative analysis for patients as well as nerve studies. She had also founded a medical research company that was testing new diabetes therapies. But it was her early interest in marine biology, her love of SCUBA diving, and her adventurous spirit that led her to join our expedition. No stranger to travel, Pam was born in Okinawa, Japan, and had lived in Hong Kong and Singapore, and had visited the pyramids, the Serengeti, and Calcutta, all before the age of twelve! It is a rare luxury to have a physician on board a ship—even my Navy submarine with a crew of 150 normally went to sea for three-month patrols with a corpsman and an instruction manual for minor surgeries. So we were delighted to have Pam, even if "neurology" was not the kind of medial emergency we considered to be of top concern.

"Doc" Pam, as it turned out, had no idea what was in store for her.

With all the additions, our ship's population swelled from thirty-four (on the *Davidson* in 2002) to forty-three, including the ship's crew. Fortunately, the 231-foot long *Mt. Mitchell*, significantly larger than the *Davidson*, was ample and could easily accommodate us all.

Somehow, through the efforts of many under the leadership of Spence, equipment, supplies, and people converged on Seattle, and the *Mt. Mitchell*. Mobilization was an intense burst of activity, a critical first step in the expedition. The sands of time began to fall through the glass, and money began to flow from the budget as ship and equipment daily charges mounted. Neither time nor expenses would stop until the ship returned to be demobilized, some weeks hence; in the meanwhile, all time spent in port and transit was overhead. The event was an exercise in time management, logistics, and team building, as it was the first chance for the ship's crew and charter team members to work together. There was the added complication of shipyard worker coordination, dock facility issues, and availability of cranes and materials. All had to come together very quickly, and all took place in an industrial environment that included the risk of injury to equipment and people.

I visited the ship on February 13 with Gary Bane and Jon Thompson, and found matters well in hand. Cutters, welders, riggers, electricians, and carpenters had been hard at work making room for twenty-foot container vans, cable spools, winches, and cranes. Everything was set in place, wires and hoses run, and testing was in progress. A new addition to the team was my twenty-five-year-old daughter Bethany, who was serving as assistant to Spence (as well as assistant to the media and education teams). Her degree in media arts and excellent organizational skills were helpful in this job, and I was proud to see her up to its complex logistics. She exhibited a work ethic that I had not previously had the opportunity to observe in action. It is a risk to involve a family member in a project, and I was relieved to see that Bethany, like my sister Susan, did not disappoint in any way.

I returned home to Maine to make my own preparations, and was happy to receive a call from Spence on February 15 that the ship was under way, right on schedule. A couple of members of the Oceaneering team were accompanying the vessel during the nine-day transit to Honolulu, to make sure all was ready for the mission.

With the important tasks in good hands, I turned to some last-minute issues that always seem to dog the start of any expedition. On February 16, just a week before I was to fly to Hawaii, I finally made contact with the media team that would accompany us. I wanted to have a chance to choose, or at least meet, the camera crew who would be on board, as I had found in the past that media folks tend to set themselves apart from the rest of the group as though they are outside observers, and this can be a challenge in such close quarters. In a previous expedition, a camera person and a still photographer got into a fight about who-was-in-the-way-of-whose shot, right in the middle of a vehicle recovery! Such a distraction in the middle of handling a ton of swinging metal on a pitching deck can lead to injury or worse. So it was important to me to know who was coming, if they had at-sea experience, and discuss the requirements in advance.

John Heubusch had told me the names of those they had selected two weeks earlier, but I had not been able to contact them or learn much about them. Adam Geiger and Colette Beaudry were a husband-wife team, recently married, and, according to their Web site, had worked together on a number of projects involving sea life. I was not able to meet them before we left, but I had a nice talk with Adam, and tried to cover some of mission requirements and issues of concern on the phone. I wished him a good trip, and would see him in Honolulu.

A few of us arrived in Honolulu on February 24, in advance of the rest of the team. The small cost in extra preparation is normally repaid handsomely in a short turn-around once the ship arrives . . . every extra hour the ship spends in port is wasted. So we try to have everybody present, all remaining supplies staged, docking arrangements confirmed, and any maintenance needs identified by the ship during transit addressed before the ship arrives.

Ted Waitt was not planning to accompany us. Rather than being restricted to the research vessel for the duration, cut off from attending to his numerous other projects, he preferred to embark on the motor yacht *Askari* (docked at an island closer to our operations area) and meet us at sea. However, he still wanted to see us off. He kindly offered to host a departure dinner in Honolulu. To arrange this, we engaged Charlotte Vick, friend, business associate, and longtime resident of Hawaii. She organized lodging and a departure event at the famous Royal Hawaiian Hotel on Waikiki Beach, the very place that Amelia Earhart stayed when she was in Honolulu. Because of her connections, she was able to arrange rates competitive with other local hotels, which turned out to be lucky since we were there several days longer than expected. The main reason for this is that Ted could not be there until February 27, so we planned the dinner for that evening, with departure early the next morning.

All of our efforts to keep a tight schedule in order not to waste time and money paid off. We had some concerns about unusually severe winter weather in the Pacific Northwest that might delay the *Mitchell's* ten-day transit from Seattle to Honolulu. But the ship arrived on schedule, unhindered by the weather, and sat idle in Honolulu for a few days while we waited for our scheduled departure. This made last-minute preparations a bit less frantic, gave us a chance to conduct ship tours (an uncommon luxury), and visit with local friends. My friend and Oahu native Ke Kai Kealoha dropped by the ship and presented me with a beautiful maile lei, a type traditionally reserved for memorable occasions. (I note that "ke kai" is Hawaiian for "deep sea," a beautiful and appropriate name for a well-wisher of a deep-sea expedition!) The pace picked up on Sunday, February 26, as the rest of the team began to arrive and personnel issues required attention. Everyone was cheerful, helpful, and excited to be on the team.

Our dinner at the Royal Hawaiian was historic and nostalgic, thanks to some great organizing by Charlotte and Jon Thompson. The hotel has almost religiously maintained its ambiance as a *grande dame* of the industry with the 1930s feel throughout the grand lobby and dining rooms. Charlotte hired the florist, who had been around since the 1930s, to create period centerpieces of large pink roses and birds of paradise. The director of Hawaii Public Radio, Jeff Ilardi, provided a sound system and a custom-created rendition of 1930s music for the cocktail hour and after the dinner. Charlotte had a personal friend,

David Cornwell, create an amazing display in the form of a 1930s darkroom with photo images, borrowed from the Bishop Museum, hung by clothes pins on "drying" cords around the darkroom. On tables in the darkroom were artifacts from the period including a typewriter, books, and a writing desk.

Ted's flight was delayed because of headwinds, giving us an extra half-hour to enjoy cocktails and all of the memorabilia. Jon Thompson, acting as master of ceremonies, welcomed everyone, thanked Charlotte, then introduced Heubusch. As Jon recalled:

> He then introduced the Institute team members and the media team, and concluded with appropriate remarks before introducing Dave Jourdan. Dave made very impressive comments about, first, Elgen Long, and secondly, Ted Waitt and the long and difficult but fascinating road to tonight. He introduced the team members. He then asked Ted to say a few words.
>
> Ted gave a most heartfelt presentation on his passion for our project, and how he had searched the world for the finest team with the best qualifications for success. That team was here tonight and would accomplish this most difficult and historic mission. Everyone was very moved and flattered to be in the presence of a man who spoke to them in awe of their capabilities and with respect as individuals. I could tell why, even as a young man, he has achieved so much.

Also present was Bill Paupe, the U.S. Consulate for the Republic of Kiribati, whose island nation spanned the vast ocean reaches surrounding Howland Island and includes Tarawa, which, frankly, we hoped *not* to see again.

The exhausted travelers retired to our comfortable rooms at the Royal Hawaiian for the night. We savored them, as our ship would leave the next morning, and future nights would be spent with few amenities.

Operations Manager Spence set the tone for the new adventure before us in his message to the team, sent a few weeks earlier:

> Take in all lines, point your bow down Honolulu channel to open waters, and set a course southwest. The mission is under way. The outside world disappears. The only news of any consequence is now inside our lifelines. The pace is busy. Oceaneering is testing their equipment, the crew is tweaking ship systems for peak performance, the navigation team meets once again to finally choose the search area, watchstanders receive training, and the education team kicks off its program. All the planning, preparations, time and effort so far have come down to this. There is anticipation for the discovery. But keep this in mind. If this was easy, the Electra would already be on display in a museum somewhere.

The technical challenges of working on the bottom of the ocean are every bit equal to those of outer space. It's extremely difficult to build and operate equipment for these depths. The hydrostatic pressure on the sonar is about four tons per square inch. That's the pressure that a stack of ten *Mt. Mitchells* sitting on top of the sonar would exert. The equipment has to be rugged and heavy, and workmanship must be exacting. The technicians who maintain and operate these systems are extraordinary.

When we reach the survey site, the Ocean Explorer 6000 will be ready for launch. We will be met there by a second ship, M/V *Askari* with Ted Waitt embarked. Once the survey starts, *Mt. Mitchell* takes up its task of mowing the lawn. *Askari* assists by taking on all other tasks, such as running boats, doing errands, providing logistic support and personnel transfers. Many of you will be assigned to a watch section, where you will monitor the sonar picture, and track navigation of the ship on the survey lines.

The survey goes continuously, 24 hours per day and 7 days per week. You'll be on watch for 12 hours a day, with no days off. In a typical 12-hour watch, nothing will happen. The ship is moving at about 1.5 knots, barely a walking pace. It takes three hours to lower the sonar to the bottom. It takes four to six hours to turn the ship and sonar around to start the next run. It takes 12 to 18 hours to configure the deck for an ROV launch. Here is the challenge. Things happen slowly out there. It lends itself to boredom, fatigue and inattention. If the airplane is imaged, it's going to show up on your display as a very small target. Your total attention will be required to spot it. Each of you needs to bring an uncommon level of self discipline and motivation to work every day. From start to finish, that's what it's going to take to make this discovery.

So, each of you should think about what it takes to keep yourself at your top performance level for an extended period. You're in the big leagues now.

Warm regards, Spence

Don't wish me luck ... luck can be bad,
and we can do the job without it.
—Author

It's déjà vu all over again.
—Yogi Berra

# Lightning Strikes . . . Twice!

**February 28, 2006; Tuesday. Just Offshore Oahu.**

As evening fell, our view of the peaks of Oahu gave way to the twinkling lights of Honolulu. On our outbound transit, we had decided to perform an operational test of the Ocean Explorer sonar using a known target, in this case a submarine wreck about 1,200 feet deep. The launch went well, and the long-range sonar worked well, as did Jeff's processing lab. We found the sub! However, the high-resolution sonar, which we have configured as a "gapfiller" to see more clearly under the path of the vehicle, did not transmit. We decided to loiter in the area while troubleshooting and repairing the problem, then redeploy in the morning to try again. Assuming it works, we would also image a nearby aircraft. The few hours' delay would give us a valuable performance benchmark and a little operating experience. Then we will head southwest at transit speed.

**March 1; Wednesday. On Our Way, Finally!**
We redeployed at first light. Two of the technicians worked through the night to make repairs while the others caught up on much-needed rest. The test was successful, and by late morning we had everything out of the water and were on our way at twelve knots. The lights of Honolulu kept us company all night, but all sight of land vanished in short order. We expect to see no land until we return.

Meanwhile, we all worked to get our personal spaces squared away and our lab areas organized. Part of this process is "stowing for sea." Although we tried to do that before we left, there is no test like a rocking ship. We had to secure a number of items as the ship heaved through some modest swells, driven by a stormy wind. It is very hard to keep everything where it belongs, and to keep doors from slamming or to avoid bumping into unyielding steel flanges. The first real surprise came to me in the middle of the night. My bunk is right next to the door, which swings inward parallel to the bunk. In

# MERIDIAN PASSAGES
## Central Pacific Edition

**March 2, 2006**
*Volume XII, Number 2*

## Heading: Sou-West
### 1,600 nm to go

In this issue

**1,600 nm To Go**

**Plan of the Day**

**Safety Reminder**

**Spotlight on the "Radio Guys"**

**Sea School**

**Classifieds**

NAUTICOS, LLC
*For official use only*

The efforts of the OTECH team last night paid off, as the Ocean Explorer was re-deployed and tested against the same targets seen yesterday. The long-range search sonar continued to perform well, and this time the gapfiller sonar did its job, too. We are now confident that we can see our target as far away as 1,000 meters, and as close as directly below the towfish. Kudos to Larry and the OTECH team!

As soon as the gear was out of the water, we turned the Mt. Mitchell's nose south west and cranked the speed up to 12 knots or so. The next major event is rendezvous with the ASKARI, about six days from now.

**Plan of the Day** *March 2, 2006*

Transit. 0001-2400.

Next event: Rendezvous at sea with M/V Askari 7 March at 1300.

The Navigation Group Meets today. Jeff Pashook, Dave Jourdan, Elgen Long, Rod Blocksome and Tom Vinson get together again to "figger things out." Main Lounge from 0900 to 1100 and again from 1500 to 1700.

The Watchstander Training postponed for a day. It will start tomorrow with Jeff and Sue Morris.

**A Safety Reminder. Proper Attire.** Hard hats shall be worn in all operations where weights are suspended, such as launching and recovering survey gear, launching and recovering boats. Buoyant work vests shall be worn whenever performing work over the side. Proper shoes shall be worn when working on deck. Shoes shall be of sturdy construction, thick soled, hard toe design, oil and water-resistant. Sneakers are suitable on deck when no heavy weights are being lifted or moved. Sandals or flip-flops are unsafe and are not permitted for deck work. Disposable earplugs should be worn when in the vicinity of noisy machinery, such as diesel engines and hydraulic power units. MacSpence, the safety dog says, "Be safe, or I'll break your knees!"

**MERIDIAN PASSAGES**

**Central Pacific Edition
F Deck, Mt. Mitchell**
*Contact:* **Extension 700**

*Editor in Chief:*
**Dave Jourdan**

*Contributors:*
**Dave Jourdan
Marika Lorraine
Carla-Rae Smith
Sue Morris**

*Photographer:*
**Marika Lorraine**

*Layout Design:*
**Bethany Jourdan**

*Published by:*
**Mantub Publishing**

Our ship's newspaper, *Meridian Passages*, included a mix of useful information, spotlights on crew members, irreverent humor, and was an outlet for latent literary talents. The paper was one of the means used to help develop a working team and foster good morale over the many weeks at sea.

the middle of the night, we took a particularly hard roll, and all of a sudden the heavy steel door flew open. For some reason I woke up with a start, and lifted my head from the pillow just in time to see the door flying at my face! It *whammed* against the bunk frame, threatening to smash my nose, then flew shut with a bang.

For this trip, Spence suggested that we have a daily ship's "newspaper," seeing it as a good way to promulgate details of the ship's schedule (the Plan of the Day). As with our whimsical 2002 *Davidson Classifieds*, I saw it as a fun way to get people on the ship involved with each other, to help document the experience, and provide some working material for the education team. Thus was born *Meridian Passages, Central Pacific Edition*.

*Passages* was a newsletter we had been publishing at Nauticos for over a decade, starting back when our company operated under the name Meridian Sciences, Inc. I coined the title *Meridian Passages* as sort of a triple pun. Our company name was Meridian; a passage is a story, and a meridian passage is the passing of a heavenly body (like the sun, moon, or a star) across one's meridian of longitude. Hence, the meridian passage of the sun is another name for "noon," and it is the moment when a body is highest in the sky. The astronomical reference appealed to me, as an amateur astronomer operating a company whose specialties included the science of navigation. So, the first edition of volume XII of *Meridian Passages* was issued on the day after we got under way. It featured news of the day, the official Plan of the Day, a spotlight on a crew member, a story or article, and a mock "Classifieds" section for fun.

Anyone could contribute (and we received a lot of material over time), but I relied heavily on cub reporter and photographer Marika (our student) for interviews and images, teacher Carla-Rae and Sue for contributions, and Bethany for layout. Marika actually had some real experience, as she worked through college as a reporter for her local television station in Missouri. I had also collected a few "sea stories" from home, including a comedy sketch about our search written by a friend, Diane Denk, which I doled out in small doses each day, serial form.

Our first issue was received with raised eyebrows and puzzled looks. But after a few days, midwatch denizens would come looking if we didn't roll the presses by our self-imposed 2 AM deadline. Our March 3 lead article addressed a common affliction of charter team members:

## MERIDIAN PASSAGES
*Central Pacific Edition*
*March 3, 2006 Volume XII, Number 3*

### Down for the Count
*Mal de Mer* Epidemic Rockets Through Charter Team

Scopalomine, Bonnine, Dramamine, ginger pills, little wristbands, full-body suds immersion . . . it's all futile when *Mal* comes to visit. No one knows who, when, or where he will strike. There are only two known sure cures . . . jump overboard, or time-lapse therapy. Most people chose the latter, which involves waiting for about two days until you get your "sea legs."

In the meantime, you can hang out on deck, getting that "natural wind-blown look" that's all the rage among the female members of the group. Or you can conduct horizontal mattress pressing exercises. Or you can just try to keep busy. As Yogi once said, "50% of it is half mental."

As Carla-Rae's perpetual smile becomes increasingly maniacal, you know it's getting the better of her. But she still managed to write up the SEA School notes and plan the next session.

Chief Mate Lawrence noted that more folks were up and about this morning, a sure sign that the epidemic is running its course. Soon enough, all misery will be forgotten.

The Sunday edition of *Passages* even included a comics page, with material gleaned from favorite cartoons archived on the many laptops brought aboard, and even a few original offerings. I quickly became inundated with contributions, and began to have trouble fitting in Spence's "real" news, in favor of gratuitous humor pieces.

## March 6; Sunday. At Spaulding's Spa.

In spite of being in transit and not yet standing watches, we kept *very* busy, to be sure we would be as ready as possible when we reached the operations area on Tuesday. Spence had organized "tiger teams" to tackle various chores: installing latches on cabinets (replacing the blue duct tape we have been using to keep them from flying open in heavy seas); fashioning hand holds in the sonar room; painting the fathometer pole; and even learning to make Kevlar cable splices for the vehicle technicians. He recruited Bethany and Marika for some "secret" project. We also began running SEA School and watchstander training. And we held daily navigation meetings to come to final conclusions about our operations area, as we had all of the brainpower in one place, a captive audience.

The secret project was revealed on Sunday. We finally had a sunny day, and I joined Spence flipping burgers on an outdoor barbecue grill for a lunch treat, while Bethany and Marika introduced "Spaulding's Spa." We were invited up to the roof of the pilot house, where we found the girls lounging in the "pool" (an inflatable boat filled with sea water) under the watchful eye of our mascot "Spaulding" (brother of soccer ball "Wilson," who starred in the movie *Castaway*; Spaulding was was a veteran of our 2002 mission). The little mascot sat in a beach chair fashioned from cardboard and looked cool in shades. There were mock coconut palms (fronds of black poly and nuts of duct tape wads) and other "tropical" plants all around. The area was decorated with signed photos of Spaulding hanging out with famous people . . . by mysterious coincidence all now missing: Jimmy Hoffa, Bigfoot, Nessie (the monster), the Lindberg baby, and even Amelia Earhart! There were extensive "Rules for the Pool," including:

NO DIVING
NO RUNNING ON DECK
NO HORSE-PLAY
NO SPEEDOS
NO TAUNTING OF THE LIFEGUARD

. . . and my favorite,

NO P IN OUR OOL

All of this was for fun, but also was designed to help build a great team. So far, the charter team was all working together well . . . not always agreeing, but all pitching in and helping the operation to succeed. The crew was 100 percent on our side, and participating in all of these activities as well as the SEA Schools.

Berthing was a bit of a complication, as the days of all-male crews are thankfully long past. Spence organized a berthing plan that was well conceived, fair, and recognized the special vagaries of life aboard a research vessel. We always consider ourselves guests of the crew, who call the ship their home much of the time. Once the crew realizes this, they become perfect hosts, and welcome us not as customers but as shipmates. We were lucky to have plenty of space, generally in the form of two-person "staterooms," clustered in groups with shared bathroom and shower facilities. Between the charter team and the ship's crew, we had eleven female members on board, and Spence had worked to establish some segregation. This way, people would not have to worry about privacy when they used the shower, and would, in general, help to minimize complications arising from a co-ed crew. So areas were established known colloquially as "Boy's Town" and "Girl's Town," and appropriate protocols were established.

Jeff and Sue, who are married, were not excepted, and occupied separate berthing areas without complaint. But Adam and Collette, being newlyweds, were very keen to be together. Spence worked things out with the "boys" so that Collette could share a room with Adam in "Boy's Town." Flexibility and accommodation are key to getting along at sea, and thankfully our team did not resent an exception made for an unusual circumstance.

### March 7; Tuesday. A New Start.

We arrived in the operations area in the early morning hours of March 7, just under seven days from Honolulu departure, nearly three years and eleven months since the winch failure in 2002 interrupted our quest. A smooth night launch was followed by hours of waiting as the cable paid out and the sonar made its way to the bottom. The OTECH (Oceaneering Technologies) crewmen were pleased with the event, and were certainly happy to be able to start collecting data.

It was time to focus on the business at hand. We had forged a great team, and I had no doubt that everyone would do his or her best. Many slow, long hours would follow as we patiently checked out the system and benchmarked it against targets and terrain imaged in 2002. We had some hope, though not a high expectation, that one of the targets we had noted in 2002 just might be the Electra. Analysis of the 2002 data after the mission, including an independent look by experienced sonar analyst Garry Kozak, had suggested that there were four 2002 targets worth a second look. We decided to spend the first two days towing the sonar past these targets, hoping a higher-resolution view with the Ocean Explorer sonar would tell us more. This would also allow us to compare our sonar imagery with the old mission, check navigation, and gain some experience in coordination between the ship drivers and the sonar operators at full depth.

To the inexperienced, the process would seem like watching paint dry. But if we are deliberate and meticulous, we should be rewarded in the end.

The Oceaneering technical team charged with operating and maintaining the Ocean Explorer and all of the attendant equipment was divided into two shifts, manning the gear around the clock. The night shift was led by Larry Tyler, who was also the overall manager of the OTECH contingent. Larry, known on board as "L.T.," hails from Chesapeake, Virginia, and was a Navy diver. He had experience diving in manned submersibles, and is one of few humans to have been as deep as 16,000 feet. L.T. was also an Emergency Medical Technician, a handy skill to have on board.

Larry's shift included Phil Goodwin, from Baltimore, Maryland, who earned the nickname "Big Sick," owing to an unfortunate and persistent sensitivity to *mal de mer*. Phil is a mechanical technician and qualified crane operator. He used to be a professional athlete and encouraged us to guess the sport. . . . After many fruitless tries he admitted he was a professional cheerleader for the Baltimore Ravens NFL football team! Dwight Heard joined us from West Palm Beach, Florida, and served as an electronics technician. The summer before, he had worked on the latest *Titanic* expedition. Mark Wilson's expertise was the Ocean Explorer, and he was the most experienced sonar interpreter of the group. Mark doesn't mind spending six months at sea because it can mean six months of free time at home in Virginia, where he can enjoy hobbies such as ham radio.

The recurring theme of the OTECH night shift: "If it's there, we'll find it."

The OTECH day shift was led by Andy Sherrell, from Owatonna, Minnesota. Andy worked on several aircraft recovery jobs including the Egypt Air, TWA 800, Swiss Air, and Alaska Air crashes . . . seeing so much aircraft debris has made him wary of flying. "Chico" as some call him, has also worked on the *Hood* and *Bismarck* deep-sea projects.

Andy's shift was manned by Chris Russell, who was a part of the *Liberty Bell 7* (Mercury space capsule) recovery and had been working off shore for thirty years. He was in the process of relocating from Virginia to Pennsylvania, and admitted to being an "enthusiastic" guitar player. His mates said he was being modest, but we never had the opportunity to find out for ourselves. Jason Predmore, from Sussex, New Jersey, was a former U.S. Marine air traffic controller. He is hoping someday to start a business in helicopter charters. David Warford grew up in Detroit and now resides in San Diego. He worked on the *Liberty Bell* project, twice on the *Titanic*, and also on the Alaska Air recovery. His deepest military salvage was from 17,251 feet, which is a record in the Guinness Book. His oldest daughter (of three teenagers) was a nationally ranked tennis player who was waiting to hear if she would gain an appointment to West Point.

The OTECH group was experienced, talented, and dedicated. The list of successful projects they had worked on was remarkable. All were used to life at sea, and proved to be excellent shipmates. We were lucky to have them on board.

While preparing to launch the Explorer, we were also looking for the *Askari* to arrive. Spence and I were excited to have the luxury of a second vessel, which could come in handy in the event of a critical equipment failure (as in 2002) or medical emergency. Unfortunately, the *Askari* was slow, and it was not able to manage moderate wind and seas in any kind of comfort. So the transit to the operating site took much longer than planned. When it became evident that the *Askari* would be almost a day late, and it would be a tremendous waste for us to loiter around waiting, logic prevailed and we proceeded with launch. I assured John Heubusch that it would take many hours to reach the first contact, that it was not a high likelihood to be the Electra, and anyway all we would be getting was another sonar picture, which would not be definitive. Identification would have to wait for deployment of the ROV. There would be time for *Askari* to catch up.

By 0500 (local time), with Ocean Explorer on the bottom, we maneuvered to make a sonar pass by 2002 Target 131. The four 2002 targets were selected on the basis of size (all appearing to be of dimensions similar to the Electra), echo intensity, possibility of being non-geologic, and other factors such as having some evidence of nearby debris. None of the 2002 targets, including those four, were judged by Tom Dettweiler as likely to be the Electra, but Jeff Morris and Garry Kozak agreed they were worth a second look. The one I was most interested in was designated Target 66. This target measured 15 × 23 meters (the Electra is 12 × 17 meters—quite close by sonar image standards). In Garry's words, it was a "unique double-edged artifact," which suggested it was not geological. I could easily imagine the dual blips corresponding to twin engines.

But we would have to wait to look at Target 66. Jeff had arranged a path through the area that took into account our starting point and hit all four spots with the least distance and easiest turns, leaving plenty of "run in" time on each target approach to allow the sonar to stabilize. We would use a 600-meter range scale, giving us a closer look than in 2002, but making it harder to hit each spot within optimum sonar range. Imagine: we had to maneuver the ship in such a way that, nearly four miles down and two or three behind, at the end of five miles of cable, the Ocean Explorer would pass 200–400 meters from the target. To complicate matters, our uncertainty in the target position was no better than 100 meters. We had a navigation point to aim for, but we also had to watch the images of terrain as they crept by on the screen at an agonizingly slow pace, and try to match that with our corresponding images from 2002. Part of the trick was to identify unique terrain features, such as ridges, to look for. Once a match was made, adjustments to the ship track could be made that, after a long time, would nudge the vehicle track a little. This took skill and patience, and was not guaranteed to be successful.

From the time of our first views of the ocean floor, we expected it to take almost five hours to reach Target 131. We needed some extra time to adjust on this first attempt. After two hours of mapping, things were going well, and we were already identifying familiar territory. In the dim and quiet Ops room, lined with flat-panel displays and video monitors, tension was building. It was exhilarating to be back in action, being part of a good team working well, and anticipating discovery.

It happened at 0741, not quite three hours into the first survey line. The talkie monitoring the survey control van on the aft deck squawked, "Loss of hydraulic pressure!" Of course, my first thought was, "Not again!" But, sure enough, our OTECH watch leader reported that hydraulic power was lost to the traction winch, as well as the storage drum and level-wind. The HPU engine was running, but no hydraulic pressure was being produced. Fortunately, the braking system held this time, and the vehicle was in no immediate danger. Spence quickly ordered a slight increase in ship's speed to bring Ocean Explorer a little higher off the bottom and await the return of hydraulic power.

OTECH technicians quickly set about disassembling the HPU; however, this exercise would take hours. Meanwhile, we could not raise or lower the vehicle. After some consideration, we realized that we could control vehicle altitude within reasonable limits by adjusting the speed of the ship. Also, we knew the terrain ahead (having mapped it in 2002), so we did not expect to be surprised by a ridge or seamount. We decided to continue on, trying to image Target 131.

Three hours later, a beautiful image of 131 appeared on our screens. It clearly did not resemble the Electra in any way.

Six hours after the casualty, the innards of the HPU were exposed, revealing the cause of the problem: a sheared pump adapter plate. In more familiar terms, this was the "drive shaft," which connected the diesel engine to the hydraulic pumps that created the pressure to drive the winch and other equipment. The likelihood of this kind of failure is probably about the same as having your car drive shaft shear in two while driving on the highway. It was considered so improbable, that no spare adapter plate was carried. As in 2002, we were stuck with no way to fix the problem.

### MERIDIAN PASSAGES

*Central Pacific Edition*
*March 8, 2006 Volume XII, Number 8*

#### Lightning Strikes . . . Twice
*Deja Vu* All Over Again

Seven thousand meters of cable out . . . threatening weather . . . hydraulic oil everywhere . . . technicians tearing into pumps and motors . . . frowny faces watching and waiting . . . video cameras capturing all . . . it could have been 2002. Four years ago, about 15 miles from here, the Amelia Earhart Expedition came to an abrupt halt after 27 days of operations. This time, we had been operating barely three hours when hydraulic power to the winch was suddenly lost.

Last time, it was due to a ruptured hose; this time, to a failed HPU (Hydraulic Power Unit). The difference was, this time the fail-safe brake on the cable held, and we were spared the excitement of a free-wheeling cable spool with wire streaming into the abyss and our sonar dropping to the bottom.

Still, we were unable to retrieve the cable, unable to maneuver, and the mission went on hold. OTECH, with the expert help of Per Andersen and his *Mt. Mitchell* engineers, went right to work. After hours of disassembly and troubleshooting, the broken part was removed and a temporary repair was under way. Shortly after midnight, the drum began slowly spinning as the repair worked. About six hours will be needed to safely recover the sonar.

Meanwhile, we rendezvoused with the *Askari*, and Mr. Waitt came aboard. We gave a quick tour of the ship and briefing of the situation. He was very supportive and encouraging, and set off in short order to head to the island of Tarawa, about 3 days from here, to retrieve new parts. Hopefully, we will be back in operation in about 6 days. The day was not a total loss . . . in fact, we accomplished a lot in the few productive hours. The 2002 data was benchmarked with the new sonar, and one prior contact was examined. Everyone worked as a team to recover from the casualty and make the most of the situation.

Yes, we were on our way back to Tarawa! Who expected that??

As described in *Passages*, we met *Askari* and off they headed, continuing west to collect repair parts while we on the *Mt. Mitchell* were limited to about two knots speed. As it would take the better part of a week for the little motor yacht to return, we also had other more expedient contingencies in mind.

First of all, we could effect temporary repairs. The adapter plate was not a delicate instrument; the machine shop on our vessel was equipped with the tools to make a replacement. A slab of steel from the side of one of OTECH's container vans supplied the raw material, the broken part provided the template, and the *Mt. Mitchell's* engineers, led by chief engineer Per Andersen, fashioned a credible twin to the failed part. This was installed, and around midnight the Ocean Explorer was on the way back to the surface. As the jury-rigged part was not machined to accurate tolerances, we dared not run the system at full speed, and the Oceaneering management back in Maryland was not keen to allow us to return the system to operation without a "real" repair. But at least, by 0630 on the morning of March 8, the sonar was back on board, and the *Mt. Mitchell* was free to maneuver.

It would take many days to go get a spare part; the only quicker way was to fly a spare part to us. This could be done by the U.S. Coast Guard, who had the aircraft, equipment, and experience to air-drop supplies at sea. We could recover a buoyant package with our skiff. There were two reasons we thought this was possible, and even likely. First of all, I had a letter from the former

Commandant of the Coast Guard, Admiral James Loy, offering assistance. Two shortcomings of that kind offer were: it was dated 1999 and Admiral Loy had since retired; and, it was from the Public Affairs Office, and although we were grateful for their enthusiasm, there was really nothing helpful that Public Affairs could do under the circumstances. On the other hand, we had also made contact with the Pacific Coast Guard Office, though our education coordinator Sallie Smith back in Maryland. Commander "Rocky" Lee was keen to help us, and was enthusiastic about using us as a training exercise for air drops. The package would be less than 250 pounds, and smaller than half of a fifty-five-gallon drum, so technically it was feasible. We also knew that the Coast Guard had previously used us for SAR (Search and Rescue) training flights, when we were overflown by a Coast Guard aircraft in 2002.

As my journal said,

> It turns out, they [the Coast Guard] were planning to do a training flight over our area anyway, and they could in principle air-drop the needed item in a floating container that we can pick up with our skiff. As of now, this needs to be briefed to the higher-ups, but meanwhile we are setting in motion the process (through Charlotte) to get the second part to the right hands in Honolulu. If that can be done, it will save us maybe a week of time! And might produce enough drama to cause our media team to wet their pants!

The "higher-ups" were the rub. . . . We learned the next day from Commander Lee that the problem with the drop was the lawyer in Honolulu who said it was "not in the public interest." This in spite of the fact that a patrol plane was already scheduled to fly over Howland Island, and it would cost essentially nothing to make the drop. Apparently, we would have to have some kind of medical emergency if we expected the Coast Guard to help.

In the midst of it all, we had time for humor. The March 9 issue of *Meridian Passages* included the following:

## SPECIAL MEDICAL ANNOUNCEMENT:

We are presently at one of those rare conjunctions of time, skills, and events that makes possible a unique opportunity for those aboard the *Mt. Mitchell*. We basically have free medical services of Dr. Pam Geddis, and she is no doubt in need of keeping her skills honed (in addition to avoiding boredom). We have several days ahead of no surveying. There are many aboard approaching "geezer status" (you know who you are) who grew up in the era of atmospheric nuclear testing and therefore should be getting regular cancer screenings. Therefore, starting at 8:00 AM Thursday morning there will be free colonoscopies on the fo'c's'le deck.

Since Dr. Geddis did not pack the necessary instruments, the tests have been delayed by one day to give the *Mt. Mitchell* engineering crew and Oceaneering a chance to once again demonstrate their prowess at improvising mechanical solutions to any problem. Tygon tubing and hydraulic oil are being provided by the ship's engineer. As soon as Oceaneering locates a "lipstick" camera and the media team gets the video recorder set up, we will be good to go.

Having exhausted all prospects of a quick repair, we settled in for a several-days wait. Wednesday evening the expedition team got a glimpse of the island that Amelia and Fred never saw. As dusk fell, a thin strip of beach bordering a scrubby patch of land appeared on the horizon. Howland is featureless except for the Amelia Earhart Beacon and some mysterious mounds that not even Elgen could identify. Something to do with Easter Island? Equatorial beaver dwellings? Yet another mystery to ponder as we floated offshore, conserving fuel while awaiting spares. At dawn, Captain Mike arranged for a beautiful view of the island, framing the sunrise. When the sun was up, we could see for ourselves how hard it was for Amelia to spot the island in the morning glare.

Howland is now an uninhabited U.S. National Wildlife Refuge. By federal law we could approach no closer than three miles without permission. According to the U.S. Fish and Wildlife's *Comprehensive Conservation Plan* (August 2007), the islands (Howland, Baker, and other remote Pacific atolls) are "special places providing habitat for many rare, endemic plants and animals. Many of these species are formally listed as federally Threatened or Endangered under the Endangered Species Act of 1973. Endemic plants and insects, and the predators they support, are especially vulnerable to the introduction of competing or consuming, non-native species. Such introductions may cause the extinction of island endemics, or even the destruction of entire island ecological communities." In order to protect the sensitive ecosystems and maintain their isolation, a Quarantine Protocol has been established that includes:

Any personnel going ashore at any island and moving inshore from the immediate area in which waves are breaking at the time of landing must have new footwear, new or island-specific clothes and new or island-specific soft gear that have been frozen (<4° C) for at least 48 hours.

Thus, we contented ourselves with views from a distance. Still, after so many years of work, it was a thrill to finally see the locus of the Earhart mystery. In an e-mail message home, Rod Blocksome reflected on that special moment:

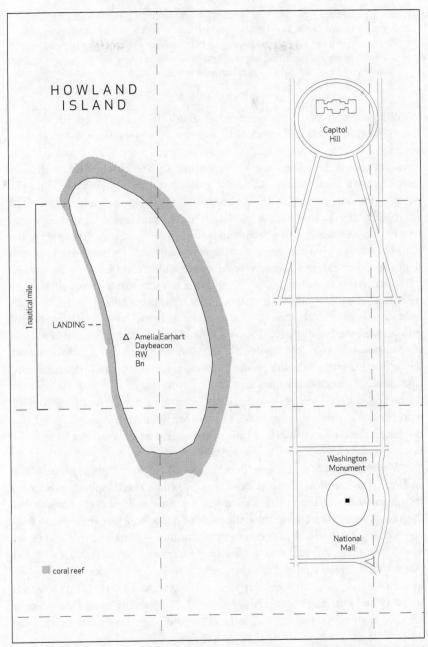

Howland Island. Now a U.S. Fish and Wildlife preserve, the small speck of land would fit neatly on the Washington D.C. Mall . . . but imagine the Mall surrounded by endless ocean.

Here on remote Howland Island stands a memorial, the Earhart Beacon, to America's most famous and beloved aviatrix. Few people have actually seen it and fewer still set foot on the island. So that morning, we quietly watched the sun rise, illuminating the Earhart memorial on Howland Island and remembering Amelia's courage and drive for aviation adventure.

We did our best to put our free time to good use. The mates practiced positioning the ship in winds and currents to support ROV operations, having mixed success. We set a "phone watch" so if we got a call from the Coast Guard we wouldn't miss it. Bethany set about organizing O-rings in the vehicle maintenance hut. Jeff continued tweaking the analysis system, as always . . . at some point in the trip, he earned the nickname "Tweak." He took advantage of the approach to the shallower water surrounding Howland Island to practice operation of the deep-water fathometer, and became an expert. Since this part of the world had never been mapped to any degree of accuracy, we needed to know the depth ahead of our underwater vehicle so we wouldn't run into a seamount.

Spence was planning and replanning our rendezvous. Jon worked with the technicians to make sure we had exactly the right part coming, and with Rod's help took accurate measurements and made a sketch, which Bethany turned into an engineering drawing. This was emailed to Charlotte back in Honolulu for verification. The deck crew painted. Rod and Tom managed to contact Cedar Rapids and ran some phone patches. Elgen re-checked fuel consumption. Marika interviewed the ship's engineering team for our next *Meridian Passages* "Spotlight." There was time for entertainment . . . reading, movies, workouts, and (of course) meals. The days really do go by quickly. . . . I had not taken the time to watch one movie, although I would plan not to miss the upcoming *Life Aquatic* and *Airplane!* festivals.

Meanwhile, the *Askari* was making poor progress. Fighting headwinds and seas, she had slowed below her normally sedate speed. Spence and I were trying to work out the optimum rendezvous time and location, considering the competing factors of getting the part as quickly as possible versus conserving fuel. We wanted to preserve our option of staying out two additional weeks if needed, and fuel was the limiting parameter. But as *Askari's* progress slowed, the tradeoff changed to the point that we realized we could have gotten to Tarawa and back more quickly on the *Mt. Mitchell*, even with the vehicle recovery and loitering time around Howland. Not wanting to wait even longer for the repair parts, we decided to head west and make our rendezvous just offshore of Tarawa.

This involved crossing the International Date Line again, and those veterans of the previous crossing led the appropriate ceremonies, welcoming the uninitiated into the Realm of the Golden Dragon.

Though the *Askari* was proving of marginal value as a support ship, the Institute's efforts ashore were more welcome, as arrangements were made to fly the repair parts directly to Tarawa, along with a few other supplies, at Ted's personal expense. On Sunday, March 12, late afternoon, the long-awaited *Askari* appeared on the horizon, bearing one repair part for the diesel HPU, and one fresh charge of Skoal for the OTECH team. The coveted adapter plate and equally sought-after tobacco were safely brought aboard. OTECH technicians immediately set about installing the new plate. The estimated six-hour repair job was completed in an hour and a half. Meanwhile, the *Mt. Mitchell* headed back east and left *Askari* in her wake.

The most effective way to do it, is to do it.
　　　　—Amelia Earhart

# The Search Resumes

Our return to the site was a rough passage. The winds and waves had increased, and the *Mt. Mitchell* was proving to be quite an uncomfortable ride in even modest weather. There were some big ground swells, which made normal activities difficult as the ship rolled and corkscrewed and lurched in unexpected ways. It was not what anybody would consider bad weather, but this ship had a very round hull and small antiroll chocks. On the other hand, the hull offered less resistance to the water, and thus could make a higher speed. That was important, as we were wasting about $1 per second while not searching!

Other than the ride, we found the *Mt. Mitchell* to be comfortable, for a research vessel. At 231 feet long and 42 feet wide, she contained significantly more interior living space than the *Davidson*, providing accommodations for fourteen crew and up to forty-nine charter passengers. With forty-two on board (crew and charter), we had just a little extra elbow room. As on the *Davidson*, we had a very ample lab space, which we used for a sonar analysis station, and "office space" for our other activities. The open aft deck was on two levels, which is where most of the ocean survey gear was installed and welded down.

The ship displaced 1,800 tons and could carry over 100,000 gallons of fuel. The rated fuel consumption for a cruising speed of twelve knots was 2,000 gallons per day; this included fuel for the generators, which provided all power for the ship and its equipment. With a planned reserve, the ship was rated for an endurance of forty-five days and a range of 11,000 nautical miles. We would be using most of this fuel during our mission.

A highlight of the *Mt. Mitchell's* NOAA service was work in the Persian Gulf to study the effects of the intentional oil spill caused by the Iraqi government during the 1991 Gulf War. She was decommissioned in 1995 after nearly thirty years of service, having contributed mightily to our scientific and practical knowledge of the sea. The hull was laid up, and for six years she sat idle until her 2001 refit as a commercial general-purpose research vessel that became operational in 2003.

The layout of the *Mt. Mitchell* was very similar to the *Davidson*, and the hull was even painted the same shade of blue. We had some extra cabins and larger spaces, which we appreciated, and greater endurance, which we needed. Of course, the crew was entirely new, except for our old friend Cap'n Joe Litchfield, who quit his job with Ocean Services, taking a pay cut and serving under the chief mate in order to continue working with Nauticos and join our quest. If you ask him why, he'll tell you, "It just got into my soul." He said he just couldn't leave the job unfinished.

Since we had last seen Joe after the 2002 mission, he had reported an exciting development—a new wife! We had seen photos of a very "shipshape" Joe at his wedding with his new bride, Vickey, who turned out to be a very accomplished oral surgeon and the pride of Homer, Alaska. Joe said that before he met Vickey he wrote to the Lonely Hearts Club and sent his picture . . . but they wrote back and said they weren't that lonely! Vickey and Joe were kind enough to come to our house for lunch when they were visiting family in Portland, Maine, and Lynn and I delighted in meeting her. Stories of Vickey became part of Joe's midwatch conversation, including a most amazing tale of her killing five grizzly bears in a week while they were building their cabin. We were suspicious that it was just a "sea" story, but Vickey later confirmed it. Joe also showed us pictures of his grandson, who he doted on, and was busy raising to be a good sailor. Little Jake could tie an expert bowline, recite the whistle signals, and at bedtime would ask to sleep in the "topside berth" with Grandpa.

We came to know and love the crew members of the Mitchell, who became our teammates in short order. Darlings of the crew were the housekeepers (stewards), Ami Pablo and Sherry Huber, and assistant cook Shirley Mira, who would keep us stocked with weekly fresh towels and linens. Sherry and Shirley, who were born in Palau, were identical twins, and it became a contest to guess their names correctly when greeting them. Along with Ami, they were always smiling and cheerful. Most of us came to think of them as our own sisters or daughters (depending on one's age . . . guess which applied to me).

At 11:30 AM every day, Shirley would be heard on the ship's PA system announcing, in a sing-song voice, "Hello-ooo, lunch is served . . . lunch is served." Reminiscent of hearing Radar O'Reilly's announcements on *M\*A\*S\*H*, or a broadcast of the day's dubious menu at summer camp, we began to look forward to this daily ritual. Shirley's ebullient inflection never failed to bring a smile to any who were listening.

Shirley had been working on the *Mt. Mitchell* for two years when her sister's military husband was sent to Afghanistan, so she recruited her as a housekeeper. If you asked how to tell them apart, Sherry will tell you that she wears a necklace with a yellow bead. But Shirley says you can tell by the smile. "Mine is better!" she says.

The master of the *Mt. Mitchell* was Michael Dunatov. Son of a son of a sailor, his early love of the sea drew him to the Merchant Marine Academy, and has over the years captained nine different vessels. We looked forward to his daily "Ramblings," appearing overnight on the mess decks white board; we were often unsure if they were in jest or for real.

Lawrence Mishefski was chief mate. He sported an eclectic background, including work for a newspaper, playing flamenco guitar at coffee houses, and fighting fires in Alaska. Lawrence could speak some Latin, Japanese, and Russian, and claimed to be able to insult your mother in Turkish.

Our chief engineer was Per Andersen. Hailing from Norway, his father and grandfather both fought the Nazis as members of the Resistance. He first went to sea as a youngster in high school, and has been on four world cruises, traversing every major body of water on earth. His engineering crew included Jay Corwin, T.J. Boudreau, and Warren Smith. Jay (who prefers, simply, "J") shared an ambition with many of the sea-going crew: to own a piece of land, in his case to raise horses. We were not surprised to learn that "T.J." (Trinity Jacob) spent time in Hollywood aiming to be an actor, as he entertained all with his wit and antics. Warren spent two years as a volunteer on mercy ships, bringing medical supplies to Third World countries.

The deck division was headed by Bos'n Jeff Shepard. He shared a sentiment with many of the crew . . . wishing he could spend more time at home with family, in his case, a daughter. The crew of the *Mt. Mitchell* spent a good part of their lives at sea, enjoying better pay and adventure, but enduring hard work and separation from home and loved ones. Hailing from Poland, Waldemar Janczak has fished all over the world. He said of his home, "It's my heaven—my sweetie is there!" Andy Gomes was in the middle of nine kids; a large familiy taught him always to lend a hand and keep people happy. He was continually cheerful, quiet, and dependable.

Our chef was Dan Nakamura, formerly with the CIA (Culinary Institute of America, that is), who suffered from debilitating seasickness the entire mission. Nothing seemed to relieve it, but still he pressed on, serving three great meals a day to the forty-two of us on board. Not able to eat much himself, he subsisted mainly on noodle dishes, earning him the nickname "Noodles Nakamura," which sounded vaguely suggestive of the Japanese Mafia. Dan was looking forward to starting a restaurant in Honolulu when he returned, and vowed never to set foot on a ship again. Ami, Shirley, and Sherry helped Dan and did everything they could to make our meals a pleasant diversion from the daily grind.

Our vessel included two large two-person staterooms that served as a dispensary and ship's hospital. We were equipped with a generous supply of medications and therapies, along with our very generous (of her time) volunteer doctor Pam. Given our isolation from the rest of the medical world, and the long time it would take to "medevac" (evacuate for a medical emergency) an ill or injured crew member in an emergency, we were very happy to have Pam along.

Doc Pam complemented the services of Amanda Becker, our very young (but very capable) third mate and ship's medical officer. At only twenty-three years of age, Amanda also was responsible for ship's navigation and safety. Hoping to follow in her father's Navy footsteps, her plans were derailed by asthma, so she shifted gears and studied at the New York Maritime College. She has an unlimited deck license, meaning she is qualified to sail any vessel in any ocean. We had no idea when we set out how much we would rely on Dr. Pam and Amanda.

## SEA School: **Nautical Terminology**

No, the "poop deck" is not where they used to "go," because we know they used the "head" for that. Captain Mike made nautical sense out of the non-sensical sea of nomenclature and lore that is part of the history of nautical terms. We know that *Mt Mitchell* has at least one of everything we need to make her a good and capable ship. Also, we learned that there is hope for those who are still suffering from *mal de mer* . . . according to *The Ocean Almanac*, although a woman aboard ship makes the seas angry, a *naked* woman calms the seas. Give it a try!

## March 13; Monday, 0400. Back in Action.

We arrived back in the operations area in the early morning hours and prepared for launch of the Ocean Explorer. Soon the sonar was in the water and on its way to the bottom. Two and a half hours later, we were collecting data and lining up for a pass by Target 66, our most promising contact from 2002. Five days and twenty-one hours had passed since we lost power to the HPU; we had consumed most all of our budget for repair time, all at once right in the beginning. There was little room left for error, bad weather, or unforeseen problems.

We began the long, slow run to image Target 66, with a bit more confidence than before since imaging of the first contact had gone so well. Adam and Collette had a few of us outfitted with lapel mikes, and tried to take charge of the Ops room as though it were a movie set. They wanted everyone positioned in a certain way . . . but this did not quite fit with the watchstander assignments and led to a bit of tension. All was worked out, and we turned our focus on the business at hand: locating terrain benchmarks to adjust our sonar track to pass by the target.

We watched the data slowly scroll down the screen, line by line. With each sonar "ping," roughly once a second, a new strip of pixels would be added to the top of the display, and an old one would fall off the bottom. We saw roughly a thousand seconds (over seventeen minutes) of raw data on the screen, but we could not advance it forward faster than it was collected. The sonar vehicle moved along the bottom at a sedate 1.8 knots, so each line of pixels represented a thin strip about three feet wide and two-thirds of a mile long (at the 600-meter range scale we were using) running across the sonar swath. One could wish it to go faster, but it would not.

As the image scrolled along, we tried to match it to terrain from the 2002 mission, displayed on an adjacent monitor. We also could study the saved history of information just collected, and try to correct everything for geometric distortions and changes in vehicle heading. The software for creating these geo-coded maps and mosaics was a truly astonishing set of programs, benefitting from the latest in computer processing technology, display systems, and data handling equipment. Not too many years ago, the U.S. Geological Survey would conduct deep-water mapping missions, saving all of the data on optical disks, and afterward, process it in a laboratory ashore. A year later, a thick document would be published with mosaicked sonar maps and annotations. Now, using programs called Isis and 20-20, the same could be accomplished in minutes, and it was practical to create near-finished mosaics in real time.

As we waited patiently, and watched intently, we struggled to find a match. As the minutes grew into half hours, we grew more and more uneasy as it was not clear that we would see familiar terrain, and the plotted position of the target steadily neared. We could not go slower, could not buy more time. Once the target area was passed, the hours of preparation would be wasted.

The Ops room was silent as the time of expected contact approached. There was nothing left to do but wait and see. The ghostly shadows of underwater hills, sand waves, and scattered rocks drifted by. We called "time," but nothing dramatic appeared on the screen. With each line of pixels we thought we might see a darkening, a sign that something corresponding to Target 66 would appear. But the next rows of pixels revealed nothing.

Finally, nearly eight hours after resuming operations, we gave up. We missed Target 66, or somehow it was gone.

We hauled in on the cable to raise the vehicle to a comfortable altitude, and increased speed as much as advisable (respecting the increased stresses on the cable and winch), and moved to a position to begin the next run. This would allow us to image the remaining two targets with one pass. Meanwhile, Jeff began pouring through the recorded data to try to puzzle out what went wrong.

It is very difficult to accurately know where the sonar is located at all times. There is no reliable instrument to measure this from the ship; acoustic pulses traveling over many miles can be distorted and cannot give a precise measure of distance and direction. That's why we have to tow our sidescan sonar near the bottom . . . the same approach tried from the surface is much too crude to detect anything as small as an aircraft (or even a battleship). On the other hand, thanks to modern navigation systems like GPS, we can, at all times, know where the ship is located to a high degree of accuracy. Unfortunately, GPS signals do not penetrate the surface of the ocean.

The best we can do is to follow a steady course and speed, and assume the sonar trails directly behind the ship at an estimated distance, called the "layback." This can be calculated from the length of cable deployed, the speed of the ship, and a model of the "catenary," or shape of the cable. This technique assumes there is no ocean current affecting most of the cable, which is usually true. Currents are normally confined to a shallow surface layer, and the bulk of the deep ocean is a very slow-moving, quiet mass of water.

This technique works quite well, but is subject to errors. The biggest problem is dynamic changes in layback as the ship speeds or slows, or changes course. So, all things considered, we expect a position accuracy of our deep ocean map at not much better than 100 meters. This is barely adequate for us to be able to reliably pass the right distance from a spot on the ocean floor using a 600-meter range scale on the sonar. But still, we should at least detect the target, even if it's not at the optimum distance. What went wrong with Target 66?

After some hours of work, Jeff determined that the layback that was used for that segment of the 2002 mission was a bit off. By carefully matching terrain features from adjacent swaths, he could find an adjustment that made a better match. Unfortunately, the direction we chose to pass through the area, as compared to the orientation of the swaths on the 2002 map, along with the layback error, served to place the target just outside of our view. We would have to decide whether to expend more time and try again to image Target 66.

That decision would have to wait, as the miles of cable trailing behind us made it horribly inefficient to turn around and make another run at Target 66 right away. Our most prudent course of action was to complete the well-planned series of maneuvers designed to image each target in sequence, then consider the merits of another run at our favorite prospect.

By the evening of March 13, we were back at it again, approaching Targets 84 and 122. Things went much smoother this time . . . five hours later, we got a good look at 84 and, in five more hours, 122 appeared on our screens. At the 600-meter range scale, these targets did not resemble the Electra in any way. Or, as is said in the search business, "No joy."

Confident that we could repeat those successes, and with time remaining on our budget for 2002 target imaging, we hauled up the sonar to an intermediate depth and headed to the starting point for another run on Target 66, our favorite.

While we were on our way to our next deep-sea event, we had other exciting business to attend to: the arrival of *Askari* and a visit from Ted. The little motor yacht had finally caught up with us, and we made plans to receive our visitor in style. The galley prepared a special lunch; we prepared detailed briefings of events and updates on our analysis work that had been ongoing.

Ted arrived in time for our daily pre-lunch operations briefing, a gathering of the operations team and ship's mates to discuss the past twenty-four hour's events and plan the next day's work. Bethany prepared the presentation, as she normally did, which included search events, coverage statistics, ship readiness, fuel consumption, weather, and any other developments. Ted climbed on board having ridden over in a small inflatable boat with an outboard motor (known as a Zodiac). The exercise required a tricky climb of about ten feet up the side of the ship using a rope ladder with aluminum treads. It was a calm, sunny day, we were creeping along slowly towing the sonar, and our passenger came aboard safely.

Ted listened to our daily briefing, where we learned from the captain that the port generator had failed overnight. The ship carries two diesel-powered generators that provide all power for the ship, other than propulsion. One is sufficient; but they are normally both operated at reduced load. Although we had not noticed the difference, the ship was now relying on a single machine for all of its internal power.

Without power from the generators, the *Mt. Mitchell* would be unable to support survey operations and would be forced to limp back to port. Once again, the expedition was at risk owing to unusual mechanical problems with critical equipment, and a demand for rarely used spare parts. The ship's engineers had been busy for hours dismantling the generator to identify the problem. We would have to wait for further updates and any prognosis.

At the conclusion of the meeting, Ted said goodbye and headed back to the *Askari*. As circumstances developed, unfortunately, that was the last time Ted set foot aboard the *Mt. Mitchell*.

## March 14; Tuesday. Approaching Midnight.

A few hours later, we were in position to lower the sonar back down and begin our second attempt to image Target 66.

It was a trying evening, as one problem after another began to accumulate, adding to the intrinsic difficulty of the exercise. The weather kicked up, and unrelated issues with the ship and equipment defeated our efforts to get the Ocean Explorer to the bottom and stable. Time was running out on Target 66.

The situation was grim: strong cross-currents and fifteen-knot wind gusts were pushing the *Mt. Mitchell* one way; thirteen tons of cable hanging off the stern was pulling it the other. The cable crane hydraulic oil was overheating, and a ship's rudder seal was leaking. Vehicle altitude was too high, and with almost six miles of cable out, there was no more left to spool. We had already missed a couple of benchmarks on the approach to the target area because the sonar was too high to see well. We had already missed 66 once. . . . Could it happen again?

This was the situation I found when I climbed up to F Deck and entered the Ops room at 2330. Spence had been called to help, and the captain was on the bridge working with Amanda. If we could not manage to hold the line and altitude, not only would we be in danger of missing the target, but we would wonder if we could run a proper survey going in that direction.

The situation began to improve immediately. The altitude began to drop as the ship managed some slower speeds. Finally, at midnight, we began to see good images from the bottom, and Jeff (with help from Jon) began to match terrain with the 2002 records, getting the first indication in many hours that we were right on track. Our confidence improved as the ship crept down the line with the Ocean Explorer in tow behind almost 10,000 meters of cable. Since the drum carried barely 11,000, we could not safely let out any more.

In just twenty minutes, we came to within 1,000 meters of the target zone, just a few minutes out, and the captain eased the ship's speed slower to allow the Explorer to sink lower. As we caught the last terrain benchmark right on line, OTECH shifted the sonar to the higher resolution 600-meter scale, and the sonar dropped down to a remarkably steady 80 meters—perfect altitude for a high-resolution pass.

There was nothing more to do; the silence hung thickly in Ops. Slowly, exactly on time, the target scanned into view, right in the middle of the record. We could not have expected a better look! Unfortunately, it was clearly not our quarry. But we could now be sure of that.

As the rush of adrenaline passed and the excitement evaporated, we began to recover the vehicle to reconfigure it for normal survey operations and start mapping new areas. Collette and Adam packed up their gear in stony silence. We were all disappointed the target was not the Electra, but we also took great satisfaction in a job well done. We spent only three extra hours over our budget of two days imaging contacts. We eliminated all 2002 targets and could move on to map the rest of the search area with confidence in the quality and navigation accuracy of the old data. Also, we gained valuable experience in operating and coordinating the ship, Nauticos, and OTECH personnel. We felt well prepared for the next phase.

Ocean Explorer was recovered on deck without incident, reconfigured for mapping, and ready for redeployment even before the ship had reached the launch point. Reconfiguration was necessary because we were using a second set of sonar sensors that operated at a higher frequency (with corresponding shorter range) as a "gapfiller." This imaged the area directly below the vehicle, which otherwise is a blind spot. To do this, the high-frequency sonar projectors were physically re-oriented to point slightly forward and overlap below the path of the Explorer. Jeff programmed the 20-20 display software accordingly. For searching, we wanted the projectors in the normal configuration. The decision to recover and reconfigure was not made lightly, but was coordinated with relocation of the ship to a new starting point.

The Ocean Explorer slid into the water and began its descent to the bottom mid-morning on Wednesday, March 15. We would not welcome it back to the surface again for the next eighteen days.

## March 15; Wednesday. Man Overboard!

### MERIDIAN PASSAGES
Central Pacific Edition
March 16, 2006 Volume XII, Number 16

**Man Overboard!**
*Askari* Crewman Dunked . . . Personnel Transfer Aborted

Drama . . . emotion . . . excitement . . . danger . . . that's television! Just what the media team has been looking for! Yesterday, we had it all! Unfortunately, the media folks were right in the middle of it, cameras secured for small boat transfer, unable to capture the event.

Fortunately, Sue was handy with her still camera, and she captured some dramatic shots of an *Askari* crew member plunging head first into the ocean, nearly becoming a sub-marine sandwich, before being hauled to safety by his mate.

It was around noon, and Adam and Colette were returning from the *Askari* (via Zodiac small boat) where they had been filming the sonar launch. Five members of the expedition team were waiting for them, planning to climb on the Zodiac and transfer to the *Askari* for a visit. The seas were choppy, with six-foot swells in a stout breeze. Unfortunately, since we were towing the sonar, the *Mt. Mitchell* could not change course to create a lee side and protect the small boat from the wind and waves.

Coming alongside, the Zodiac was tended to the side of the *Mt. Mitchell* with a "painter" line, attached to the ship. A ladder was rolled down the side for the passengers to ascend. Equipment was passed up, including the video camera, wrapped in plastic. Although this exercise had been completed successfully several times already, the rough conditions made the eight-foot ascent with the boat bobbing six feet up and down quite daunting. Adam and Colette managed to scramble up, with some difficulty.

All of a sudden, the crewman tending the line was in the water! We all saw a face of sheer terror as he clung to the painter, keeping himself from between the boat and ship. In a few moments, with great effort, his mate fetched him back aboard. He was shaken, but OK, poorer by one ball cap. Personnel transfers were secured for the day. Lunch on *Askari* could wait!

And now, for the *rest* of the story. As our slow and deliberate mapping of the ocean floor began, the *Askari* was free to maneuver and enjoy all that the vast reaches of the Central Pacific had to offer. Of course, since everywhere was the same, there was no real advantage in freedom of movement. The only attractions in the area were Howland and Baker Islands, and we had briefed the Institute folks on the U.S. Fish and Wildlife protocol to visit there before we left home. Unfortunately, they had not followed through with this, so no arrangements were made to set foot on the only specks of land within hundreds of miles.

In fact, the only opportunity to visit was with each other! So, Ted kindly invited our gang for visits to the *Askari*. This involved making the small-boat transfer in the Zodiac, an inflatable craft that could safely carry five or six people in calm seas.

John Heubusch and some of his Institute compatriots made the trip one day, followed by Adam and Collette for an overnight stay and filming fest on the *Askari*. The next morning, they were to return, and the Nauticos brain trust was invited for lunch. That included Elgen, Jon, Spence, and me, with John Heubusch along. Sue and Jeff were on the docket for lunch the next day.

I had not paid much attention to these transfers, considering it not really my business, but as we lined up at the ship's rail at the appointed hour, I began to feel uncomfortable. The seas and winds were not exactly calm, and as we watched the Zodiac approach it was clearly fighting the elements, bucking and sloshing through the waves. I realized that, contrary to our other ocean operations, we had been given no briefing on procedures and safety measures. No life jackets were provided. Including the two boat crewmen, we would be pushing the capacity of the boat. We had two spry, but aging members of our party, one with a bum shoulder, and were facing an eight-foot descent down the vertical side on the hull on a rope ladder, with the sea surface lifting and dropping by most of that distance. As each man dropped into the craft, he would fall into the laps of the others clinging to their seats.

I turned to Amanda, who had been detailed to oversee the event, and asked her to send for life jackets immediately. They were quickly gathered, and as we donned them the drama unfolded.

One of the Zodiac crewmen tended a "painter" line, keeping the small boat fast to the ship. Suddenly, as the ship rolled and a wave crested, the line snapped taut and the crewman was jerked from his perch. As the man fell into the sea, the real danger became apparent: he was briefly trapped between the steel hull of the ship and the pitching, corkscrewing boat. The Zodiac's engine was running to keep up with the *Mt. Mitchell*, so one could easily imagine a rap on the head and a limp body plowing under the small boat and into its spinning prop. Somehow, the man in the water held on to the painter line, and his mate, driving the Zodiac with one hand, steered away from the hull, but kept close. The driver reached over the opposite side like a mailman delivering a package and plucked him out of the water.

Witnessing this, I immediately turned to Spence and said, firmly and deliberately, "It's time to secure this exercise!" He looked at me and said, "I agree," and that was that.

Minutes later, I spoke to Ted on the radio telephone and explained the situation, and told him I decided for safety reasons to not try any more personnel transfers until the weather eased. The captain backed me up on this. I apologized for missing lunch, which we were really looking forward to. He said I made the right decision, and we would reschedule.

That evening, in spite of the weather, the Zodiac returned to collect John. The captain rationalized that one fit person with prior experience could make the transfer safely. The *Askari* then departed the area, never to return. Apparently, Ted had pressing business back home relating to another project, and he needed John for his public relations expertise. We guessed they were satisfied with our technical competence, and had agreed to fund the full twenty-one-day survey. Pat was left behind to serve as our liaison to WID, along with our cross-trainers, Laura and Mike.

I didn't realize it at the time, but my last opportunity to develop a working relationship with Ted disappeared with the *Askari*.

Also staying with us was Dr. Pam, who had been given the option to bug out with the *Askari*. She had not volunteered for the extended mission, being assured that there would be an opportunity to come home before we returned to port. In fact, John thought that *Askari* would return in a couple of weeks, and she could probably transfer off then. Pam thought about her practice back in San Diego, the comforts of home, her lingering seasickness—but decided to stay on board with the team nonetheless. We were quite impressed with her commitment, and looked forward to keeping Doc Pam with us. We would soon enough learn just how lucky we were.

When men come to like sea life, they
are not fit to live on land.

—Samuel Johnson

When you are fed up with the sea, put an oar over your
shoulder, and keep walking until someone asks you
what you have on your shoulder, then settle there.

—Anonymous

# Life at Sea

With Ocean Explorer on the bottom and performing well, our team set about the long and tedious task of mapping our primary search area. We would plan to tow the sonar back and forth as in 2002, covering a new area that represented our remaining highest-probability region. Day by day, line by line, mile by mile, we would build a detailed map of the ocean floor to a resolution of one square meter, looking for anything unusual, anything bright and hard-edged. Even if we found such a contact, we would not deviate from our plan to map the primary area; there would be time to investigate contacts at the end. We would plan to survey until the end of the month, leaving a few days to investigate contacts.

All was not routine, however. The ship's engineers had been working tirelessly to repair the port generator. The first thing they did was check for leaking coolant, but that wasn't the problem. They then removed the injectors and did a pressure test. The test showed there was a leaking head. It seemed that the more troubleshooting they did, the worse the problem became. Soon we became concerned that the damage was not repairable at sea, which would present a serious dilemma. Having to rely on a single generator for a few days while making repairs was one thing—choosing to continue to operate 1,700 miles from home port on a single unit was another thing altogether. I was reporting these developments to WID daily, and I could imagine my esteem in their eyes eroding with each message.

Further investigation showed cracks in one of the cylinder heads. That's when the time-consuming task of removing the heads and everything attached began. All the parts were thoroughly cleaned and new gaskets and seals were added. This was a tedious process because the engines were complicated and unique: two V8 diesels bolted together, making it harder to take apart and put back together. The group changed watch schedules and sacrificed sleep to allow someone to work on the generator full time. Even with ear protection, the hammering of the main engine diesels pounded in one's chest—and it was *hot* down there!

Each day the captain reported at our progress meeting that a new problem had been encountered:

| | |
|---|---|
| 15 March | Port generator head removed, and the spare will be put on today. |
| 16 March | Port generator ready for testing this afternoon. |
| 17 March | Generator very close to being operational. |
| 18 March | Port generator has a water leak; replacing water pump. |
| 19 March | May need to cannibalize bow thruster for a replacement compression ring; the running unit is overdue for an oil change. |
| 20 March | Compression ring from original head used; testing in progress. |
| 21 March | Discovered that the spare metal gasket for the generator head is the wrong type; cannot re-use the old one. A new one must be fabricated from copper stock. |
| 22 March | We are cutting copper rings for seals; new leaks have been found and repaired. |
| 23 March | Port generator test will be run this afternoon. |
| 24 March | Port generator running in parallel with starboard. |
| 25 March | Port generator declared repaired! |

So, finally, after nearly two weeks of anxiety and round-the-clock work for the engineers, we could relax about the port generator. Expecting the *Askari* to return to the site soon, we sent a request for replacement spare parts to be brought to us, including the correct gaskets.

When it was all over, we held a small ceremony to recognize the work of Engineer Per Anderson's crew—in particular, Jay Corwin. Among other trinkets, Per was presented with an attractive copper mobile fashioned from the scraps and trimmings of sheet copper used to fabricate the head gaskets.

### Nautical Term of the Day: **Lucky Bag**

Articles left adrift, such as your personal junk, found in a public or work space, such as the Ops Center, may be confiscated or otherwise collected in the "Lucky Bag," without regard to rights of ownership, and re-contributed in an arbitrary manner without prejudice.

Most of our days were filled with our primary job of surveying the bottom, and all of the attendant tasks involved with keeping the process running smoothly. Data analysis, archiving, equipment maintenance, and clerical work kept us busy when we weren't actually sitting at a monitor. Carla-Rae ran the SEA School and developed educational mini-projects; Rod and Tom ran "phone patches" back home and kept up with their ham radio buddies; and the ship's newspaper was published each night.

There was certainly time for reading, movies, and other fun. Sundays and holidays were recognized with some kind of merriment. A leprechaun visited the ship on St. Patrick's Day and had his picture taken with the crew. Sue, Marika, and Bethany took over the galley on occasion, gave the cooks the night off, and made pizza for the crew (Bethany drawing on her prior experience as a "pizza artist" at Pie-casso Pizzaria in Stowe, Vermont). Near the end of March we recognized the midpoint of our survey with a "Halfway Day" celebration, including a miniature golf tournament and sailboat races. The golf course was designed around deck fittings on the fo'c's'le (which also served as hazards). Spence had the forethought to bring a putter, some balls, and a practice cup. The rolling of the ship added a unique challenge to the course. The sailboat races were held on a short course in the water-filled inflatable boat on the upper deck. In the final heat, Amanda's boat beat Captain Mike's in a close finish.

On March 20, we marked the passage of the sun from south to north declination, meaning it crossed the equator heading north. Spring had arrived! We calculated that the spot on the earth that the equinox occurred was somewhere near the Galapagos Islands, and held a contest to see who could make the closest guess.

It now being Spring, Easter was around the corner, but it would occur just after we planned to be home. Not wanting to miss the opportunity to recognize it in our own special way, we concocted a mock Easter celebration:

## HOLIDAY WEEKEND COMING!!

This Sunday will mark a special *Mt. Mitchell* holiday . . . Easter-ish! Just in case we are not still at sea for real Easter, we will have a provisional celebration, complete with an Easter-ish Egg Hunt and other festivities. This will be preceded by the traditional April Fool's Day on Saturday, and the holiday weekend will kick off with Pretty Good Friday. SEA School will take a Spring Break, Friday through Monday. Special movies will be shown in the Lounge in lieu of SEA School.

Over the weekend, we held an April Fool's Challenge to see who could make the biggest fool of whom, without being deliberately cruel. Jokes about the Electra being found were considered to be in poor taste. That day's edition of *Passages* was riddled with subtle (and not so subtle) errors, and we held a contest to see who could find them all. The First Annual Central Pacific Film Festival included such classics as *A Shot in the Dark* (prequel to the *Pink Panther*) and *Airplane!* And it was rumored that the Easter-ish Tuna might make a visit on

Sunday, hiding roe around the ship.

Not all of our diversions were irreverent. Through our faithful education coordinator back ashore, Sallie Smith, we learned that one of the astronauts aboard the International Space Station (ISS) was a ham radio enthusiast. That got Rod and Tom to thinking, and then to designing, and then to building. The result was featured in the daily newspaper:

## MERIDIAN PASSAGES
*Central Pacific Edition*
*March 23, 2006 Volume XII, Number 23*

### From Sea to Space
The Radio Guys Try to Contact the Mother Ship
November Alpha One Sierra Sierra . . . this is Whiskey Zero Charlie X-Ray X-Ray Maritime Mobile, Region 3 aboard the Research Vessel *Mount Mitchell* calling. . . ."

Rod's plaintive calls reached over the airwaves, trying desperately to make contact with the space ship whizzing overhead. It was our only chance . . . he just HAD to get a reply. . . .

"We must be on you, but can't hear you . . . pretzels are running low. . . ."

But it was useless. The orbiting space station dropped over the horizon, leaving just a few meager "data packet bursts" to tantalize us.

Actually, this is not a science fiction story. Inspired by our chance viewing of the Hubble Space Telescope passing overhead the other night, the Radio Guys decided to see if they could get in touch with the Space Station. Turns out that one of the current residents, Astronaut Bill McArthur, is a ham, so he talks Rod & Tom's language. They spent the day at one of their favorite activities, crafting a special hand-held antenna that could be pointed at the Station as it flew overhead. (Don't they have enough antennas already??) A few emails to NASA (including some help from Sallie Smith) got them the orbital transit times for this part of the world, and they were ready.

Comm-Tom held the antenna, SEA-Rae marked the transit times, and Rod-io manned the radio. Doc Pam attended in the event of injury. The Media Team was on hand to record the event, and a crowd of rubber-neckers gathered.

As the transit began, Rod began his calls. "NA1SS" is the U.S. Amateur Radio Call Sign for the International Space Station. "WØCXX" is Rod's call sign. "Maritime Mobile" identifies us as aboard a ship on the high seas. "Region 3" is the ITU (International Telecommunications Union) region of the world we are in, as agreed by international treaty.

Sadly, Rod's calls were not answered, and we were all disappointed. Maybe the astronauts were asleep? Maybe they were afraid to be asked to teach a SEA School? Anyway, the Station will pass overhead regularly, and our hams will try again.

They did try again, and were successful. The ISS orbits the earth once every ninety minutes, and its path carries it in view of a particular point at irregular (but predictable) intervals. The station is in view for up to fifteen minutes (depending on its elevation above the horizon) at each pass, offering us a chance to have a few short conversations with Astronaut Bill McArthur. It was thrilling to imagine what we were able to accomplish, and to make a connection between explorers probing the bottom of the ocean and those living in outer space.

Of course, most was not fun and games. Day after day the Ocean Explorer chirped away, our ship handling and coordination was refined, and our map of the ocean floor grew. As the mission progressed, the team worked efficiently, and we continued to be amazed by what we were seeing on the ocean floor. One feature that was of great interest was a distinct line, several hundred meters long, imaged earlier during our target runs. Clearly not of geological origin, it seemed mysterious at first until Jeff correlated it with the 2002 event log and realized it was the drag mark left on the ocean floor when we recovered NOMAD at the end of the last mission. The fact that the Ocean Explorer sonar could easily detect this narrow (barely one meter wide) furrow in the sand was very encouraging, and gave us increased confidence that the Electra would not escape our notice.

The generally flat and smooth ocean floor below us was sprinkled with a handful of truly awesome volcanic calderas, all close to two miles in diameter, rising generally a couple of hundred meters from the seafloor. Our fathometer on the ship would detect these "bumps" in the terrain hours before the sonar would pass over them, so we had some warning and were careful to gain a little altitude as the Explorer approached. By making composite images from multiple adjacent passes, we could build a mosaic of these craters, yielding some beautiful pictures. One of the calderas had a strange-looking structure emanating from one side; we arranged to fly by that spot again later when investigating a nearby contact and saw a dramatic image of a field of lava tubes streaming from a vent in the crater's rim. Looking like a bundle of ropy dreadlocks, we wondered just how fresh were the lava flows that caused them. Lava tubes are formed when a flowing river of magma begins to cool on the top, forming a crust over the still-flowing stream, and then the flow abruptly stops. The still-liquid rock flows out, leaving the empty tube surrounded by solid rock. I had seen (and even hiked into and through) lava tubes in the crater at the top of Haleakala, the volcanic peak forming most of the island of Maui, and could imagine how these looked on the ocean floor. I certainly wished we had a science team on board to help investigate this phenomenon.

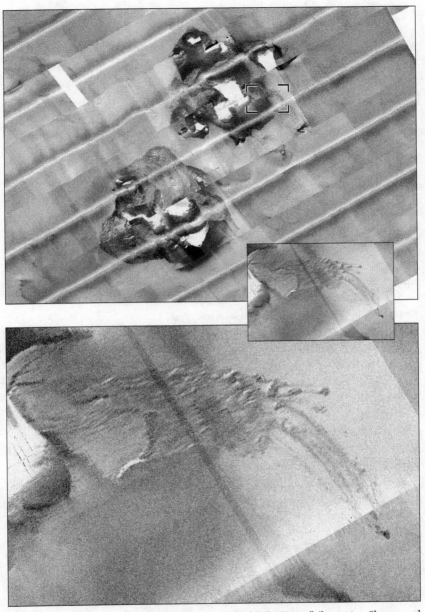

Lava tubes emanate from a volcanic feature dubbed "The Twins" (honoring Sherry and Shirley). These resemble similar features found on land, and could have been formed quite recently, geologically speaking. The box in the upper drawing is shown in the inset and expanded in the lower box. White area are shadows, where the sonar signal was blocked by ridges. (Courtesy Waitt Institute for Discovery.)

Though these features were beautiful and intellectually exciting, they were a bit of a worry for our search. The area covered by these craters was very small, but the ridges created "shadow zones" that the sonar could not "see" into, at least not without another pass to allow a look from a different angle. Our map of the ocean floor would include a few hiding places, small in percentage, but more than large enough to hold many Electras. And was there evidence of fresh lava flow? Without a geologist aboard, we couldn't tell if the features were thousands of years old or decades-recent. There was a tiny, but non-zero, chance that the Electra was consumed in a subsea volcanic outburst, never to be seen again.

April Fool's Day marked a major milestone in the expedition: we completed the survey of the primary search area. At 2044 on Saturday evening, the Ocean Explorer lifted off the bottom after nearly eighteen days of continuous surveying at depths approaching 20,000 feet. Over that time we added over 650 square nautical miles to the area searched in 2002, making the area searched to date by the Nauticos team nearly 1,300 square miles, about the size of the State of Rhode Island! This region was mapped at a resolution of one meter, so that we could see objects smaller than an automobile. We did miss a few spots, owing to calderas, ridges, and one small stripe missed in 2002, when we were having winch control problems early in the mission. Still, our overall coverage exceeded 95 percent, and we judged our likelihood of detection of an Electra-sized contact to be very high.

The performance of Oceaneering's Ocean Explorer was nothing short of spectacular. Since the broken HPU that cost us five days in the beginning of the mission, we had experienced not one moment of down time. Our rate of coverage was over one and a half square miles each hour, half again better than the NOMAD performance in 2002. I am quite sure that our efforts represented the largest contiguous area of deep-ocean floor ever mapped. It was quite an achievement, and we could take pride in it.

However, there was little justification for pride. We had not yet found the Electra.

There was still hope as we began the next phase of the operation. We had a collection of promising contacts scattered across the region that we intended to investigate, first using high-resolution sonar passes as we had earlier in the expedition, and then using the ROV for visual identification. Nothing was nearly as compelling as we expected the Electra to be, and there was great debate among the experts on board exactly how the plane would appear on the sonar screen.

This debate frustrated Elgen, as he was expecting that some of the best sonar experts in the world would be in better agreement on this basic issue. What Elgen understood intellectually, but failed to come to grips with emotionally, was that we were purposely operating on the edge of the sonar's ability to detect such a target. Just as a radar "blip" cannot be resolved into an aircraft at long range, the sonar could not resolve any real detail at the swath width we were using. This was a trade-off between greater coverage and less certainty. We wanted to be sure we would detect the Electra, but we would not know for sure we had until we got a closer look with a higher resolution (but shorter range) setting.

The time "wasted" between turns was also a source of immense frustration to the less experienced. Between Oceaneering and Nauticos, we had decades of experience with military, academic, and commercial mapping systems, and had worked with equipment from all around the world. No one knew a better way to cover an area effectively with a towed sonar except by methodically and patiently "mowing the lawn," line by line, with agonizingly deliberate turns in between. Everyone new to the process had the same set of ideas to get around this, all of which had long ago been proven not to work.

There was a new and better way, however, and I had talked to the Institute about this early in our relationship. Autonomous Underwater Vehicles (AUVs) were an emerging technology that would soon be available to operate at the depth we needed. In fact, Jeff had been working with a military system the past year that could, for quite a high price, be built for a commercial client. I had worked with this technology in military and academic programs my entire career, and was delighted with the opportunity to promote it. The main advantage of an AUV is that it has no cable attaching it to the ship, so it can turn easily and, in principle, can travel faster. Its disadvantages are lack of power and complexity of navigation, as well as unproven reliability. All power must be supplied by on-board batteries, which limits speed, sonar range, and endurance. Able to operate for only about a day at a time, these systems are normally used in pairs, one surveying while the other is charging batteries on the support ship. In deep water, the transition from surface to bottom to resume a lane of mapping adds uncertainty to navigation, and there is no tether to keep the vehicle on track, so it can drift off line. Navigation systems are much more complicated, and must rely on anchored acoustic beacons for some operations. Also, communication to the surface is very limited, so one has to wait until the vehicle returns to know in detail what it has found.

Besides the high cost (as much as five million dollars to build a pair), the AUV benefits for the Amelia project would be marginal because of the great depth and long search lanes. Also, the remoteness of the site coupled with unproven reliability of a new technology made the risk of failure or even loss of the system unacceptably high. Still, there are major advantages to such a system, in particular the ability to quickly go to a designated spot on the ocean floor and image a contact. For this reason, I have suggested a "hybrid" approach, using a single AUV to investigate contacts and supplement a survey, while a towed sonar is doing the bulk of the mapping.

Another emerging technology is "synthetic aperture sonar," a device modeled in theory after the radar of the same name used in military and satellite applications. The idea is that the larger the antenna or sonar array, the greater the range and resolution. This is analogous to the size of a camera or telescope aperture; the bigger the lens, the finer the image. One can create an artificial, or synthetic, array by putting many smaller ones in a precise geometric arrangement. Or, one can artificially create the illusion of a large array by careful timing of information from the same array as it moves through different spots. This is the principle used in synthetic aperture sonar. If it could be made to work, one could map huge areas at high resolution in much shorter times. Unfortunately, the precision required to know the changing location and accurate pointing has so far defeated development of this technology much beyond the experimental stage.

So, our team had the best sonar devices, the most reliable equipment, the latest in computer processing, and some of the top operators in the world. But we remained limited by the physics of the ocean and the mechanics of long cables. By industry standards, we were doing remarkable, unprecedented work. But the Institute was, understandably, interested in results.

We planned a meeting to review our collection of sonar contacts and assess them. It was meant to be an open-exchange-of-ideas working session, to make sure we covered all bases and made the best choices for using our remaining precious time at sea. Jeff Morris and Mark Wilson, lead OTECH sonar analyst, had prepared a summary of targets complete with enhanced imagery, and were prepared to lead the discussion. The rest of the gathering, including the entire operations team, would engage in discussion, make observations, ask questions, and suggest priorities. I had intended to sit in the back and observe the team go through the planned process, reserving objective judgment after letting everyone have their say.

I climbed the ladder up to the Ops room, just a few minutes before the meeting was to start and, to my surprise and consternation, found that the entire room was set up like a theater with people wearing lapel mikes and occupying assigned seats. I planned to sit in the back so not to influence the debate, but Adam and Collette wanted me to sit in front so I could be seen on camera leading the discussion. I was completely surprised by this development. It was too late to protest, as the character of the meeting was irretrievably altered. Needless to say, it was not the kind of session I envisioned, and not the method of leadership I used. We pressed on, but in that setting everyone clammed up except for the presenters, and we ended up with a "staged" event that was less than productive as a useful assessment.

After that episode, we decided to have a navigation team meeting at 4:30 AM, both to accommodate watch schedules and to avoid excessive attention and get some real work done.

The Ocean Explorer was retrieved, the "gapfiller" sonar projectors were re-configured, and the sonar sent on its way back to the depths, returning to the bottom after less than twelve hours from the moment we stopped surveying. Among other things, we were happy to get a chance to load more cups . . . our supply of crushed Styrofoam souvenirs was sparse!

We had identified a small collection of targets that we felt were worth a look in high resolution. It was our hope that one of these would be compelling enough to warrant deployment of the ROV for visual identification. Otherwise, we would search a little more, and then on the last two days make at least one ROV deployment on our best target.

For now, our best hope was Target 87, which we came to call the "Blue Crab," based on the sonar image's resemblance to the tasty Chesapeake crustacean. None of the sonar blips was as big as we thought the Electra would appear, so our expectations were muted. Still, after weeks at sea, and day after day of surveying, we were eager to change gears and take some closer looks.

One encouraging thing we had noted in our review of the new survey: the frequency and density of notable contacts in the 2006 region were the same as in the 2002 region. This, despite using a different sonar and operating team. If one sonar was out-performing the other, we would expect some difference in the two datasets, and we would wonder if we missed anything. Also, the contacts we imaged from the 2002 data were all smaller than the Electra. If this held true for our new batch of contacts, it would suggest that we were seeing everything there was to see.

It is remarkable to think that, with the possible exception of the Blue Crab, there was no evidence of *any* manmade object on the ocean floor in an area the size of Rhode Island. This was not unexpected, as we knew there was little commerce through the region and no significant war activity, but it served to remind us that we were in a truly remote corner of the planet.

So, with the Ocean Explorer at depth, chirping away at the ocean floor, we approached Target 87, the Blue Crab, with guarded excitement. The sonar touched down only a hour and twenty minutes from the target area, so we didn't have too long to wait. As Rod Blocksome wrote in his journal:

> We are approaching the "Blue Crab" target using high resolution sonar. [Adam and Collette] rush in at about ten minutes prior and start ordering people around, installing microphones through their zippers, etc. It was quiet with the Ops room full of people watching the sonar screens. From the geology nearby, I was afraid we might pass directly over the target and thus not see it because of the small blind spot directly below the sled.
>
> All of a sudden there it was on the right edge of channel 1 (left sidescan)—just a little past the first return. It was a few seconds before we realized we had the target. It was hard (bright) and sharp but a bit small. Most people's reaction was "Oh! That was it?"

Unfortunately, this time we were "too" close . . . the sonar passed directly over the target! We could see it clearly in the gapfiller, but we had never fully adjusted for the distortions caused by the unusual geometric arrangement of the sonar projectors, so it was inconclusive. The main arrays picked up nothing of use. We saved the data for further analysis and began to maneuver the ship for the run to the next target, number 88.

I set my disappointment aside and steeled myself to continue the search for Amelia.

Disasters are the confluence of improbable events.
—David Katz

# Medical Emergency!

April 4. Tuesday, 12:18 PM YST.

**W**e had the fuel. We had the time, and we had the will. We had a plan. What we needed was the funding to stay out to sea a bit longer and continue the search. We had looked just about everywhere we thought likely, but we had one more area to examine that had some real merit. All of our assumptions about Amelia's flight seemed pretty solid, hard to seriously question. Sure, there were lots of *unlikely* but possible places the Electra could be, but had we looked in all of the *likely* ones yet?

Among the assumptions we questioned, thanks to research done by David Dunlap, was whether Amelia used the wrong position for Howland Island. That assumption fit the scenario very nicely, but what if it was wrong? We knew from David that someone tried to send her an updated chart, though we had no evidence that she received it or used it.

But what if she did?

Changing assumptions such as that one opened up a new area to examine—or, to be more precise, raised the probability of success in some regions that we had previously considered too unlikely to warrant the investment of precious search time. We could search most of those areas in a few days' time, and leave the final day to deploy the ROV and see for sure just what the Blue Crab target was. Then we would be low on fuel, and reaching the limits of the Institute's patience and crew commitments. But the cheapest survey days are the ones you add to the expedition once you are already on station, having mobilized, transited, and deployed your equipment. Another $125,000 might turn a $2 million expedition from just another good effort into a rousing and dramatic success.

I had sent a message to Lynn back in Maryland expressing my hope that we might get some more time. I'm sure she was personally disappointed by the prospect of extending the mission and wanted us all back soon, but she was the model of encouragement in her reply:

Glad to hear that you may have a little more time. Remember the *I-52* was found in the little more time that Tom [Dettweiler] managed to squeak out of Paul [Tidwell, the expedition leader] when he wanted to give up!

I knew from experience that discoveries usually come when all means are nearly exhausted, or a little extra effort can be mustered. Lynn's message was a welcome reminder, and I was grateful for her support.

During the previous midwatch, we had completed the process of imaging likely contacts with high-resolution sonar, and decided to make best use of our time by positioning the ship to resume search in a new area. The next morning, we had our daily progress meeting, and afterward I spoke to Ted on the radio-telephone. I explained the situation, described our plan, and discussed some options. By the time we finished, I had the go-ahead to extend the mission a few more days.

By that time we were already on the first line of the new search area. I hung up the phone and relaxed for a moment. Then Spence appeared, with the words, "We have an emergency."

Flying down the ladders I reached the berthing space to see a tangle of bodies on the deck. At the center of attention were twins Shirley and Sherry, writhing in convulsions. A group of crewmen, led by Pat Sullivan, were trying their best to keep the two women under control so they wouldn't hurt themselves. Pat explained in a few terse and clear words the situation, and I grasped the seriousness of it immediately. I turned to Spence, and told him to secure search operations, retrieve the Ocean Explorer, and make best speed to the nearest medevac location. Having set those actions in motion, I turned my attention to the twins, and helped with the immediate efforts to safely move one of them to another compartment.

The 2006 Amelia Earhart search mission had come to a dramatic close, only a few miles from the location that the 2002 mission had ended under similarly unexpected serious circumstances.

A lot had happened between the time I left the operations briefing to call Ted, and Spence's appearance. I was so intent on my conversation that I failed to hear the ship's PA announcement:

"Dr. Pam, Dr. Pam, please report to berthing area four immediately!"

Rod and many of the others were at lunch in the mess deck, having concluded the morning meeting. In his journal of events, Rod recalls:

Pam was not at lunch at the time. Jason immediately jumped up from the table and dashed out, heading for the emergency. He is a former Marine and had emergency first aid skills. The mess was suddenly quiet as each of us looked around to see who was not here and began pondering what had happened.

My first thought was there had been an accident and someone was injured. Thank God we had a doctor along. She should be able to handle just about anything. Back to eating, but it's quieter now. No one is joking. Ten to fifteen minutes pass and the Captain comes in and briefly announces that it's Shirley Mira. She is having convulsions. Pam and Jason are attending her. Her twin sister, Sherry, is also with her. He says it looks serious. Larry and Pat go to help Pam. Dave confers with the Captain and the decision is made to start bringing up the sonar sled as we are going to have to get under way for some medical help.

The rest of us pitch in and help clean up the dishes and the Mess. I learn how to use the scalding industrial dish washer and start doing dishes. This freed Ami so she could go help with Shirley as needed. Others pitched in and did similar chores.

I'm thinking this must be epilepsy and it will be over any time now. Best thing to do is stay out of the way of the doctor and the folks attending Shirley.

An hour later, Rod finished with the dishes and headed down the passageway to the ladder leading to his cabin. At the ladder top is the entrance to the "hospital," and another ladder going down to "girls town"—the women's berthing spaces, including Shirley and Sherry's cabin. Rod met Pam just coming up-ladder and asked how Shirley was doing.

Her eyes were wide as she exclaimed, "Still seizing and now Sherry is also!"

Rod replied in amazement, "You mean both twins are having seizures?!"

"Yes!—this is just too weird! We're going to have to separate them."

"Do you need help moving them?" Rod offered.

"No, I think Pat and Jason can handle it. We're going to bring Shirley up and put her in the big padded sofas in the Lounge. But here's what you can do—gather up all the cleaning chemicals Sherry uses and make a list of what they contain for me."

Rod replied that he would get right on it. Grabbing his notebook from his cabin, he went to look for Ami, who worked with Sherry cleaning the rooms, heads, mess, and galley. Along the way he collected Marika, and together they filled a plastic tub with all of the cleaning supplies the women used. They start reading the fine print and making a list, noting some nasty sounding chemicals in the industrial strength cleaners and disinfectants. Rod writes down the phone numbers to call for physician assistance in case of swallowing or eye contact. They finished the list and gave it to Pam, who paused long enough to scan it and shake her head—she didn't think those were the cause. Besides, Shirley worked in the galley and wouldn't have been using them.

Meanwhile, I was in the berthing spaces with Pat, Jason, Larry, and several others. Both twins were experiencing violent convulsions requiring several men to keep them from harming themselves in the confined spaces, with steel bulkheads and sharp metal edges to fixtures in the room. Pat had taken charge of moving one of the women to a different room, and it was a great comfort to have him around in such a situation. He directed several of the guys to bundle Sherry up in a blanket and they managed to move her (while convulsing) into another room across the passageway. With four of us attending each woman, we felt that we had some measure of control, although I can attest to the uncommon strength of a body, even a slim female, undergoing severe convulsions.

As the underwater equipment was being retrieved, we headed southeast toward the island of Kanton, the nearest place with an airstrip, over 450 miles away. Once we were able to make full speed, we could be there in thirty-six hours.

The twins continued convulsing, sometimes violently. Four of us were holding little Shirley, who is small but has a lot of strength. She would come out of it for a little while, talk to us, ask about her sister, and want to get up, but we kept her on the carpeted deck surrounded by pillows. Then her eyes would flutter and she would start again. This went on steadily for over four hours. The same was going on in the next room, and the twins seemed to be feeding off each other's anxiety. As no end was in sight, we decided to separate the women and set up more comfortable and manageable surroundings for them. During one of her lucid spells, we carried Shirley up to the lounge and placed her on one of the couches, moved against another couch so she could not fall off. Surrounded by cushions, and with at least one person watching at all times, we felt she was as safe as we could manage. Sherry was set up in another space under similar conditions. Still, the seizures kept returning.

Rod was concerned for our ship's doctor, who we had suddenly come to rely on more than we ever expected. His journal reflected his concern. . . but Rod was one to channel that anxiety into action.

> After encountering Pam, I could see she was under intense pressure. She was chasing around having to do things that really didn't require a doctor's skills. I knew the outcome of this situation depended heavily on her. So I offered to be her "nurse" to take some of the pressure off her so she could concentrate on figuring out what was wrong with the twins and getting them treated.
>
> I explained to her "my only qualifications are my wife is an RN so I know a tiny bit of the routine and lingo—but I'll do anything you need—but you'll have to explain how and what to do."

It took her about a milli-second to "'hire'" me. "Come with me," she says.

At this point I had not seen either twin. I was thinking back to the very few times many years ago when I was around someone who was having an epileptic seizure. It's not a pretty sight.

As I followed Pam down the passageway, I had a moment of "second thoughts." What if I make a mistake? We're dealing with human beings—not electronics equipment. This could be emotionally very tough as I had become good friends with the twins—especially Shirley, since I kidded around with her at nearly every meal—and they are about the same age as my own adult children.

We stepped into the Lounge. The lights were dimmed. There on the sofa is Shirley, eyes closed, teeth clenched, and shaking uncontrollably. Pat is holding Shirley's head, stroking her cheek and smiling as he spoke reassuringly to her. A couple others were holding her hands and feet down.

It was a gut-wrenching sight, and you could see the fear and apprehension in the eyes of those holding her—except for Pat. Seeing Pat calmly handling the situation suddenly made it "click" for me. All the apprehension and doubts cleared from my mind. We had to do everything possible to help these gals—so let's get on with it.

Pam is checking pulse, respiration, etc. Soon Shirley's convulsions start building up to larger and more violent motions. Her breathing comes sharp and in short pulses—sometimes barking noises. It's very wild and she would be throwing herself all over the place if it weren't for the restraining hands holding her. Then she "froze stiff"—no breathing. We watch. We call her name— "Breathe, Shirley" — "Take a breath, Shirley." Many seconds tick by. Pat is working around into position to start CPR when suddenly she takes a gulp of air. What a relief!

Pam leaves. I follow. In the passageway, she tells me, "Try not to scare folks, but I want you to make a list of everyone on the ship. Find out who has had CPR training, when they took the training, and if they ever had to use it for real."

Everyone on the ship wanted to help. Amanda, of course, was working side by side with Pam, and had formal responsibility as the ship's medical officer. Pat was a source of great comfort to the twins, and his calm handling of the crisis was reassuring to us all. Similarly, Larry Tyler, the OTECH team leader and our third most qualified medic on board, was a cool-headed, unflappable leader. Carla-Rae was to put in many long hours caring for the twins in the days ahead. She had her moment of fear and self-doubt. Once over it, she was solid as a rock and a tremendous help.

We gave the girls oxygen, and the Doc tried a small amount of valium as well as some other treatments as suggested from consultation with other physicians over the satellite phone. Nothing seemed to be helping.

Now, we were sure the Coast Guard would help us—we were no longer seeking spare parts to keep a commercial expedition going. We had a true medical emergency! But shortly after we headed to Kanton, the Coast Guard informed us that the airstrip was unsuitable, and they would only send an aircraft if the emergency was life threatening. Faced with the prospect of risking an aircraft and crew, Doc Pam and Captain Mike debated the condition of the twins and concluded that we could manage for the additional time it would take to make it to an island with a safe airport. So we turned around and headed west, once again for Tarawa, about two days away at best speed. We expected to conduct a medevac there with the Air Force.

Again to Tarawa! Who *ever* would have believed *that*?

By then we were coming to terms with the situation, which was transitioning from an immediate life-threatening emergency to a long-term life-threatening ordeal. The *Mt. Mitchell* was being transformed into a hospital ship and, with ocean search operations suspended, all available hands found a new role supporting our remade identity.

Pam and Rod directed Bethany to organize a "med watch." She made an hourly sign-up sheet and posted it in the mess. We needed two people with each twin around the clock, needing to restrain them from hurting themselves and be prepared to do CPR and fetch the doctor if necessary. Either Pam or Amanda were up and about at all times. "Nurse" Rod, with Tom's help, started a written log on each woman to record the timing, duration, and characteristics of the convulsions. Periodically, Pam reviewed this log and issued instructions while flying down the passageways and ladders, running to Ops for satellite phone calls, conferring with the captain, going through the dispensary medications, and trying to keep an eye on the twins.

Others pitched in to help in more mundane ways. The ship's routine had been disrupted, especially the all-important tasks of preparing, serving, and cleaning up after meals, normally the twins' main jobs. Fortunately, we had a number of volunteers to pick up the slack. Jeff Palshook and Dwight from the OTECH team took turns with galley duty, as did Bethany, Carla-Rae, and others. Marika supplemented Rod as another Doc assistant.

Rod's crash course in nursing continued. . . .

Pam grabs a drug bottle and syringe from the dispensary cabinet. "Come on, we're going to give Sherry a shot." We find Sherry convulsing with two people protecting her from hitting anything. Pam tells us we have to hold her immobile on her side for the few seconds it will take to give her the medicine. The adrenalin in this 120-pound gal made her super strong, but the three of us managed to hold her still. After the shot, we watch . . . and wait. . . . Nothing happens. The seizures continue.

We go up a deck to the dispensary and unpack IV bags, tubes, etc. Pam is reading the labels. She gets one prepared and off we go to the Lounge to see Shirley. Pam now hits me with something unexpected which again drives home the seriousness of the situation.

"I want you to double check me to calculate the dose of this drug—It's Dilantin," says Pam. "Now what is the concentration?"

"5 mg/ml" [Rod replies.]

"Good," says Pam. "Now I want to give her a 1 mg dose—so calculate how much you would put in the syringe."

Geez, I'm thinking, this means the concentration will change with the amount of saline in the IV bag. I start working out the math on my notebook and it's quickly apparent to Pam I didn't understand the question. Stopping me, she says,

"Here, don't be too much of an engineer on me. This is the ratio." (Writes the equation on my notebook.) "What's the answer?"

"Oh, that's easy—its 0.2 ml."

"Good."

She fills the syringe and hands it to me. Now we go over to Shirley. Pam puts the IV needle into a vein in Shirley's arm. Blood spurts momentarily as she connects the IV tube and tapes it down. The drip starts and she shows me how it should look when working normally. Next she puts the drug into the IV. We wait and watch. Not much change.

We prepare a second IV and syringe and go visit Sherry. Same routine. Capt. Mike comes in—satellite phone call for Pam. As she starts to go up to Ops, she hands Sue and me several sheets of paper holding the ship's inventory of medicines. Pam points to one drug and says to find it and carry it with me.

Sue and I go through the drugs, finally locate the correct one (taking a queue from Pam, we both verify it), and I slip it in my pocket—not knowing what Pam plans to do with it. Soon Pam's back from the phone call.

Over the next couple hours, Pam gave each twin a couple more doses of the antiseizure drug—still no changes. The seizures continue with varying intensity and durations for both women. The hours dragged by and the sun set off the bow of the ship as we drove straight west at top speed for Tarawa.

By nightfall, we were twelve hours into the crisis, and were making no progress in effective treatment of our patients, other than keeping them stable. Knowing our medevac site, and confident that we were doing all we could, I considered our options for continuing the mission. A quick look at time, distance, fuel supply, and the calendar told a discouraging tale. Even if we were able to quickly transfer our patients and return to the operating site, we would not arrive until sometime on April 9, and even if we extended to return to Honolulu as late as the April 17, that would only give us two days to work. Although we could deploy equipment and get some additional surveying done, there would be little return for the effort and expense, and that assumed the medevac would take place with dispatch. So, I did not recommend we take that course. Rather, I informed Ted that we would complete our medevac and return directly to Honolulu from Tarawa.

Further searching for Amelia Earhart would have to wait for another mission.

So my thoughts returned to organizing the medevac. As events would prove, this turned out to be far more complicated than we could have imagined.

Rod remained focused on the twins. At one point, he wondered what the drug was that Pam told him to keep handy. She explained that the antiseizure drug she is giving them could impair their breathing. "In case that happens, you have the antidote in your pocket." The seriousness of this business hit him again.

Back to the dispensary. Pam gets out another drug—capsules of Diazipam. "Count these, take three out for each gal, then write the remaining quantity on the bottle. I put the three pills in paper coffee cups and also get an additional cup of water and we take them to each gal. Attendants are to try and get them to swallow the pills whenever they can sit up. They get them in Sherry without much trouble but Shirley's not able to take hers for some time. I check on them about every 15 minutes. During one check on Shirley, I see the cups are gone.

"Did she swallow the pills?" I asked the med watch.

"No, seizures have prevented it."

"What happened to the pills?"

"Don't know."

I go back to Pam to get more. She's talking to Captain Mike. When he hears my story, he gets very apologetic and says he saw the cups and thought he would clean up the area a bit. So he tossed them all in the trash.

Geez. We have three days before we reach Tarawa and with an exact count on these pills, three get trashed! Mike felt bad, but it just pointed up how much we have to be alert and thinking clearly as we deal with this crisis.

The situation is very stressed. The drugs should have some effect, but they don't. Tarawa is still a long way in front of us as the ship is making top speed—about 12 knots. Then at 9:30 PM a remarkable thing happens. Shirley opens her eyes, smiles at everyone there, and in a couple of minutes starts chit-chatting with us.

What a relief! It's over—now if Sherry would just do the same thing. About 30 minutes more, and Shirley feels steady enough to go use the bathroom; coming back, she says she's sleepy and bingo—back into convulsions for the next 45 minutes.

About an hour later, Sherry comes around and talks to us. We learn that she can hear everything going on around her during the seizures—she is just unable to respond. She goes to sleep at 12:30 AM and is quiet except for minor twitching motions.

As dawn approached, Sherry had been sleeping peacefully for several hours. Shirley had a rough night and was just beginning to quiet down.

### April 5; Wednesday. Medical Emergency, Day Two.

Though the seriousness of the crisis we were facing did not diminish, the ability of the people aboard the *Mt. Mitchell* to cope with the situation improved. For many on board, duties had not changed, as the ship continued to motor along (though at a quicker pace) and require the normal level of attention. For others, such as Doc Pam and Amanda, what had been a routine and comfortable cruise had in a flash become a crisis of indefinite duration and uncertain outcome that drew on all their time, focus, and skills. For most of the charter team, the day-to-day duties that had been learned and honed over the weeks were substituted by entirely new tasks requiring a completely different set of abilities. It is to the credit of all, that adaptation to the new circumstances was essentially complete by the next morning.

I was able to take a few moments to send a brief message to Lynn back home, very terse. Of course, she had already been alerted by Charlotte. Lynn replied:

Charlotte is trying to get through, but all lines are busy. She is thinking that she would not send you to one of the islands Capt Mike is talking about, but rather to meet Coast Guard somewhere around Kanton. She is trying to reach you to get more info before calling the Coast Guard. Lynn.

By then, of course, we were heading away from Kanton. A flurry of messages were passed that day, including referrals to specialists who had previously treated "Micro-Asians" and might have some insight to the seizures and their possible psychosomatic nature, alternative island destinations, medical facilities on those islands, and prospective medevac options.

Through it all, Charlotte Vick was an indispensable resource. With a background in private industry and government, Charlotte was adept at working in a multicultural, multinational arena. She had arranged hotel rooms, helped us get our much-needed spare parts, and would be handling the public relations in Hawaii when we returned. Having followed most of the major ocean policy and technology developments for the past thirty years, Charlotte was completely invested in ocean exploration and the future of the seas.

The twins remained much the same, still lapsing into convulsions from time to time. The periods in between seemed better, and they even were up and in the mess room for a little food that evening (although one of them had another attack at that time). Either they were improving or we were getting used to their condition. Rod had quite a scare when he was helping the 120-pound Shirley down a ladder in rolling seas when another seizure hit. Fortunately, Jason was handy and helped avert a hazardous tumble down the steel steps.

During periods when the women were lucid, Doc Pam conducted private interviews with each of them, attempting to understand the circumstances of the onset and their medical history. The cause of their condition remained a mystery, despite consultations with physicians and hospitals around the world, including the Mayo Clinic.

### April 6; Thursday. Medical Emergency, Day Three.

As we proceeded steadily toward Tarawa, our medevac options began to deteriorate. It seemed that those not on board personally witnessing events were assessing the situation as less dire than we were. When queried, Doc Pam had to admit that under our care the twins' condition was not getting worse, and we were able to keep them from further harm for the time being. The Coast Guard concluded that our situation was not life threatening, and so an evacuation in Tarawa was again "not in the public interest." It certainly was frustrating to us that JAG (legal) officers in Washington, D.C., made that diagnosis. So, we began exploring civilian medevac capabilities, with the tireless help of Charlotte, and even considering just holding on and making best speed to Honolulu, a trip of about six days. Timing worked against us, as top speed would get us to Tarawa the next day at midnight, and there was no point in arriving there in the middle of the night, or even much before noon. This was just as well, because the low speeds we had been traveling for the last few weeks while surveying had caused unburned oil to build up in the stacks, which tended to catch fire from the heat of the engines at full power. (We learned this on our first attempt, turning the *Mt. Mitchell* briefly into a Roman candle!) With a chance to slow down, the engineers got busy with the unpleasant task of removing the oily lagging (insulation) in the stacks and replacing it.

Further complications affecting our efforts to quickly evacuate the twins came courtesy of the insurance industry. Facing looming liabilities, the ship owner's insurance company insisted on certain steps, which may have looked quite logical on paper in the beginning but made no sense to us now in the central Pacific. As the issue involved *Mt. Mitchell* crew persons, it really was the ship's problem to handle, and we had to follow their lead. The crew, in turn, were beholding to the ship's owner, Global Seas, who dealt with their insurance company. Global Seas had to worry about the health and safety of its crew, as well keep their obligations to the mission funder who had chartered the ship. As far as I could tell, the Institute put no pressure on Global Seas and cooperated fully, but the company had to manage unfolding events to minimize their exposure to legal action. Soon, it seemed that everything we were doing was being second-guessed by folks from Seattle to Washington, D.C., and we were being directed to take steps that we knew were fruitless, but were designed to satisfy some established protocol or deflect an imaginary lawsuit.

Chief among these steps was a demand that, once we arrived in Tarawa, we take the twins to the island hospital for "evaluation and treatment" prior to expecting a medevac flight. We had been to the island, and we knew the medical facilities and expertise there were inferior to what we had available on the *Mt. Mitchell*.

I confessed to a shipmate at one point that I felt rather helpless. The Institute in San Diego was in charge of the mission, Global Seas in Seattle was in charge of the medical situation, and I lacked the legal authority to direct anything. From the moment I ordered the survey to be suspended, I relinquished any control over events. My shipmate gave me a searching look, and wondered why I felt that way. I think he expected me to take charge of the situation and set us on a path to resolution, but I felt I had to defer to the captain and others in this case. It was a very frustrating feeling, especially for one who is used to taking charge and solving problems.

## April 7 (8); Friday (Saturday).
## Medical Emergency, Day Four. Arrival at Tarawa.

In the course of the transit, we shifted from Time Zone −12 (Yankee Standard Time) to +12 (Mike Standard Time) as we crossed the International Date Line heading west. So our arrival in Tarawa was on Saturday morning, local time.

During the night, our patients seemed to be improving, as judged by having more and longer periods of lucidity. When lucid, they resisted being confined and begged to be allowed up from their beds. Amanda told them that if they stayed awake and free of seizure for two hours, they could take a walk. Shirley wanted to go up to the bridge and see Spence, and Sherry wanted to go to the Wet Lab, her favorite place to relax. This usually included a smoke— which Sherry was desperate for—but Pam would not allow the twins to have any kind of stimulant, including cigarettes and coffee. Shirley made the mark and got her trip to the bridge, but Sherry fell asleep. When she woke up a bit later, ready to go, Amanda told her she had to wait a bit longer.

A facet of Sherry's personality previously unknown to us erupted as anger. Her pleading turned to furious demands. As she was being walked back to her bed from the bathroom, she surprised her attendant Andy with suddenly acquired mobility and just kept going, right out the other door! Before she could be stopped, she somehow made her way down to her berthing area. Andy followed her but, short of him tackling her, she was unstoppable. Marika was sitting outside the room where Shirley was sleeping. Sherry barged in, closed the door, and locked it! Through the door came the sounds of raised Palauan voices, as Sherry woke Shirley and began to shout at her. According to later translation, the gist of the "conversation" was a diatribe of accusations against Shirley, blaming her for all of the bruises, the IV's, and drama. As the crew scrambled to locate the master key, Sherry finally opened the door at Amanda's demand.

We arrived at Tarawa Atoll in the morning, and docked smoothly at the island of Betio, the same place as in 2002. We first spied the island lights in the wee hours of the morning, and watched them go by a few miles to starboard as we circled around to the other side of the atoll, where the passage through the coral reef had been cut for shipping traffic. That took several hours (it's a pretty big atoll), and it was well after sunrise before we reached the harbor entrance and the pilot boat came alongside. I noted that it was the first land we had seen in thirty days, to which Carla-Rae reminded me of our glimpse of Howland Island from several weeks ago. She was technically correct, even though all we saw was some low-lying beach scrub from miles away, so I amended my comment to say it was the first *inhabited* land we had seen in thirty-eight days.

There was an ambulance waiting on the pier—a very good sign! After clearing customs (quite expeditiously, especially considering that it was a Saturday), the (for the moment, ambulatory) twins were quickly escorted off the ship and, with Doc Pam, Pat, and Rod, headed off to the hospital. We didn't expect to see Shirley and Sherry again.

Rod rode seat belt-less in an ancient SUV, aggressively driven by the island customs agent, following the ambulance over a grievously potholed road. The hospital was located on Bikenibeu, one in a chain of islets strewn along a narrow line marking the south side of the atoll. About forty-five minutes' drive from Betio, it was near the largest island in the chain, which included the airport. Rod learned that the agent was also the head of the Tarawa Bureau of Tourism, and his uncle operated a ham radio station on the island. Suddenly, he veered off the road, and Rod saw the ambulance disappear in the distance as they took a side trip to meet the uncle, over Rod's protests.

A short visit and tour of the ham "station" satisfied everyone, and Rod was finally able to convince the customs agent of the importance of arriving at the hospital the same time as the ambulance. Rod was imagining the chaos that would ensue if both women were to go into violent seizures with only Pat and Pam available to control them. Apparently, this impressed the agent, as once back on the main road, he drove wildly, passing cars, dodging potholes, and gunning the engine hard after each obstacle. As a measure of safety, he turned on his hazard lights.

In defiance of all odds, the battered SUV and its contents arrived safely in Bikenibeau. Rod described the events that followed:

We arrive at the hospital emergency entrance just after the ambulance had unloaded. I jump out and go inside to find both gals setting upon a crummy, dirty gurney with an unpainted plywood top. Both are smiling and chatting with Pat while Pam is talking to the hospital staff. I thought this was a bit primitive for a waiting room. Later I realized we were in the hospital emergency room—such that it was.

After a bit, Sherry starts convulsing so Pat lays her down and I take Shirley into another room on the other side of the admissions office. There is a similar gurney but with the luxury of a 2-inch mattress pad on the plywood. Five minutes later, I have my hands full as Shirley starts into convulsions. During this seizure episode, a Kiribati Nurse comes in. I'm thinking— "Good, some trained help—finally."

The Kiribati nurse asks me, "What's wrong with her?"

"She's having convulsions"

"Oh!" . . . and she walks out of the room.

Later, I have Shirley back but from the sounds in the next room, Pat is having a much tougher time with the more muscular Sherry.

The Kiribati nurse returns to ask me her name, birthday, and other information and takes Shirley's pulse and blood pressure. Next Pam comes in with another nurse to draw blood from Shirley. The nurse fumbles around and Pam has to talk her through how to do it properly. I'm starting to realize this hospital isn't going to be any help for us. Pam quietly tells me what's going on and what she's seen. It's appalling.

Shirley is doing OK now; Pam says, "Take pictures of everything now while you have the chance." I get the camera out and start clicking away. The place is filthy and in pitiful disrepair. The more I looked and shot pictures, the more appalled I became. I thought, "At home you wouldn't bring your pet to a vet's office if it looked like this."

Pat continues to attend Sherry, but Shirley is ready to walk. So Pam escorts her on a tour of the hospital to visit the VIP ward where she and Sherry will stay if they elect to remain in the hospital. I follow along—taking pictures of things that Pam is pointing to behind Shirley's back.

We must have been a very odd sight to the staff, patients, and visitors we encountered by the looks on their faces. They probably wondered which movie or

TV star this good-looking island gal was. She just had to be someone famous to be so gently escorted everywhere—and a paparazzi photographer trailing along taking photos!

Upon returning to the emergency room, we found Sherry lucid and ready for a walk. So now the entourage through the hospital enlarges to two movie stars—twins—plus a bodyguard—and that pesky paparazzi still pursuing them. We get quizzical looks from all the bystanders—patients and staff alike. It's a much needed comic relief for all of us.

Their potential hospital room was very plain but clean. No air conditioning—none anywhere in the hospital. The ocean was only 25 yards from their room. Bathroom was very primitive and unsanitary. No staff available to tend to them during seizures. So to keep them from injuring themselves, they would be strapped into the beds at night. Pam explained everything to them. We walked out on the beach while they thought about their decision. I took more pictures. Their decision: don't want to check into the hospital.

Good.

The obligatory visit to the Tarawa hospital complete, the group made their way back to the ship to try to convince those directing our fate that a medevac was warranted and necessary. . . . Meanwhile, time and money were slipping away.

Having no duties to attend to while this was going on, the rest of us (except for the ship's in-port watch section) headed for town. Repeating our path of four years earlier, we set out on foot and wandered down the pier and to the main street. Much had not changed, though those of us who visited in 2002 noticed some differences, generally for the better. In fact, the level of sanitation seemed to have improved substantially. There were trash bins all around that had collected a lot of the litter, and the odor of sewage, though present, was milder. We also noted a lot of new construction of small buildings and docking facilities. There was a major renovation of the dock in progress, in cooperation (and presumably funded by) the Japanese government, and a large gymnasium funded by the ROC (Republic of China) under construction.

Our first stop was the bank, so we could get some Australian dollars, the accepted currency here. I knew from experience that they would accept American dollars, but one-for-one (with the 2:3 exchange rate in their favor). Several of us were able to get Aussie bucks from the ATM, which we shared around. The next order of business was finding a beer, which was plentiful and sold everywhere. Some members of our group were way ahead in this regard, and one handed me a Tiger beer, brewed in Singapore. Even though it was only 10 AM, we didn't hesitate to down one. I can't say it was the best beer I've ever had, but it was certainly welcome.

After reliving most of the sights, sounds, and smells of Betio, we encountered another group from the ship who told us that our island "liberty" time had been extended from 1300 to 1700, as the ship was not expected to leave anytime soon. With a few extra hours to kill, my group decided to look for a restaurant called "Mary's," which Jonathan Blair, Tom V., and Rod had visited back in 2002. Also a hotel, it was apparently where most foreign visitors stayed when stranded on the island owing to some imagined opportunity for commerce.

We flagged down the first bus we saw. The busses were actually vans, usually nine-passenger, and came by just about every minute. Even though all of the signs were in English, we could not puzzle out the difference between them. Nor could the driver or any passenger understand where we wanted to go, or acted like they had ever heard of Mary's. Eventually, we concluded we were on the wrong bus and got off, even though we were headed in the right direction. We knew that Mary's was just on the other side of a causeway-bridge that connected Betio with the next island in the atoll, so we had some idea of where we were going. We got in another bus that seemed hopeful, and after lots of discussion (both with us and between each other) the driver and passengers concluded that we were going where we wanted to go. Somehow, after all of this, we arrived at Mary's, a pleasant little oasis of good food in a shady, restful setting.

We returned to the ship, having satisfied ourselves that we had seen the best Tarawa had to offer. We were shocked to find the ship gone from the pier! However, as we peered into the lagoon, we spied (to our relief) the *Mt. Mitchell* moored in the harbor some distance away, although we had no way to contact them and no idea how to get there. There was no shade on the pier, so we walked back toward town again to rest and consider our options (none), when we saw a rented van with Sherry, Shirley, the Doc, and helpers returning from the hospital.

Unable to raise the *Mt. Mitchell* on the ship-to-shore phone, Pat used his Iridium phone to call (at great expense) someone in Seattle, who relayed a message back to the ship. Soon, a small boat was on the way to collect us.

As we made our way back to the ship via several round trips in the little Zodiac rubber boat, we heard the horrifying details of the visit to the hospital. Rod described the unsanitary conditions, including dogs walking around peeing on the furniture, lack of facilities (they had no phone or fax, much less medical equipment), and absence of trained staff. They could not efficiently draw blood. They asked Pam to do everything for them. In the pictures that Rod took, one could see papers tacked up everywhere with basic how-to instructions for treatment of medical conditions written in big magic marker. I suppose they sufficed as procedural reminders, but they looked very crude and rather comical.

This was the hospital that the insurance people insisted we take our patients to for evaluation before they would authorize a medevac aircraft! The hospital doctor, who had no way of making a report back to Seattle—even if he had anything to report—eventually went home.

Pam was somehow able to find humor in it all: "In most trips you have a weird experience to tell about. . . . We're having four per day!"

By evening, after Pam spent two hours on the phone, we learned that an air ambulance was coming (from Alabama) at great expense, but not due to arrive until Monday (local time, two days hence). Though we would have been happy to leave the twins at a hospital in the care of competent medical professionals and begin the long transit back to Hawaii, this was not an option. We didn't have a suitable place for Sherry and Shirley other than the ship. Though the episodes were subsiding, they were still happening and we were no wiser about what we were dealing with—if any permanent harm was being caused by their state or if it would become drastically worse all of a sudden.

Back in Honolulu, Charlotte was doing what she could to help. She called Dr. Henry Preston, a doctor with Straub Hospital and Clinic in Honolulu, because he had worked extensively with Micronesian patients. As an internal medicine doctor, he really couldn't provide a great deal of assistance for problems at a distance. Without the right diagnostic tools on board the boat, no doctor would have been able to determine what might actually be wrong. Upon consultations with a few medical resources, it was suggested that the best hospital to handle such a medical evacuation would be Queens Medical Center in Honolulu.

Through her own sources, Charlotte was able to find out that the medical aviation services in Hawaii were in a bad state. One company had recently entered bankruptcy and another was having some difficulties as well. She was able to find an aircraft suitable to do the job; however, the ship's sources found what they deemed a better alternative.

Global Seas also sent a representative to Honolulu to meet the twins when they arrived. Charlotte took her to dinner, showed her the hospital, and shared all the information she had gleaned from her research. Having done all she could, Charlotte waited for the twins to arrive.

On top of it all, I broke off a chunk of a tooth filling! Though in some discomfort, I hated to mention it to Pam under the circumstances, but it turned out there was a nifty kit for temporary filling repair, and Larry volunteered to be Mr. Dentist. He told me to meet him in the mess deck a little later, and when I entered he had a saws-all in his hand, ready to operate! Pam assisted for Larry-Doc, and he patched me up, at least temporarily.

April 8 (9); Saturday (Sunday).
## Medical Emergency, Day Five. Stranded in Paradise.

The day was far less eventful, as the *Mt. Mitchell* remained our little floating hospital. Most everyone had their fill of sightseeing, and preferred to remain on the ship, essentially at sea. Tom and Rod were an exception, taking advantage of the free day in an exotic location to visit the ham station, renew their license, and make plans to conduct another overnight "DXpedition" to the delight of amateur radio enthusiasts around the globe. Pam, who had been under tremendous pressure without a break for several days, spent a relaxing few hours ashore with Sue, Marika, and Ami.

Some months later we discovered an interesting book that reminded us of our experiences in Tarawa. *The Sex Lives of Cannibals: Adrift in the Equatorial Pacific* (Maarten Troost, 2004) is about neither sex nor cannibals, but is a hilarious travelogue of a two-year stay on Tarawa by a twenty-six-year-old would-be novelist. His descriptions of the limited food options, putrid sanitary conditions, bizarre island characters, and incessant blaring blasts of the island's only song, "La Macarena," were quite accurate. If Global Seas' insurance carrier had read the book, we would never have been sent to Tarawa in the first place.

Upon reflection, despite all of the disparaging descriptions, I am glad I visited Tarawa, and am happy to have met some of the friendly people and seen such exotic sights. As Spence reminded us, most people in the world have no better, and are born to their lot by chance. If they can find any measure of happiness, we should have no worries about our own wonderful, comfortable lives.

April 9 (10); Sunday (Monday).
## Medical Emergency, Day Six. The Twins Depart.

The ship readied the small boat to take the twins ashore in the morning for transportation to the airport and the medevac flight, and bring Tom and Rod back to the ship after having spent the night ashore "DX-ing." Shirley was feeling and looking good, in high spirits, and said goodbye to everyone aboard. She and Amanda went ashore at 10 AM, all aboard seeing them off with waves and shouts of good wishes. All was not well, however; Sherry was seizing, and a second trip was necessary.

Sherry was mostly unconscious and looked dreadful as she was lowered by Pat, Larry, and Phil into the small boat, Phil cradling her in his arms for safety and comfort. We told her good-bye, which she could only acknowledge by slightly squeezing our hands. Pam, looking exhausted but smiling and waving, climbed aboard, and all were lowered into the harbor. It was sad to see them leave after all the work, fun, and drama we had shared over the last six weeks.

The return trip brought everyone and everything back to the ship, except for the twins, Pam, and Amanda, who would be flying to Hawaii on the air ambulance. Spence (who is a licensed captain) would serve as mate, substituting for Amanda. We also took on a former crewman from the *Askari* who had been stuck on Tarawa for some weeks, to take over mess duties in the twins' absence.

Colette and Adam had left the ship the day before. They were both desperate to leave, as they were not expecting we would be gone so long. They tried to arrange a charter flight to some intermediate destination that would eventually take them to Honolulu, but it was rumored that they missed it. The crew began making bets on who would get to Hawaii first!

We don't have to make this easy.
We can always do it the hard way.

—Captain Spence King

# Homeward Journeys

We departed Tarawa early in the afternoon of April 9 (April 10, local time) with very mixed feelings. On the one hand, we had not found the Electra, and we were heading back without some of our shipmates. The transit, over 2,000 nautical miles into a stiff wind and heavy seas, promised to be long and uncomfortable. On the other hand, there were many positives. We were going home after a long and eventful journey, and we had accomplished the survey goals we set out to achieve. Those of us experienced with deep-sea searches knew that our methodical elimination of territory meant that we were improving our odds of eventual success. And Ted Waitt was keen to continue the program. He sent me a message to this effect while we were in Tarawa:

> Well, I viewed our mission as pretty much being over when we got off the phone. We were past the point of diminishing returns without a serious regrouping effort, and we'd already accomplished what we set out to do. Very unfortunate about the twins, and I wish them a full and complete recovery. You made the right call to terminate at that point. Safety first. I hear they are doing better now, so that is good.
>
> Like I told you when your wife asked me the question, "What if we don't succeed?," my response was, "Well, then we'll know where it isn't." I still hold that view, and I now believe we have the biggest fact yet. A large area where we know it isn't. That changes the models.
>
> I'd like to regroup and convene a meeting to de-brief on the mission, and look in detail at the possible scenarios and where exactly we'd go when we return. So, let's set something up a few weeks after your return.
>
> I have every intention of succeeding on this quest, and I have no intention of giving up. I was assuming multiple missions. I will look at some additional facts, get a few other opinions, make some improvements, and do whatever it takes to improve our chances of success. It is out there somewhere, and I intend to find it.

Again, I probably had a more realistic set of expectations than you. I put our chances of success below 25% so I'm not surprised or disappointed. We're playing the odds here. I view our mission as completed successfully, but the job isn't done yet. We didn't find the target, but we know more than when we started. I wish all of you a safe and smooth trip home. Talk to you soon.

Though I would quibble with Ted's assessment of probabilities, this was all very encouraging. It *was* a successful mission, and we were glad Ted recognized that.

It was a sad day for the *Meridian Passages* staff today:

## MERIDIAN PASSAGES
*Central Pacific Edition*
*April 9, 2006 Volume XII, Number 40*

### Paper to End Publication
Look for *"Passages* LITE" in the Near Future

Sadly, and with deep distress, we must announce the FINAL ISSUE of the *Meridian Passages*, Volume XII. There are many reasons for the demise of this formerly popular and top-flight publication. The 10 most serious are:

1. Circulation has been dwindling as of late. With the departure of the media team and key members of the crew, we have lost 13% of our readership.
2. More significantly, the female readership has decreased by 45%. Since this is a significant demographic of the Paper, our underwriters have balked at continuing to fund the lavish banquets, generous expense accounts, and company cars that our staff members enjoy.
3. The printer is running out of yellow toner.
4. The Paper lost a key contributor when it failed to land the popular public opinion pundit, T. J. Boudreau, and his column, "This Is What I F**ing Think," which will soon appear on the EIB Network.
5. The printer is running out of cyan toner.
6. The Editor has been conscripted to help navigate us to Honolulu.
7. The staff has been engaged to write reports, pack gear, and otherwise make ready to go home.
8. The printer is running out of magenta toner.
9. Our medical insurance rates were skyrocketing as a significant fraction of our readership were reported to be experiencing distress when they read the Paper.
10. We have run out of Spotlight people, new material, and pretzels.

So, the Editor wishes to offer his sincere THANKS A LOT to our Dedicated Staff, including: Contributors Spence "Spider" King, who made up the Plan of the Day; Marika Lorraine, who gave us our daily Spotlight, and has learned how to terrorize young reporters when *she* becomes an Editor; SEA-Rae Smith, who kept us up to date on SEA School; Sue Morris, who headed the Irreverent Mirth Department; Rod & Tom who provided the Phone Patch Diaries; and Bethany Jourdan who created the layout, was late with the comics, and occasionally told us when to go to bed already. Also, THANKS A BUNCH to all of the various Contributors who provided plagiarized articles, random opinion pieces, bogus classified ads, altered photos, and endless bizarre events to report.

Finally, THANKS to Snyder's of Hanover, who provided the pretzels that kept us going through the long Central Pacific nights.

Is this the end for *Passages* and the publishing empire that founded it? Maybe, maybe not. There is still news and we make it. So stay tuned for the new "*Meridian Passages* LITE *Edition*," coming soon to your Mess Room. Don't miss a SEA School session, navigation team meeting, or ship emergency because you didn't read the Paper (LITE)!

And THANKS, THANKS, THANKS for being such a great crew. It has TRULY been a privilege. Sincerely, your Editor, Dave Jourdan.

We did continue the paper with the "Lite" edition, a single page, printed in black and white, until the day before we reached Honolulu. It was good that we did, because we had big news the very next day.

Doc Pam, Amanda, and the twins were on their way, and we were eager for news of their safe arrival in Honolulu and a chance to visit a real hospital. But they still had quite a journey ahead of them, and were anxious about a cramped flight in a small aircraft, designed for two patients and two medical attendants, with an extra pilot for the long flight ahead. In order to accommodate the twins, plus Pam and Amanda, the air ambulance would arrive with only one nurse in addition to the pilots. If Sherry and Shirley experienced seizures in flight, the other three would have to do their best . . . a continuing circumstance for Pam and Amanda.

An exhausted Pam arrived with her charges at the airport. In her words:

By the time we arrived at the airport at Bonriki, Sherry was lucid and walking. We drove out onto the tarmac and there waiting for us was this nice shiny jet [a Hawker 800—Ed.] along with an RN and pilots—all looking very professional and impressive in their white uniforms. We unloaded and must have looked quite bedraggled because it was not obvious to them who were the patients. They were prepared to have to carry two very sick women aboard the aircraft. Instead, they saw Sherry walking along and Shirley looking very chic in her sunglasses climbing aboard.

I explained the situation, who we were, and other details. Soon we were buckled in and taking off from Tarawa. On the left side of the aircraft, from fore to aft, was the exit door, Amanda, myself, and Sherry on a stretcher. On the right side was the luggage bin with an LCD display of altitude and air speed. Next was seated an extra pilot, then Shirley on a stretcher, and behind her was seated the RN.

As we climbed and headed out over the vast Pacific, I settled back into the luxurious seat and immediately drifted off to sleep. I imagine the others did also.

The jet continued to eat up the miles over the ocean as I slept.

For the first time in days Pam was able to relax. Her journey had been long and eventful—six weeks at sea, battling seasickness, facing a mysterious illness that she had meager means to combat, and dealing with responsibilities she had scarcely imagined. Finally, she was seeing the end, ready to transfer her patients to a competent medical authority, confident that she had done her very best to deliver the twins in a stable and safe condition. Her account of the flight continues:

Suddenly, I was awakened by the smell of smoke. As I opened my eyes, the cabin was filling with smoke and the plane was in a very steep dive. I looked forward and both pilots had on oxygen masks and one of them was flipping through a manual.

The extra pilot saw me and said, "Don't worry, we've lost an engine but have enough fuel to make Honolulu on one engine. We're going down to 10,000 feet to depressurize the cabin and get rid of the smoke."

My eyes were glued to the LCD display of altitude and air speed on the luggage bin wall. But the extra pilot kept getting between me and the screen. The altitude is coming off fast. We get to 10,000 feet but continue right through it without leveling off.

These thoughts were racing through my mind: "We're going into the ocean! I wonder if they will find us? Are we joining Amelia?" Everyone was very tense when suddenly the plane pulls out at 4,000 feet and the smoke clears from the cabin.

During all this, both twins relapse into convulsions.

Ten thousand feet was wishful thinking, as was the promise of making it to Honolulu on one engine. Concerned about how long the aircraft could remain aloft, the flight is directed to make an emergency landing at the nearest location.

It's a tense 45 minutes as Hawaiian air traffic control vectors us to the nearest airport on the Island of Kauai. We touch down and as the plane slows, fire trucks and emergency vehicles race alongside and surround the plane as we stop. The door is popped open and in rushes a guy in a full hazmat suit. He grabs me and as he hustles me out of the plane, I look into his face mask and see tears streaming down his face.

"You're alive, you're alive—thank God!" they are all exclaiming as they pull us from the plane and away from it.

Everyone is whisked off to Wilcox Hospital in Lihue.

Only later, after things calmed down a bit, did Pam and Amanda learn the reason for the particularly emotional outpouring from the rescuers.

Only three weeks earlier, a Hawaiian medevac plane lost an engine and did a full emergency landing on Kauai. The pilot lost it as he touched down. The plane cart-wheeled down the runway and all three aboard were killed—all friends of the airport emergency responders. And now they were afraid they were going to witness a repeat of this tragic accident.

This is also the reason for our medevac plane coming all the way from Alabama. The Hawaiian medevac planes were all grounded pending the accident investigation.

The scene at Wilcox Hospital was one of confusion. They were not expecting us—Queens Hospital in Honolulu was—but we never showed up. Hotel rooms were not readily available. No one had a car. The aircraft crew had left their entire suite of luggage in Honolulu to save weight and so had no change of clothes.

Of course, we didn't know all these details at the time, just the astonishing news that the plane was forced to land on Kauai. We wouldn't learn the whole story until we had dinner with Pam in San Diego many weeks later. Our information was confined to brief reports sent to Captain Mike that he would transcribe to the mess deck's white board. Around midnight on 11 April we learned:

No substantive news on Shirley and Sherry.... They are still on Kauai with Dr. Pam and Amanda, awaiting a decision to move them to Oahu or the mainland, which is forthcoming soon. Pam is flying to Honolulu, then San Diego tomorrow and is "totally freaked out" at the thought! Valium was administered mixed with vodka in an IV drip 30 ml/hr; only minor convulsions were experienced but much euphoria.

At least we knew they were safe! And certainly Kauai had medical facilities that could properly care for the twins and relieve the strain from Pam and Amanda. We were hoping to find out what was really wrong with Sherry and Shirley, and their prognosis for recovery. However, from our viewpoint, the mystery deepened. At noon the next day, the captain reported:

News @ Noon: Shirley and Sherry's tests were all negative (MRI and EEG). They will be delivered back to Mississippi in a couple of days on the same air ambulance that took them from Tarawa. . . . We certainly hope that the plane won't have the other engine go out when flying back to the mainland! The twins will have more tests done when they get home.

Dr. Pam will be poured onto a [commercial] plane later today to get back home. I'm sure right now she is feeling no concern at all.

I certainly would not have been keen to fly on that same aircraft!

In Honolulu, Charlotte had ambulance services on alert and was awaiting the arrival of the patients at Queens. The plane was overdue and she was starting to worry. After lots of calls to Seattle and the *Mt. Mitchell*, she finally found out that the plane was in Kauai. Undaunted, Charlotte scrapped all of her arrangements and shifted gears to support the new circumstances, starting with sending the Global Seas representative to Kauai and alerting all who had been on call to help with the situation.

Charlotte's next thought was for Doc Pam and Amanda. Amanda's duty was with her shipmates until they were safely on their way to the mainland. Pam was reluctant to let go of her charges, but realistically there was little she could do once they were admitted to the hospital. Charlotte convinced her to fly to Oahu, and arranged an appointment with a spa in downtown Honolulu for some serious TLC. They spent the afternoon together, Pam recounting the dramatic events of recent days, until it was time to return to the airport for her flight home to San Diego.

## MERIDIAN PASSAGES
*Central Pacific LITE Edition*
*April 10, 2006 Volume XII, Number 41*

### Castaway in Kauai
Medevac Takes a Dive, Doc Pam "Really Concerned"

Our big story is the never-ending saga of the Great Race to see who gets to Honolulu first: the Twins, Collette & Adam, or the *Mt. Mitchell*. Taking an early lead were C&A, who then stumbled when their flight outta here left before they did. Their current whereabouts are unknown.

The smart money was on the Twins (accompanied by Doc Pam and Amanda), who left the ground on *Medevac One* early this afternoon. However, four uneventful hours into the flight, things returned to normal as one of the two engines failed. The cabin filled with smoke, the crew went on oxygen, and the plane shed 20,000 feet of altitude in 5 minutes to raise cabin pressure. Both Sherry and Shirley began seizures, and we're not too sure about Pam & Amanda.

Apparently, they did their job well as usual, as the plane made a safe emergency landing in Kauai, about 45 minutes after the emergency began. Fire and rescue trucks lined the runway as they landed.

Everyone was safe, but a very concerned Pam was heard to comment, "Just get me back on that boat!" Apparently, she feels safer with us!

No word on when the gang will be able to resume their journey to Oahu…the *Mt. Mitchell* could beat them yet!

## April 13; Thursday. Navigating by the Stars.

Spence knows that "a busy sailor is a happy sailor," and although we had a lot to do involving breaking down gear, packing, report writing, and cleanup, it was not as busy as running a survey. So Spence found useful chores for everyone. In my case, more practice at celestial navigation was in order, and we set about navigating the week-long voyage back to Hawaii.

When we tried this in 2002, though we had success, our efforts were hampered by having to use a 1930s vintage air navigation sextant (technically known as an "octant") to take our measurements. The R/V *Davidson* did not possess a sextant of its own; in fact, ships rarely carry them any longer. One mariner friend of mine said his boat had a sextant, mounted in a glass case with a hammer and a sign: "FOR EMERGENCY, BREAK GLASS." The instructions went on to say:

> If you are lost, determine your position as follows: Unmount the sextant and take it to the bridge. Look for a passing fisherman or other competent sailor. Hail him, and offer to give him the sextant if he will tell you your position.

Fortunately for us in 2002, Elgen had brought his old octant along for fun, and kindly let us use it. With practice, it worked pretty well. But this time, Spence thought ahead and suggested we bring a sextant of our own. Surprisingly, these instruments are still made and for sale by a company named Celestaire, located in the very nautical town of Wichita, Kansas. I'm sure there is a story behind that. The company catalog offers a range of devices from a plastic "beginner" model ($39, plus $23 for the carrying case) to a traditional Cassens & Plath model for $1,500 (case included). We opted for a very nice Astra sextant, with wooden case, for $500. (I am also the very proud owner of an antique working sextant given to me as a gift from the Nauticos Corporation staff when we merged with Oceaneering in 2003. It sits prominently on display in my office, and I will *not* take it to sea!)

When we broke out the instrument earlier in the expedition for training, a number of crewman (Merchant Marine types) proudly fetched their own, otherwise collecting dust in their lockers. So we had several sextants available this time.

The other crutch we had was a very accurate wrist chronometer—actually, my $100 Freestyle Tide Watch, synchronized to GPS time. In the old days, carrying accurate time around on a ship was very difficult and, in fact, was not possible at all until John Harrison invented a marine chronometer (the culmination of a life's work) in the late 1700s. For his efforts, he won a £20,000 prize ($12 million in today's dollars) given by the British Parliament. He only got part of the money, however, not long before he died. You can read about this fascinating history in the book *Longitude: The True Story of a Lone Genius Who Solved the Greatest Scientific Problem of His Time* by Dava Sobel (Walker Publishing Company, 1995).

We set about navigating the 2,000-nautical-mile voyage from Tarawa to Honolulu much as we did the 600-mile transit to Tarawa in 2002: using only the ship's course by compass, speed by engine setting, and the sky. No GPS or other electronic means, other than using the watch for accurate time. Over the prior few days, this worked quite well, although not when it was was cloudy and rainy, when we could get little information . . . a practical lesson in the limitations of the art. Several others developed a taste for taking readings and we compared our answers. Spence and the others computed their fix calculations on the computer, but I was the only one foolish enough to be doing it "by hand," using only a Hewlett Packard reverse-Polish calculator (the same model used by Columbus and Magellan), supplied by Rod.

## Nautical Term of the Day: Reverse Polish

This is actually not a nautical term at all, but it bears explanation for non-geeks who think I am being politically incorrect. According to W. Marshall Leach Jr. (Professor of Electrical and Computer Engineering, Georgia Institute of Technology), "Polish notation was described in the 1920s by Polish mathematician Jan Lukasiewicz as a logical system for the specification of mathematical equations without parentheses." There are "prefix" and "postfix" versions of this, the latter referred to as "reverse Polish notation," or RPN. Anyone who has used a vintage Hewlett Packard calculator has noticed that there are no parentheses or "equal" keys, and one has to key in "1-enter-1-plus" to get "2" (rather than "1-plus-1-equals").

There is a notable history of Polish contributions to mathematics and computing, including the breaking of the German Enigma cipher in 1933, a feat considered by many to be one of the two most critical scientific events leading to the end of World War II (the other being the development of the atomic bomb).

The morning was clear after a couple of cloudy days, and I managed the first star fix (just before dawn) that we had in thirty-five hours. We got only one sun line and one moon line in that timeframe. But in the morning I obtained sightings of Jupiter and Venus, and the stars Arcturus, Vega, and Aldebaran. All five lines crossed within a mile! It showed us right on course, but a little behind, owing (probably) to the wind.

Meanwhile, while "browsing" through *Bowditch*, I found some new information on my new favorite star name (taking the place of Betelgeuse): Zuben el genubi. It's the second brightest star in Libra, and its name is an Arabic word meaning "southern claw." Sounds like it could be a distant cousin of Obi-Wan Kenobi. The sky is full of wonder. . . .

The Race: The Twins are OK, in the hospital in Kauai, and have had no seizures since they arrived. They are in the lead, but the *Mt. Mitchell* gained 300 miles yesterday. Collette & Adam's whereabouts are still unknown.

Our long voyage to Hawaii became more dramatic as the seas and winds rose. The wind fetched up quite a swell, and as we were plowing right into it, we experienced regular up and down high-speed elevator rides. This was hard to get used to, especially for those bunking in the forward part of the ship. Even if it didn't make you queasy, anything not lashed down wanted to fly all over the place, so everyone had to be very careful where to leave things, and to hold onto whatever one was working with. This made equipment breakdown and packing quite a challenge, and even working on the computer difficult. It's hard to have "one hand for the ship, one hand for you" when you're carrying a box that needs two hands! I benefited from great isometric workouts by trying to clutch the chair with my thighs at all times.

Most of the ship's crew hardly noticed, and to some of our party it was great fun. Sue, Laura, and Marika were observed "riding the bow," standing on the very nose of the fo'c's'le deck hanging on as the ship pitched in the seas. I caught them on camera from a safe vantage point at the top of the pilot house, just as they were about to be inundated by the spray from a bow wave. It was great fun for those who like roller coasters.

My personal condition began to deteriorate. . . . I could not seem to shake a headache, making it hard to concentrate. Soon, full-blown nausea set in, reminiscent of sea sickness. As the days of transit wore on and the heavy, confused seas persisted, I began to spend more time in my rack, unable to work without regular visits to the head. At first, I attributed it to a bad case of Channel Fever.

## Nautical Term of the Day: **Channel Fever**

This is the mental disease you get when you are on the way home, and all you can think about is the shipping channel that takes you to the dock. There are many symptoms: irritability, fatigue, depressed sense of humor, lower initiative.

But clearly there was more to it than that. It was Lynn back home in Maine who made the diagnosis.

> I am wondering if the headache that you cannot shake could be your tooth. In any case that is what I will tell the dentist. You have a dental appointment at 5pm on the day you get in. Bet your sinus headache will go away when they get the tooth fixed. Meanwhile you need some antibiotics for the infection. Do they have any on the ship? Just some amoxicillin would help!

Of course, I had lost that filling and had a hole in my tooth! Though it was patched temporarily, there was a path for infection. I sought out Larry-Doc and, sure enough, antibiotics were available. By the next day, thanks to Lynn, I was feeling almost fine.

## April 16; Sunday. Last Day at Sea.

We finally relented this morning and compared our celestial track with GPS position, and found that we were only 3 1/2 miles off after a week of navigating by stars, compass, and ordered speed. More than good enough to find Oahu!

In the end, of course, everybody did make it home. Adam and Collette appeared in Honolulu, then continued on their way east. Pam made it to San Diego, worse for wear, but in one piece. The twins safely flew on that air ambulance all the way to Alabama, diagnosis yet unresolved. And Amanda with a big smile was waiting for us on the pier in Honolulu.

## MERIDIAN PASSAGES

*Central Pacific Edition*
*April 15, 2006 Volume XII, Number 46*

**FINAL ISSUE!!**

Open Letter to the Editor: On behalf of all of us on the *Mount Mitchell*, we would like to thank the Editor, staff, and contributors of *Meridian Passages* for their entertaining columns, witty commentary, off-beat news, fun with Photoshop, and Spotlight features. Producing *Meridian Passages* often came at the end of long days and long watches, and we appreciate your dedication and effort. Even after screwing up the comics last Sunday, this is one of the best papers available anywhere in the free world. Thank you, Cap'n Davey and friends.

And the Editor Says . . . Aww, shucks! And THANKS AGAIN for all the help and appreciation! ALSO, kudos to the Dean of SEA School, SEA Rae, for a very successful semester. Great job!! See you next mission. . . .

You haven't seen a tree until you've
seen its shadow from the sky.

—Amelia Earhart

Chapter 14

# The Curse of Amelia
# (and Other Sea Tales)

Why we haven't found the Electra yet, and "how close are we"?
Could it be. . . ?

### A Twisted (Bread) Tale

According to reliable sources, it is clear that our ship has been hit with the
"Amelia Curse." It means that we were getting really close to the target and she
wasn't happy.

"Amelia" means "twin" in Sahalie, a lost language of the Central Pacific.
Back in 1852 a well-known witch doctor of the Jumongula tribe of the Sahalies
prophesied that in one hundred and fifty-four years a steel canoe would travel
with a weird assortment of people to a distant ocean looking for a bird made
of a strange material that was "buried" in very deep water. On that steel canoe
would be "amelias" (twins in Sahalie) from a far distant land—maybe an island.
Those amelias would be cursed and would assure that the bird made of strange
material would never be found.

He foretold that one of the "weird assortment" of people on the steel canoe
would have a supply of "a funny twisted bread." This twisted bread contained—by
its very shape—an energy field that would cause the amelias to perform strange
dances that would distract the crew and doom the mission to be incomplete—
*misceion-interupt-alulu* in Sahalie.

Despite the warning about the potential twisted results that would be
caused by baked bread, one of the weird people disregarded this prophesy and
took a large supply on board—and the rest is history just as the witch doctor
said. I know these things to be true. How else can you ever expect the strange
goings on during this mission to be explained?

It's entertaining to indulge in a little "associative learning" and come up with
some false associations that "explain" our failure to find the Electra so far. For
example, it is interesting to note that early during the 2002 mission we had some
trouble with the winch level-wind and were forced to run the NOMAD sonar

at too high an altitude for a few hours (see Chapter 4). This resulted in a strip of about 10 miles long by 0.4 miles wide that we missed, right in the highest probability area. This amounts to 4 square miles—small in comparison to the overall area, only a few tenths of a percent, but not insignificant. And large enough to hide 70,000 Electras! Though on a regular line we cover a square mile an hour or better, it would have taken almost half a day (including a turn) to go back over that short strip, and we favored continuing our regular grid, planning to cover the missed strip in the end. Of course, the end of the 2002 mission was premature due to the hydraulic failure and we never covered that spot.

In the 2006 mission, I had hoped we would cover this strip during the approach to one of our initial target imaging runs, but the diesel drive shaft failure precluded this. We then proceeded to search new areas of high probability, not willing to invest the time to search a few particular square miles. After finishing the new area, we were moving to a secondary area that was adjacent to this missing strip and would have given the chance to extend a line and cover it efficiently. We were within a couple of miles of that line when the medical emergency brought the mission to a halt. Again, circumstances thwarted our efforts to look in that spot.

A "curse"? Of course not. But an opportunity? Maybe. My "dream scenario" is that the aircraft is in that small strip. In the next mission, I will be sure to cover that! Wouldn't it be a great story if, all along, it was in the first place we meant to look? Remember my quote introducing Chapter 7:

*The sea does not give up her secrets lightly.*

A more rational way of looking at this is that the endeavor of deep ocean exploration is very complicated and difficult, fraught with opportunity for mishap. Teams are brought together for short periods of time to perform demanding tasks that no one gets the chance to do often enough to become routine. It just isn't easy, and every day brings a new challenge. So, it's easy to imagine a mysterious evil (or mischievous) agent in the works.

Another useful way of imagining the difficulty of this endeavor is by analogy. I have mentioned before that the area we have covered so far is equivalent to the acreage of the state of Rhode Island, which sounds impressive. But that is hard to visualize, as no one can easily relate the size of Rhode Island to something familiar, like one's backyard or a typical parking lot. Most people can grasp the size of a football field, so let us consider relating that size to the Amelia search area and see if that helps.

The Electra measures about 55 feet in wingspan by 38.6 feet in length. The plane could be contained in a rectangle with an area of about 2,100 square feet. Now, imagine shrinking this down to the size of a typical contact lens, about half an inch in diameter. The ratio of the areas is about 1.5 million to 1; length about 1,200 to 1. By this analogy, Elgen's "Area of Probability," about 6,000 square miles, would fill nearly two and a half football fields, including end zones. The area we have searched so far, 1,200 square nautical miles, would be about half a football field in area.

Let's say you're a football running back, quick and elusive. You take the ball at the fifty-yard line, break a couple of tackles, head for the sideline, reverse field, hurdle another would-be tackler, and streak for the end zone. Another cut back, and you meet a bruising tackle just at the goal line, but manage to tumble into the end zone for a touchdown! You jump up to do a little victory dance, but are feeling kind of woozy, and so your teammates help you to the sideline. As you take a seat on the bench, you realize you have lost a contact lens.

Now, you have run all over half the field, and you really don't know where you lost it, though you are pretty sure you had it before that last play, so it's very likely to be in that half of the field. How would you find it? The relative scale of this problem is the same as searching for the Electra in a 1,200-square-mile area.

To extend the analogy, consider that it is night, and the field lights are off. You are armed with a small penlight that can illuminate only a two-inch diameter area. To search carefully, it takes a full minute to search a two-inch-wide strip five feet long with your penlight. Five feet is equivalent to the effective swath width of the Ocean Explorer sonar, by our scale ratio. Each minute, you advance another two inches, and by this means, little by little, you can cover a five-foot-wide swath over the sixty-yard length of the half-field, from the fifty-yard line to the back of the end zone. At this deliberate rate, it would take eighteen hours to cover one swath. Considering that you have to take breaks for meals, sleep, change batteries in your penlight or whatever, it will really take you all day and night to cover that single swath. In order to thoroughly cover the entire area, more than a month of painstaking labor could be required to find that contact lens.

I could carry this further to note that the field is covered with divots, and that you are suspended from a crane fifteen feet over the field dangling your penlight and a little lipstick camera at the end of a piece of dental floss, but I hope the point is made.

We have not yet found the Electra; in fact, we probably have not found anything man-made of significant size on the ocean floor. This is in itself not surprising, as we are working in such a remote corner of the globe that the Electra is about the only thing we expect to find out there. We are sorely disappointed that the search has not found the plane so far. But this is a statistical problem: we have an area of highest probability (that we have searched already), adjacent to areas of lower (but still significant) probability that we plan to search. These remaining areas are small enough to cover in one more long mission. Statistics say that we will almost certainly be successful if we carefully search all areas of high probability, so, the next mission should do it, and in that sense we are very close.

Of course, statistics also say that the Electra could have ended up in an unlikely, but possible, location. But that is, by definition, unlikely.

Further statistical gamesmanship suggests that, since Nauticos has so far always found its quarry in the most probable location, it's about time for an outlier! Now, I know a true statistician would shudder at such a statement, since probabilities are not influenced by past results. My point is that there are unlikely scenarios to consider. Besides just being in an unlikely (but possible) location, the plane could have nestled in one of the small patches of rough terrain that dot the (otherwise benign) abyssal plain, hiding in a rock outcropping that makes it very hard to detect. Or it could have fallen into one of the volcanic calderas, lurking in the shadow of a ridge. Even worse, we see at least one caldera that shows recent (in geological terms) activity, including lava tubes. Without some geological expertise and more data, I can't discount the exceedingly unlikely possibility that the Electra was caught in an undersea eruption and buried. It could be right there, but will never be found, at least not with today's technology.

These scenarios are all extremely unlikely, though it will be possible for us to examine some of the rough areas and shadowed spots more carefully with some time in a future mission. It is wise to "close out" an area as thoroughly as possible before declaring, almost for sure, that the Electra isn't there.

What was wrong with the twins, Sherry and Shirley?

This remains quite a mystery. Even when they arrived at a modern hospital in Kauai, their condition continued to baffle doctors, and, as far as we know, no conclusive diagnosis was ever advanced. Among a battery of tests, it was reported to us that their EEGs were normal, even while experiencing seizures.

Once they were safely back to the mainland, their symptoms subsided and soon disappeared. The last news we heard before our ship reached Hawaii and our team dispersed was from Greg Shuey (operations manager at Global Seas):

> I don't know what to tell you about the twins. They are doing fine but I don't think anybody really knows the nature of the illness except that it appears to be a psychological thing and not related to a medical condition. Very strange and most unfortunate, but as we all know, strange things happen at sea.

Well, this was not very satisfying, especially since these "strange things" brought a multimillion-dollar operation to a dramatic halt. While I can offer nothing more satisfying myself, I can relate a few possibilities we have considered, in the category of "informed speculation."

Charlotte Vick has lived in and worked with Pacific island communities for over thirty years, and had some observations from her own experiences:

> When I first heard about the attacks experienced by the twins, I was concerned because I had seen and heard of other similar instances of such ailments or afflictions [among people in Pacific islands]. There are various terms for it in different island cultures, but they are similar to what are described as "possessions" in Western parlance. In the Marianas, the term is *tautau'mona's disease*. Albert Wendt, a Samoan author, wrote a book about a *matai* (chief) that experiences this entitled *Pouliuli* [Longman Paul, 1977].

Charlotte went on to say that during an extended stay on the island of Palau, she had witnessed a woman having a seizure at a funeral, and was told not to worry, it was "normal." The other witnesses left her alone, and in a while she recovered. Charlotte referred to this behavior as "Palauan Cultural Stress Syndrome." It certainly fit the symptoms expressed by the twins, and we could certify that they were under an unusual burden of stress.

Another interesting idea is that this behavior was an example of a condition known as a "folie à deux"—literally, "double madness." Besides being the excellent name of a record album by the alternative punk rock band *Fall Out Boy*, as well as a winery in Napa Valley, folie à deux is defined by the *Merriam Webster Dictionary* as "the presence of the same or similar delusional ideas in two persons closely associated with one another." The *Princeton University Wordnet* describes this as, "the simultaneous occurrence of symptoms of a mental disorder (as delusions) in two persons who are closely related (as siblings or man and wife)." Though the twins didn't seem to be sharing delusions as such, they certainly exhibited symptoms of a mental or psychological disorder. This can occur when the individuals concerned "live in close proximity and may be socially or physically isolated," which fit our situation pretty well. It is said that this condition can be resolved without medication once the source of disturbance is removed.

In researching this possibility, I noted that the same syndrome shared by more than one person may be called folie à trois, folie à quatre, folie à famille or even folie à plusieurs (madness of many). It occurred to me that we "Ameliacs" could form a club and call it the "Folie à Plusieurs Society."

I may count myself among those relatively few who "went down to the sea in ships, doing business on the mighty waters" (Psalms 107:23, RSV). It is a privilege that bears reflection. It is a circumstance rich in contradiction. At once, you are isolated from society, yet in close company with your shipmates. You are immersed in nautical traditions of organization, timeliness, protocol, and routine, yet always subject to the random whims of the sea and nature. You have almost nothing impeding your vision, but a limited set of things to see. You have set aside any work that seemed essential to do on land, and replaced it with an entirely different set of tasks that are essential to do at sea.

Under these circumstances, the relationship with shipmates, the value of tradition, the nightly wonders of the heavens, and the satisfaction of accomplishing small but important jobs take on a great significance. When we return home and resume our land lives, we find that we have a new appreciation for these things, and find the ways ashore curiously lacking. No matter how eagerly a sailor looks forward to returning to port, to reunite with friends and family, to enjoy the comforts of home and hearth, once ashore he soon begins to recall fondly the ways of the sea.

This sentiment was captured well by Carl Hoffman, author and veteran of the 2002 Amelia expedition:

> By several strokes of good fortune I have more than once found myself on small ships looking for treasure lost at sea—the most recent for 50 days in the middle of the Pacific Ocean. Our quarry was Amelia Earhart. On the first day I paced the decks like a caged rat. I felt cut off, out of the loop. There was nowhere to go. I opened my cabin door to check the telephone answering machine that didn't exist. I sent a flurry of emails to friends and family, checked for replies. I waited for newspapers that weren't being delivered. I fretted about unpaid bills and wondered if the kids were doing their homework.
>
> As the days passed, I forgot about it all. Except for the sea and sky around me, I sought nothing, save the treasure down there. I turned off the satellite phone. Stopped reading the daily faxed news briefing. George Bush? Kobe Bryant? Iraq? Who cares! My 41-year-old aches and pains disappeared. I got as brown as an old penny. I stood my watch gazing at the sonar image sea bottom for hours at a time, leaned on the ship's rail for hours thinking about nothing while watching albatrosses soar in the thermals and delighting in the rhythm of the rolling ship, the clouds, the dawns, yet enervated by the singularity of

the quest. "Today's the day," my ship-mates would say, each and every day, and each and every day that's how it felt.

Embarking on a long sea voyage, I have discovered, is about the only remedy left to escape the fierce gravitational pull of our too-busy lives. A secluded house or a hotel isn't the same. When you're on land, people find you. You check your messages, you return calls, you fret about deadlines. A ship is different. Sophisticated satellite telecommunications notwithstanding, when you're on a mission at sea you're, well, "at sea." Sorry, you say later to all the people who couldn't reach you, I was "at sea." They understand. The boss leaves you alone.

On a research vessel your entire life is reduced to sleeping and eating and working, subsumed to the matter at hand, while you're engulfed in a wilderness of clouds and waves and stars as far as the eye can see. Patience and observance are always rewarded. Flying fish the size of sparrows shoot from the bows; everyone should see a fish fly at least once in their lives. Whales spout in the distance. Porpoises leap from the ship's bow wake. At night the Milky Way is so thick it looks like fog. On a ship surrounded by 360 degrees of sea and sky the view is compelling, almost hypnotizing. For my 50-day voyage I brought a stack of books. I read one. There is, in the middle of the ocean, just too much of nothing to watch.

In the old days, I think, people were engulfed in pastoral silence and solitude all the time. And whenever they embarked on a journey, be it hours, days or weeks, they were cut off; they were, metaphorically at least, at sea. Not anymore. How many people, I wonder, go their whole lives without indulging in quiet reflection at the rail of a ship on a long and tiring voyage? It is, I realize (and here I must stress, I am addicted to my cell phone as much as everyone else), a luxury more precious than the softest sheets.

I enjoyed Carl's romantic musings, and from my perspective as an ocean explorer making occasional forays to the sea on research vessels, I could relate to it easily. In fact, I even included his story in an edition of *Meridian Passages*. But as I thought about it further, I realized that while there is some truth in the story and it's a valid point of view, the reality for most seafarers is quite different.

Cap'n Joe, for one, says, "It's only romantic to those that haven't done it." He wasn't talking about a South Pacific run, with fine weather, good food, and easy work . . . for some of us. For the team up in Ops, it's like an office job—except the office leans a bit and you don't go home at the end of the day. It's not the same as stints in the engine room, day after day with the heat, noise, and grease. Or twelve-plus hours, seven days a week working the survey gear back aft, or all the back-breaking work that goes on with the deck gang to keep us afloat, not to mention the cooking and cleaning that keeps us fed and comfortable. It's easier to be "romantic" when you don't have to spend a week rebuilding a diesel generator, or reassemble an HPU in the rain, or cook all day when you're seasick.

Now, consider doing it in Alaska, and imagine you are spending most of the time in cold, drenching winds, heavy seas, and primitive surroundings. And *much* harder work, exhausting physical labor. And some real hazards, even for the experienced sailor. Joe doesn't want to tell some of his stories . . . friends he's lost and close calls he's had.

He will tell you, though, that, "Cruise ships don't go to the Bering Sea in January." I wonder why?

After midnight the moon set and I was alone with
the stars. I have often said that the lure of flying
is the lure of beauty, and I need no other flight to
convince me that the reason flyers fly, whether they
know it or not, is the esthetic appeal of flying.

—Amelia Earhart

# Epilogue

The search for Amelia Earhart's Electra continues—on reef-fringed islands, in dark tropical jungles, in dusty archives, and in the deep sea. Someday, surely, the plane will be found, the mystery will be solved, and the quest will end. What will it mean? What is the value of all of the time, treasure, and toil devoted to the decades-long search? What continues to drive explorers to seek an antique hunk of aluminum and steel, with no "real" treasure on board, good for nothing more than a museum piece?

Why, after over seven decades, are books still written, movies still produced, and interviews still granted? Why do armchair explorers fill the blog-waves with heated arguments about who has puzzled out the solution to a mystery that has yet to be solved? Why do school kids, born sixty years after Amelia's disappearance, write essays about the famous flyer and read newly published children's books about her life and achievements?

What's with all this fuss about Amelia Earhart?

From my perspective as an explorer, I can point to the challenge of solving the greatest aviation and undersea mystery of the century. Finding the Electra would surely be a triumph of technology and expertise, and one could imagine its discovery fostering a new era in undersea exploration. As a successful businessman in the undersea profession, I have worked with my team to create plans and projections that offer a vision of how that achievement could be used to promote and fund future opportunities, leading to new discoveries.

From the broader professional perspective, I can imagine the discovery of the Electra would be an inspiration to explorers, engineers, historians, artists, aviators, women, children—all of the people fascinated with Amelia and her exploits. We lament that America is losing its world leadership in science and technology, and that young people no longer choose these career fields in sufficient numbers. Perhaps, here is a way to help reverse that trend, presenting the legacy of Amelia and her technological feats with the story of the deep-sea discovery and aircraft salvage as examples of the thrills and rewards that such careers can offer.

And who knows what world-altering discoveries lie in wait, deep in the sea, if we only seek them?

But there is also something about Amelia—her beauty, daring, and drive; her compassion, wisdom, and independence; and the sad, tragic end of her young life—that make her the classic heroine. A life of service in the public eye, a world traveler who called kings and presidents friends, a touch of passion with a famous partner, and a death shrouded in mystery, Earhart lived a remarkable life in fascinating times. There is Amelia appeal for everyone.

I know it is possible that we may never find what we seek, though I remain confident in eventual success. Regardless of the outcome, have we gained anything from all of our toil? My old friend and college classmate Admiral James Stavridis, who has commanded battle groups and spent more than his fair share of time at sea, had these words for me. I leave Jim's wisdom as the closing thought.

Dave,

As one who has followed the sea for 30 years now, I truly found your cruise journal fascinating from start to finish.

In the end, a ship is a ship; and warship or research vessel, it seems that the sense of camaraderie, the roll of the deep sea, the joy of coming home, the pang at separating from shipmates . . . it all rings so true.

I'm sorry you didn't find what you sought, of course: but in the end, I'd guess what you gained—the adventure, the friendship, the experience of going to sea yet again—was more than worth the time and trouble of the voyage.

Godspeed and open water to you, my very good friend, in all your future voyages.

Search on,
Jim

# Appendix A: Crews & Support Teams

## 2002 Mission: R/V *Davidson*

| Name | Organization | Position |
| --- | --- | --- |
| Elgen Long | | *Expedition Leader* |
| Dave Jourdan | Nauticos | *Program Coordinator* |
| Tom Dettweiler | Nauticos | *Operations Manager* |
| Tom Bethge | Nauticos | *Operations Assistant* |
| Spencer King | Nauticos | *Operations Assistant* |
| Shawn Dann | Nauticos | *Operations Tech* |
| Mike Davis | Nauticos | *Electronics Tech* |
| Jay Ellis | Nauticos | *Operations Tech* |
| Julie Nelson | Nauticos | *Corp. Counsel, Diesel Queen* |
| Sue Morris | Nauticos | *IT and Vehicle Tech* |
| Jeff Palshook | Nauticos | *Navigation Analyst* |
| Jon Thompson | Nauticos | *Exhibitions* |
| Jonathan Blair | Nauticos | *Media* |
| Rod Blocksome, NYØV | Rockwell Collins | *Communications* |
| Tom Vinson, KØDAS | Rockwell Collins | *Communications* |
| Bragg Sherrer | NAVO | *Rider/Sonar Analyst* |
| Robert Witzleb | NAVO | *Rider/Weather support* |
| Dave Everhart | Ocean Services | *Master* |
| Joe Litchfield | Ocean Services | *First Mate* |
| Rod Brumbaugh | Ocean Services | *Second Mate* |
| R. J. Callahan | Ocean Services | *Chief Bosun* |
| Mel Kufeldt | Ocean Services | *Chief Engineer* |
| Leroy Rubinas | Ocean Services | *Engineer* |
| Paul Bingel | Ocean Services | *Engineer* |
| Jesse Sims | Ocean Services | *A/B Seaman* |
| Ron Curran | Ocean Services | *A/B Seaman* |
| Harold Story | Ocean Services | *A/B Seaman* |
| Bruce Nelson | Ocean Services | *A/B Seaman* |
| Bryan Lampi | Ocean Services | *A/B Seaman* |
| Scotty Swistchew | Ocean Services | *Cook* |
| Jerzy Plata | Ocean Services | *Asst. Cook* |
| Carl Hoffman | Freelance Journalist | *Media* |
| Bill Mills | BMA Productions | *Media* |
| Kristin Whiting | NGS | *Media* |

## 2006 Mission: R/V *Mt. Mitchell*

| Name | Organization | Position |
| --- | --- | --- |
| Elgen Long | | *Expedition Leader* |
| Dave Jourdan | Nauticos | *Program Coordinator* |
| Spencer King | Nauticos | *Operations Manager* |
| Sue Morris | Nauticos | *IT Tech* |
| Jeff Palshook | Nauticos | *Navigation Analyst* |
| Bethany Jourdan | Nauticos | *Operations and Media Asst.* |
| Jeff Morris | Nauticos | *Sonar Analyst* |
| Jon Thompson | Nauticos | *Exhibitions* |
| Rod Blocksome, NYØV | Rockwell Collins | *Communications* |
| Tom Vinson, KØDAS | Rockwell Collins | *Communications* |
| Larry Tyler | OTECH | *OTECH Team Leader* |
| Andy Sherrell | OTECH | *Watch Leader* |
| Mark Wilson | OTECH | *Sonar Analyst* |
| David Warford | OTECH | *Operations Tech* |
| Chris Russell | OTECH | *Operations Tech* |
| Phil Goodwin | OTECH | *Operations Tech* |
| Jason Predmore | OTECH | *Operations Tech* |
| Dwight Heard | OTECH | *Operations Tech* |
| Michael Dunatov | Global Seas | *Master* |
| Lawrence Mishefski | Global Seas | *First Mate* |
| Joe Litchfield | Global Seas | *Second Mate* |
| Amanda Becker | Global Seas | *Third Mate, Medical Officer* |
| Jeff Shepard | Global Seas | *Chief Bosun* |
| Per Andersen | Global Seas | *Chief Engineer* |
| Jay Corwin | Global Seas | *Engineer* |
| T. J. Boudreau | Global Seas | *Engineer* |
| Warren Smith | Global Seas | *Engineer* |
| Waldemar Janczak | Global Seas | *A/B Seaman* |
| Andy Gomes | Global Seas | *A/B Seaman* |
| Dan Nakamura | Global Seas | *Cook* |
| Shirley Mira | Global Seas | *Housekeeper* |
| Sherry Hubler | Global Seas | *Asst. Cook* |
| Ami Pablo | Global Seas | *Asst. Cook* |
| Collette Beaudry | SeaLight Pictures | *Media* |
| Adam Geiger | SeaLight Pictures | *Media* |
| Carla-Rae Smith | Nauticos | *Teacher at Sea* |
| Marika Weiner | Nauticos | *Student representative* |
| Pam Geddis, MD | | *Doctor at Sea* |
| John Heubusch | WID | *Institute representative* |
| Pat Sullivan | WID | *Institute representative* |
| Mike Dessner | WID | *Institute crossdecker* |
| Laura Walters | WID | *Institute crossdecker* |

## Other Key Supporters of the 2002 and 2006 Missions

| Name | Organization | Position |
|------|--------------|----------|
| Crawford MacKeand, WA3ZKZ | M.I.E.T. (retired) | *Radio Analysis* |
| David Dunlap | | *Aviation Consultant* |
| Charlotte Vick | Nauticos | *Logistics ashore* |
| Garry Kozak | GK Consulting | *Sonar analysis* |
| Colleen Hughes | Nauticos | *2002 Seattle-Honolulu rider* |
| David Yole | Nauticos | *2002 Seattle-Honolulu rider* |
| David Dettweiler | Nauticos | *2002 Seattle-Honolulu rider* |
| Eric Jourdan | Nauticos | *2002 Seattle mobilization team* |
| John Vezina | Global Seas | *2006 Tarawa-Honolulu crew* |

## Collins Amateur Radio Club Members and Associates, led by Rod Blocksome and Tom Vinson

| Name | Organization | Position |
|------|--------------|----------|
| Bryan McCoy, KC0YSQ | Collins ARC | *Experiments and simulations* |
| Charley Snodgrass, KC0CD | Collins ARC | *Navigation analysis* |
| Don Grimm, WA0WJM | Collins ARC | *Navigation analysis* |
| Gary Bishop, NQ0V | Collins ARC | *Data gathering and collection* |
| Tom Heifner, WE0F | Collins ARC | *Statistical analysis* |
| Barry Brown, K0YLU | Collins ARC | *RCI pilot for experimental flights* |
| Roger Hatcher, WB9OMY | Collins ARC | *Antenna modeling* |
| Mike Zonnefeld, W0LTL | Collins ARC | *Logistics and experiments* |
| Dan Roessler, WD0HOJ | Collins ARC | *HF Propagation expert* |
| Dave Graham, WA0YDO | Collins ARC | *HF operator during mission* |
| Barry Buelow, W0IY | Collins ARC | *Analysis and Support* |
| Mike Zonnefeld, W0LTL | Collins ARC | *Analysis and Support* |
| Dave Schmoker, KJ9I | Collins ARC | *Analysis and Support* |
| Fred Spinner, W0FMS | Collins ARC | *Analysis and Support* |
| Joe Culwell, WB0YFL | Collins ARC | *Analysis and Support* |
| Lisa Carrara | Rockwell Collins | *"Voice of Amelia Earhart"* |
| Gary Belcher, KH6GMP | Kailua Kona, HI | *Radio Phone Patch Support* |
| Kimo Chun, KH7U | Honolulu, HI | *Radio Equipment Support* |

# Appendix B: Chronologies

## 2002 Mission Operations

| Day/Time *(local)* | Local Zone | Event | Mission ET *(Days/Hrs)* | | Event ET *(Days/Hrs)* | | Comments |
|---|---|---|---|---|---|---|---|
| 22 Feb 13:00 Fri | EST | Trucks depart MD for Seattle | | | | | |
| 24 Feb 10:00 Sun | PST | Begin mobilization | | | | | |
| 28 Feb 18:00 Thu | PST | *Davidson* departs Seattle | 0 | 0.0 | | | |
| 07 Mar 07:00 Thu | EST | Fly to Honolulu | 6 | 10.0 | | | |
| 10 Mar 18:00 Sun | HST | Departure dinner at Seafood Village | 10 | 2.0 | | | |
| 11 Mar 15:00 Mon | HST | *Davidson* arrives Honolulu | 10 | 23.0 | 10 | 23.0 | Transit Seattle to Honolulu |
| 12 Mar 15:30 Tue | HST | Under way from Honolulu, transit OPAREA | 11 | 23.5 | 1 | 0.5 | In Honolulu |
| 14 Mar 08:00 Thu | HST | NOMAD tests | 13 | 16.0 | | | |
| 19 Mar 00:00 Tue | YST | Arrive OPAREA Launch NOMAD | 18 | 10.0 | 6 | 10.5 | Transit to OPAREA |
| 19 Mar 18:22 Tue | YST | Begin survey operations | 19 | 4.4 | 0 | 18.4 | |
| 04 Apr 08:08 Thu | YST | Complete Area A, southern portion | 34 | 18.1 | 15 | 13.8 | Time to survey primary area |
| 04 Apr 14:00 Thu | YST | Resume survey operations | 35 | 0.0 | 0 | 5.9 | |
| 08 Apr 06:59 Mon | YST | Complete southern extension. | 38 | 17.0 | 3 | 17.0 | Time to survey primary area |

| Day/Time (local) | Local Zone | Event | Mission ET (Days/Hrs) | | Event ET (Days/Hrs) | | Comments |
|---|---|---|---|---|---|---|---|
| 08 Apr 14:45 Mon | YST | Resume survey operations | 39 | 0.8 | 0 | 7.8 | |
| 14 Apr 23:03 Sun | YST | Complete Area A, central portion; Depart OPAREA | 45 | 9.0 | 6 | 8.3 | Time to survey primary area |
| 18 Apr 08:00 Thu | MST | Arrive Tarawa for refueling | 47 | 18.0 | 2 | 9.0 | Transit to Tarawa |
| 19 Apr 07:00 Fri | MST | Depart Tarawa | 48 | 17.0 | 0 | 23.0 | |
| 20 Apr 11:30 Sat | YST | Arrive OPAREA Launch NOMAD | 50 | 21.5 | 2 | 4.5 | Transit to OPAREA |
| 21 Apr 07:44 Sun | YST | WINCH FAILURE | 51 | 17.7 | 0 | 20.2 | |
| 21 Apr 22:00 Sun | YST | Recovered NOMAD | 52 | 8.0 | 0 | 14.3 | Recovery of NOMAD |
| 23 Apr 02:00 Tue | YST | Depart OPAREA | 53 | 12.0 | 1 | 4.0 | Working options to continue |
| 30 Apr 06:00 Tue | YST | Arrive Honolulu | 60 | 16.0 | 7 | 4.0 | Transit to Honolulu |
| 30 Apr 16:00 Tue | YST | *Davidson* departs Honolulu | 61 | 2.0 | 0 | 10.0 | In Honolulu |
| 06 May 06:00 Mon | YST | Charter team returns home | 66 | 16.0 | | | |
| 11 May 04:00 Sat | YST | *Davidson* arrives Seattle | 71 | 14.0 | 10 | 12.0 | Transit Honolulu to Seattle |
| 13 May 11:00 Mon | YST | Demob complete | | | | | |

EST   Eastern Standard Time (–5 GMT)
PST   Pacific Standard Time (–8 GMT)
HST   Hawaii Standard Time (–10 GMT)
YST   YANKEE Standard Time (–12 GMT)
MST   MIKE Standard Time (+12 GMT)
ET    Elapsed Time

# 2006 Mission Operations

| Day/Time (local) | Local Zone | Event | Mission ET (Days/Hrs) | | Event ET (Days/Hrs) | | Comments |
|---|---|---|---|---|---|---|---|
| 08 Feb 08:00 Wed | EST | Trucks depart MD for Seattle | | | | | |
| 10 Feb 05:00 Fri | PST | Begin mobilization | | | | | |
| 15 Feb 14:00 Wed | PST | *Mt. Mitchell* departs Seattle | 0 | 0.0 | | | |
| 24 Feb 07:00 Fri | EST | Fly to Honolulu | 8 | 14.0 | | | |
| 24 Feb 10:00 Fri | HST | *Mt. Mitchell* arrives Honolulu | 8 | 22.0 | 8 | 22.0 | Transit Seattle to Honolulu |
| 27 Feb 18:00 Mon | HST | Departure dinner at Royal Hawaiian | 12 | 6.0 | | | |
| 28 Feb 09:00 Tue | HST | Under way from Honolulu | 12 | 21.0 | 3 | 23.0 | In Honolulu |
| 01 Mar 08:00 Wed | HST | Begin transit to OPAREA | 13 | 20.0 | | | |
| 07 Mar 01:08 Tue | YST | Arrive OPAREA Launch OE for target survey | 19 | 15.1 | 6 | 18.1 | Testing & transit Honolulu to OPAREA |
| 08 Mar 00:24 Wed | YST | HPU casualty Recovering OE | 20 | 14.4 | 0 | 23.3 | Deployment for target imaging |
| 10 Mar 06:00 Fri | YST | Offshore Howland Island | 22 | 20.0 | | | |
| 10 Mar 11:00 Fri | YST | Depart OPAREA for Tarawa | 23 | 1.0 | 2 | 10.6 | Recovery of OE & transit offshore Howland |
| 13 Mar 17:00 Mon | MST | Rendezvous *Askari* Depart for OPAREA | 25 | 7.0 | | | |
| 13 Mar 04:34 Mon | YST | Arrive OPAREA Launch OE for target survey | 25 | 18.6 | 2 | 17.6 | HPU repair time 5d 20.9h from casualty |
| 13 Mar 07:08 Mon | YST | OE on bottom for imaging Target 66 | 25 | 21.1 | | | |

| Day/Time *(local)* | Local Zone | Event | Mission ET *(Days/Hrs)* | | Event ET *(Days/Hrs)* | | Comments |
|---|---|---|---|---|---|---|---|
| 15 Mar 00:48 Wed | YST | Liftoff bottom Moving to Line 1 launch point | 27 | 14.8 | 1 | 20.2 | 2002 target imaging 2d 3.5h total tgt imaging |
| 15 Mar 10:26 Wed | YST | Launch OE to begin search operations | 28 | 0.4 | | | |
| 01 Apr 20:44 Sat | YST | Liftoff bottom Primary survey completed | 45 | 10.7 | 17 | 19.9 | Time to survey primary area |
| 02 Apr 04:25 Sun | YST | Launch OE for target survey | 45 | 18.4 | | | |
| 03 Apr 18:18 Mon | YST | Recovering OE to resume search operations | 47 | 8.3 | 1 | 21.6 | 2006 target imaging 4d 1.1h total tgt imaging |
| 04 Apr 03:56 Tue | YST | Launch OE to resume search operations | 47 | 17.9 | | | |
| 04 Apr 12:18 Tue | YST | MEDICAL EMERGENCY Recover OE - | 48 | 2.3 | 0 | 18.0 | Survey of secondary area |
| 04 Apr 15:25 Tue | YST | OE on deck Secure operations Depart for Tarawa | 48 | 5.4 | | | |
| 08 Apr 08:00 Sat | MST | Arrive Tarawa | 50 | 22.0 | 2 | 19.7 | Transit for medical emergency |
| 10 Apr 14:45 Mon | MST | Depart Tarawa | 53 | 4.8 | 2 | 6.8 | In Tarawa for medical support |
| 17 Apr 12:30 Mon | YST | Arrive Honolulu | 61 | 2.5 | 7 | 21.8 | Transit to Honolulu |
| 18 Apr 06:00 Tue | YST | Charter team returns home | 61 | 20.0 | | | |
| 18 Apr 10:00 Tue | YST | *Mt. Mitchell* departs Honolulu | 62 | 0.0 | 0 | 21.5 | In Honolulu |
| 27 Apr 08:00 Thu | YST | *Mt. Mitchell* arrives Seattle | 70 | 22.0 | 8 | 22.0 | Transit Honolulu to Seattle |
| 29 Apr 11:00 Sat | YST | Demob complete | | | | | |

EST    Eastern Standard Time (–5 GMT)
PST    Pacific Standard Time (–8 GMT)
HST    Hawaii Standard Time (–10 GMT)
YST    YANKEE Standard Time (–12 GMT)
MST    MIKE Standard Time (+12 GMT)
ET     Elapsed Time

# Appendix C: SEA School

**A** uniquely Nauticos approach to deep ocean operations incorporates a team-building concept in which the skills and experience of individuals from every functional area of the company are melded into a single capable team. This philosophy yields a widely diversified set of skills that enhances the overall capabilities of the team. While some team members may have little or no experience at sea aboard ships, they bring unique skills and fresh perspective to the mission. Nauticos encourages all employees to seek these special opportunities for assignments at sea. We are a stronger and better company when our employees appreciate the rigors of going to sea, and respect the complexity of the problems that must be solved in working in the deep ocean. That perspective should be embraced in all our business relations.

Nauticos "SEA" School is established to familiarize team members with all aspects of the ship, the operations, and the systems that they will be working with. Because some team members will be working in a wholly unfamiliar environment, it is essential to teach the skills and share the knowledge that will help them contribute to the mission objectives. Nauticos and its associates include some of the world's foremost authorities on many subjects, which make this an extraordinary learning experience. Because we will all be learning from each other, instructors may tailor their topics appropriately for the audience and operations. Instructors are encouraged to introduce new topics as the mission progresses and a need is recognized. Any team member may serve as instructor.

Most of the lectures are optional, except for safety lectures, which are designated ALL HANDS.

## SEA School Topics, 2002 Mission

| | | |
|---|---|---|
| 3/13 | Shipboard Safety: ALL HANDS | Spence and Joe |
| 3/17 | The Amelia Earhart Search Project | Dave |
| 3/21 | Discovery of the *Dakar* | Dave |
| 3/22 | Shipboard Electrical Safety: ALL HANDS | Shawn |
| 3/25 | Amelia's Last Flight | Elgen |
| 3/26 | Radio Analysis of Amelia's Last Flight | Rod and Tom |
| 3/27 | The "Real Deal" Amelia Earhart Analysis | Jeff P. |
| 3/28 | Renavigation of Amelia Earhart's Flight | Dave |
| 3/29 | Discovery of the Japanese carrier *Kaga* | Jeff P. |
| 3/30 | Discovery of an Ancient Shipwreck | Dave |
| 4/1 | Sonar Theory and Interpretation | Tom D. |
| 4/2 | Isis . . . The Eye of the Hectopus | Bragg |
| 4/3 | Global Positioning System | Tom B. |
| 4/4 | Renavigation Theory | Dave |
| 4/5 | Photography 101 | Jonathan |
| 4/6 | National Geographic Today | Kristin |
| 4/7 | Discover the World of Ham [Radio] | Tom & Rod |
| 4/8 | Practical Knots | Spence |
| 4/9 | Fancy Knots | Spence |
| 4/10 | Celestial Theory | Spence and Elgen |
| 4/11 | "Monkey Method" of Celestial Sight Reduction | Spence |
| 4/12 | The Octant | Spence and Elgen |
| 4/13–14 | Shoot a Sun-line | Spence |
| 4/15 | The ABC's of Welding | Spence |
| 4/16 | Weather by Robert | Robert |
| 4/18 | Camera Obedience Training | Bill |
| 4/23 | The Life and Times of an NGTV Photographer | Bill |
| 4/24 | Astronomy 101 | Dave |
| 4/25 | Discovery of the *I-52* | Dave |
| 4/26 | Duct Tape and Tie Wraps | Sue |
| 4/27 | A Day in the Life . . . | Carl |
| 4/28 | The Radio Guys Land in Tarawa | Rod & Tom |

## SEA School Topics, 2006 Mission

| | | |
|---|---|---|
| 3/1 | Shipboard Safety: ALL HANDS | Spence |
| 3/2 | Amelia's Last Flight | Elgen |
| 3/3 | Sonar Theory and Interpretation | Jeff M. |
| 3/4 | Discovery of the *I-52* | Dave |
| 3/6 | Sonar and ROVs | Larry |
| 3/7 | Radio Analysis of Amelia's Last Flight | Rod and Tom |
| 3/8 | Renavigation of Amelia's Last Flight | Dave |
| 3/9 | Practical Knots | Spence |
| 3/10 | Colonization of Howland Island | Rod and Elgen |
| 3/11 | Fancy Knots | Spence |
| 3/13 | Discovery of the *Dakar* | Dave |
| 3/14 | Nautical Terms and History | Capt'n Mike |
| 3/15 | Your Time Has Come | Elgen |
| 3/16 | Designing a Mega Exhibition | Jon |
| 3/17 | Four Myths about Amelia's Last Flight | Rod and Tom |
| 3/18 | The Truth Behind the Pictures | Adam and Colette |
| 3/20 | What We Do in the Real World | Pat and Pam |
| 3/21 | Behind the Scenes with an Investigative Reporter | Marika |
| 3/22 | Radio Guys Comedy Tour | Rod and Tom |
| 3/23 | Greybrow and the Horse Canoe | Elgen |
| 3/24 | Photoshop 101 | Bethany |
| 3/25 | Astronomy 101 | Dave |
| 3/27 | Connecting the Bottom of the Ocean to Space | Sue |
| 3/28 | The Marine Industry | Capt'n Mike |
| 3/29 | History of Technology Development at Collins Radio | Rod |
| 3/30 | Catching a Comet | Carla-Rae |
| 4/10 | Celestial Theory | Spence and Dave |
| 4/11 | How to Make 100 Million Bucks | Jon |
| 4/12 | Battle of Midway | Jeff P. |
| 4/13 | Renavigation and Discovery of the *Kaga* | Dave |
| 4/14 | Discovery of an Ancient Shipwreck | Jeff M. |
| 4/15 | Duct Tape from Spaulding to Wallets | Sue and Bethany |

# Index

# About the Author

**D**avid W. Jourdan is the founder and president of Nauticos, a company devoted to the exploration of the deep ocean. He studied physics and engineering at the U.S. Naval Academy and Johns Hopkins University, and served as a U.S. Navy submarine officer during the Cold War. As a physicist at the Johns Hopkins University Applied Physics Laboratory, and as leader of Nauticos, he became an expert in the exploitation of undersea environmental data, and has supported many scientific, archaeological, and military programs. He has written about diverse technical topics including underwater navigation, oceanographic survey, remote sensing, underwater vehicles, ocean exploration, and ocean renewable energy applications.

Jourdan and his Nauticos team managed ocean operations for The Discovery Channel during the live broadcast from the wreck of the *Titanic* in 1998. He is responsible for the discovery of the Japanese aircraft carrier *Kaga*, sunk at the World War II Battle of Midway in the Pacific, and the Japanese World War II submarine *I-52* in the Atlantic, both at depths exceeding 17,000 feet. His team discovered the missing Israeli submarine *Dakar* in the Mediterranean at 10,000 feet and he has led two deep ocean expeditions in search of Amelia Earhart's lost Lockheed Electra airplane. He has spoken to military, business, and scientific organizations across the country about his major discoveries and has appeared on the National Geographic Channel, The Discovery Channel, and the *Today Show*.

Jourdan was named Maryland Small Business Person of the Year in 1999 and is an International Fellow of the Explorer's Club. He has been active in many humanitarian programs, including Rotary International since 1994, and has traveled to Africa to support initiatives to combat AIDS and provide fresh water to rural communities. Jourdan lives with his excellent wife Lynn in the coastal Maine village of Cape Porpoise.